OCEANOGRAPHY

OCEANOGRAPHY

The Last Frontier

EDITED BY

RICHARD C. VETTER

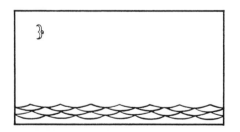

Basic Books, Inc., Publishers

NEW YORK

THE AUTHORS

D. James Baker, Jr., is Assistant Professor of Oceanography at Harvard University. He is a member of the board of editors of the journal of *Geophysical Fluid Dynamics*.

George S. Benton is Chairman of the Department of Earth and Planetary Sciences at The Johns Hopkins University. He has been president of the American Meteorological Society and was head of the 1969 U.S. scientific delegation to the U.S.S.R. He was also chairman of panels on air-sea interaction (1960–66) for the National Academy of Sciences.

Wallace S. Broecker is professor of geology at the Lamont-Doherty Geological Observatory of Columbia University and on the advisory committee to the Geochemical study of the oceans (GEOSECS) program.

Wilbert McLeod Chapman (1900–1970) must be listed, biographically, as a biologist, educator, oceanographer, ichthyologist, and consultant. Dr. Chapman has written more than 250 papers in his field.

Jacques Cousteau is director of the Oceanographic Museum in Monaco. In 1943, during his service in the French Navy, Captain Cousteau invented the aqualung. Since 1950 he has been leader of the Calypso Oceanographic Expeditions (Calypso being the name of his underwater vehicle).

George E. R. Deacon graduated in chemistry from King's College, London. In 1949 he was made director of the newly-formed National Institute of Oceanography. Dr. Deacon has served on several international marine science committees.

Margaret Deacon is a modern history graduate from Somerville College, Oxford. She is a research assistant in the Science

Studies Unit at Edinburgh University and is author of two papers on the history of oceanography.

JOHN EWING is a Senior Research Associate in Oceanography at the Lamont-Doherty Geological Observatory of Columbia University and is in charge of the Observatory's Marine Seismology Department.

ROBERT G. FLEAGLE is Chairman of the Department of Atmospheric Sciences at the University of Washington. He has been chairman of the Committee on Atmospheric Sciences of the National Academy of Sciences and president of the Meteorology Section of the American Geophysical Union.

GLENN A. FLITTNER is professor of biology and director of the Bureau of Marine Sciences at California State University, San Diego. He served for nearly a decade as Leader in the fishery-oceanography program of the Fish and Wildlife Service of the U.S. Department of the Interior.

PAUL M. FYE has been the director of the Woods Hole Oceanographic Institution in Massachusetts since 1958 and has served as President of the Institution since 1961.

EDWARD D. GOLDBERG is professor of chemistry at the University of California's Scripps Institution of Oceanography in San Diego. Dr. Goldberg is an editor of three journals, *Earth and Planetary Science Letters, Journal of Marine Research,* and *Environmental Science and Technology.*

H. R. GOULD is research scientist with the Esso Production Research Company in Houston, Texas. Dr. Gould has also authored many published works in his field.

DONALD W. HOOD worked on the Manhattan Project at the University of Chicago and was a participant in the birth of the Atomic Age. Dr. Hood has continued as a research participant at Oak Ridge, Tennessee. He is now Director of the Institute of Marine Science of the University of Alaska.

DOUGLAS L. INMAN is professor of oceanography at the University of California's Scripps Institution of Oceanography in San Diego. He has been an advisor to the United States and several foreign governments on problems relating to shore processes, coastal engineering, and the location of harbor sites.

C. E. LUCAS is director of fisheries research with the Scottish Office and Director of the Marine Laboratory, Department of Agriculture and Fisheries for Scotland. He was chairman of the Consultative and Liaison Committees of the International Council for the Exploration of the Sea and of the Advisory Committee on Marine Resources Research of the Food and Agricultural Organization.

NELSON MARSHALL is professor of oceanography at the University of Rhode Island. He has held active advisory roles with several government and private organizations.

WALTER H. MUNK is associate director of the University of California's Institute of Geophysics and Planetary Physics and director of the Institute's La Jolla Laboratory. He has served on several panels of the President's Scientific Advisory Council.

MELVIN N. A. PETERSON is associate professor of oceanography at the University of California's Scripps Institution of Oceanography and is chief scientist for the Joides Deep Sea Drilling Project, which is a part of the U.S. National Foundation's National Research Program of Ocean Sediment Coring.

WILLARD J. PIERSON, JR. is a professor with the Institute of Oceanography at the City University of New York. His areas of specialization are geophysical random processes, ocean waves, air-sea boundary processes, and turbulence. Dr. Pierson is a member of the Earth Resources Advisory Subcommittee of the National Aeronautics and Space Administration.

DONALD W. PRITCHARD is professor of oceanography at The Johns Hopkins University and is director of the Chesapeake Bay Institute of the university. He is a past president and fellow of the Oceanography section of the American Geophysical Union.

COLIN S. RAMAGE is professor of meteorology at the University of Hawaii and associate director of the Hawaii Institute of Geophysics. Between 1962 and 1964, he was scientific director for meteorology of the International Indian Ocean Expedition and edited a monograph series on this Expedition.

JOSEPH L. REID, a research oceanographer, was attracted to his profession during World War II naval service as an anti-submarine warfare officer. He served as coordinator of the NORPAC expedition of 19 ships from the United States, Japan, and Canada. Dr. Reid served for several years as secretary of the Eastern Pacific Oceanic Conference, an annual meeting of oceanographers.

GORDON RILEY is research professor of biology and director of the Institute of Oceanography at Dalhousie University in Halifax, Nova Scotia, Canada. He has served as president and trustee of the Bermuda Biological Station.

ALFRED SHERWOOD ROMER, Harvard University professor emeritus of zoology, is an authority on the 500 million years of history of the backboned animals on earth. He served as president of the XVI International Zoological Conference, held in Washington in 1963. From 1946 to 1961, Professor Romer directed Harvard's Museum of Comparative Zoology.

JOHN H. RYTHER is chairman of the Department of Biology of the Woods Hole Oceanographic Institution and consultant to the National Science Foundation, the National Institutes of Health, and other private and government organizations. Dr. Ryther was scientific director of the U.S. Biological Program of the International Indian Ocean Expedition from 1959 to 1965.

KARL K. TUREKIAN is professor of geology and geophysics at Yale University. He is one of two Yale geologist members of the Scientific Planning Team for the U.S. Government's Apollo moon-landing project. He is also director of Yale's Kline Geology Laboratory, and is research associate in meteorites at the university's Peabody Museum of Natural History.

HAROLD C. UREY is professor of chemistry-at-large at the University of California in San Diego and a Nobel Prize winner. He is also a consultant in lunar sciences for the U.S. National Aeronautics and Space Administration and an advisory member of the Space Science Board of the U.S. National Academy of Sciences. He was the discoverer of the hydrogen atom of atomic weight and a participant in the research for production of heavy water and for the production of U235.

WILLIAM G. VAN DORN is a research oceanographer in the Division of Oceanic Research of the University of California's Scripps Institution of Oceanography. His background in oceanography includes participation in most of the nuclear weapons tests in the Pacific. Dr. Van Dorn was in charge of the Island Observatory Program in Oceanography for the International Geophysical Year.

RICHARD C. VETTER was coordinator of the Voice of America Forum Series on Oceanography and is executive secretary of the Ocean Affairs Board, National Academy of Sciences—National Research Council. Before assuming his present position in 1957, he was an oceanographer with the U.S. Office of Naval Research.

FREDERICK J. VINE is at the School of Environmental Sciences, University of East Anglia, Norwich, England. Dr. Vine was the 1968 recipient of the Arthur L. Day medal of the Geological Society of America for "outstanding distinction in the application of physics and chemistry to the solution of geological problems."

EDITOR'S PREFACE

Interest in the oceans (at both national and international levels) has burgeoned explosively during the past ten years. Many look to the sea as the source of food for future generations. Others visualize a vast storehouse of mineral wealth in and under the ocean's waters. For a growing number, the sea's coastal regions offer a refuge for recreation. Certainly, these expectations are great; many, but not all of them, can be fulfilled.

As our numbers and our demand for resources increase, reality intercepts imagination, and we discover that one use of the sea competes with and sometimes prohibits many other uses. For example, coastal fisheries often depend upon the waters of brackish bays and estuaries as spawning grounds, but industrial development of coastal areas and waste disposal from urban regions can change the coastal oceanic environment enough to mar the fragile reproductive fabric of a fisheries population. Man's activities, even farther afield, can affect the oceans. The pesticides that protect inland food crops and the chemicals that keep the vast continental heartland fertile are eventually washed into the sea. There, they too can alter nature's balance and bring about changes in the physical, chemical, and biological oceanic realms.

Many of the chapters in this volume speak to this conflict directly or indirectly. Although the original instructions to the authors emphasized the identification of scientific problems and how they are studied in the oceans, in many chapters the reader will find an underlying awareness that we face many difficult decisions as to how we will use the sea in order to enhance rather than erode its value.

The authors of this volume originally prepared their chapters for a series of radio broadcasts for the Voice of America "Forum Lectures" broadcast to a worldwide audience from late fall 1969 through early spring 1970. The authors were carefully chosen from among the leaders in the field of ocean science to cover the broad range of topics that must be studied if we are to understand the complex problems of the sea. Within these chapters, the reader will glimpse the excitement felt by all ocean scientists as they attempt to unravel complex topics ranging from Harold Urey's "The Birth and Growth of the Oceans" to Glenn Flittner's "Fishery Forecasting for Food from the Sea."

The contrast between popular "Sunday supplement" articles on the vast riches of the sea and the careful, guarded hopes of the experts writing in this volume is obvious. For example, Wib Chapman explains that although we can obtain more animal protein from the sea for human diet, the oceans alone cannot meet men's future food needs. Man must also have carbohydrates, starches, and sugars, which will, for the foreseeable future, come from traditional land sources.

Beginning with the exciting introduction by Captain Jacques Cousteau, the chapters proceed to describe the early evolution of the oceans, their chemical cycles and geophysical turmoil; lead the reader into an understanding of the motions of the ocean field; elaborate on life in the sea and the uses of coastal waters; outline the complex features of international cooperation in ocean affairs; and end with Paul Fye's visionary look at prospects for the future. The reader will discover a many-faceted collection of concepts that, taken together, constitute a modern ocean scientist's view of his mysterious realm.

While this collection of essays was being assembled in the summer of 1970, both Wilbert M. Chapman, author of the chapter "Fisheries of the World," and Milner B. Schaefer, a close friend of Chapman and equally renowned as an authority on ocean fisheries, died. These two giants of intellect and human compassion were world leaders in showing how men can learn to wisely use the ocean's bounty. Both of them vigorously tested their own ideas, as well as the ideas of others, against the truths learned through the careful, factual observation of their first love—the sea. They are deeply missed. It is fitting that this book be dedicated to them.

1973   RICHARD C. VETTER

CONTENTS

CONTENTS

OCEANOGRAPHY

INTRODUCTION

Captain Jacques Cousteau

On July 20, 1969, my research ship *Calypso* was anchored in Beaver Inlet on the South side of the island Unalaska in the Aleutian Islands, Alaska. Deep under our keel in about 600 feet of water chief pilot Raymond Coll was aboard one of our small diving saucers, "Minisub I." He was exploring the submerged glacier canyon exactly at the same time as Armstrong was setting his historical foot on the soil of the moon. Half of my crew had gathered around the sonar telephone system that enabled me to communicate clearly with Raymond Coll at the bottom of the sea, while Armstrong's voice came to us from the moon by radio through a loudspeaker near the underwater telephone on the fantail. My friends were holding their breath realizing the importance of the moon landing and anxiously waiting to be sure that both astronauts were safe while walking in such an alien environment. I relayed the news into the depths to Coll, who shared our excitement.

This instantaneous link between men on the moon and on the bottom of the sea was a fine example of what technology could achieve in modern times. But the episode had a much deeper meaning for me. Armstrong and Coll were talking at the same time about what they were seeing. The astronauts moved and walked on a barren, hostile and lifeless moon world, while the oceanaut described crowds of large shrimps, graceful fangorgonians, and packs of large king crabs, trying to hide in the sediment. If the moon is sterile, what about the other planets in our solar system? Prospects there are not very promising either. Venus probes have reported temperatures that are incompatible with life, and very recently Mariner VI and Mariner VII have shown Mars to be almost as dead as the moon. We may have to become accustomed to the discouraging thought that man probably is the only thinking creature in the solar system and the next sun is very far away, out of reach for at least one generation.

Standing on the moon, the lonely ambassadors of mankind looked back at their earth. It was glowing with color and beauty. Our planet clearly is a water planet mostly covered by oceans, shrouded with clouds of water vapor.

Of course, we are not yet sure that the earth is unique in the universe, but we already know that it is an exceptional planet. It is so because of the abundance of life; life is there because of a number of rare circumstances—chemical composition of the atmosphere, for example, and because there is an unusual quantity of water on board our space ship. It is because a few of us very recently have had the privilege to compare and judge, from outer space, that we can fully realize today that we are the fortunate tenants of a priceless property, the earth. Very unexpectedly, Apollo XI, crowning the many results of NASA's space program, has rendered an immense service to marine sciences and to conservation.

Too often public opinion has been led to question whether government funds had not been too lavishly allotted to space research and too sparsely to oceanography. This is a very unfortunate question. There is no antagonism, no rivalry between the science of inner and outer space. Both fields must and can be investigated diligently. At first sight the oceans are immense. Everyone knows that they cover two-thirds of the earth, which is called the water planet for that reason. The deepest trenches in the Pacific Ocean are almost 30 per cent deeper than the Himalayan Mountains are high. The sea is also a formidable reservoir of energy, as we unfortunately experience when large ships are destroyed in tropical storms or when coastlines are damaged by tidal waves. So, obviously on our scale, the oceans are very large, but on the scale of the earth they are, in fact, a mere trace of moisture. To realize this fact we must use figures.

If we were to build a large, accurate scale model of the earth's globe, 3 meters in diameter (that is about one story high), the average depth of the oceans would be only 1 millimeter thick, or about $\frac{1}{25}$ of an inch, and the maximum depth of the deepest trench would be represented by less than 3 millimeters. On another scale, if the earth was the size of an egg, the oceans would represent less than one drop of water. This comparison shows why the sea is so vulnerable, why it is so precious.

If man has the privilege to exploit the sea, he also has the duty to protect it. It is now easier for us to think about our earth, about ourselves as being tightly integrated into a larger complex, the solar system, and exploration of the solar system also includes exploration of the inside of the earth and of its oceans. In this field much remains to be discovered and understood. The sea is still a weird, alien, if not a hostile environment. We must urgently explore it to understand it and to realize how much each man is directly or indirectly concerned by the sea whether he lives near the coastline or in the heart of a continent. It is generally believed that life originated in the oceans, and some of the primitive forms of life looked very much like organized sea water.

It is in the sea that the fundamental first phases of evolution took place and the first vertebrate was born. Many more forms of life exist in the sea than exist on land or in the air. But in the sea as on land, the basic process of productivity of living matter is photosynthesis. The energy of sunlight is used by microscopic algae to transform nutrient salts into living vegetable organisms—the prairies of the sea—which are eaten by minute animals, the zooplankton, which in turn are eaten by larger animals, thus building what is known as the marine food chain. The tonnage of plankton algae produced in the ocean every year provides a good measurement of the global productivity of the sea.

An important by-product of this photosynthesis process and of the growth of the phytoplankton is the purification of our atmosphere. The carbon dioxide produced by our industrial civilization and by burning fossil fuels in large quantities dissolves partly into the sea, and the phytoplankton fixes the carbon from the carbon dioxide and liberates oxygen in the same manner as our forests do on land.

The total dependence of marine life on sunlight in the sea has as a consequence the existence of marine seasons. In the spring the sea blooms. Another consequence of the photosensitivity of the plankton to light is its giant daily vertical migrations which I call the pulse of the ocean. During daytime the plankton descends into the sea in order to protect itself against overillumination, and in the evening it moves upward to the surface. Quite often I have observed these giant vertical migrations through the porthole of my diving saucer submerged at a depth of 300 meters in the open sea. After sunrise or before sunset I saw waves of planktonic organisms moving up at speeds from 7 to 10 centimeters per second. It was a fascinating sight and only direct observation could make one aware of the mechanism of this fantastic migration. The pulse of the ocean affects billions of tons daily.

When daylight penetrates into the sea, the warm colors, red and orange, are quickly eliminated. At a depth of 50 meters, green, blue, and purple are the only remaining colors of the spectrum. And yet if we bring down artificial light, landscapes and deep sea animals will blaze alive with bright pigments that were not intended to be revealed. At a depth of 300 meters enough monochromatic light is still diffused to enable us to see the shapes of rocks or the motion of fish. At 1,000 meters, even in the most favorable circumstances, it is eternal night for the human eye. Visibility is often poor on the estuaries, harbors, or cities, but water is generally clear or very clear in the open ocean or at great depth. When the water seems to be crystal clear, divers have hardly 30 meters of visibility, which is comparable to a London fog.

For all of these reasons sight is not as important a sense for marine animals as it is for land animals. On the contrary, sound and pressure waves travel faster and farther undersea than in the air, and they are bounced back by the bottom. The lower sound frequencies even penetrate into the soil. Thus the ocean is an acoustic world. These properties are used to map the ocean by echo sounding or to probe the thickness and nature of the bed rocks by seismic surveys. But man is not the only one to use echo sounding. Many sea mammals, especially dolphins, also do this. In the Atlantic Ocean, sixty miles west of Gibraltar, out of sight of any land, I have observed a herd of dolphins heading directly toward the narrow straits. They were producing many quacks and squeaks as sonic feelers kept them informed about the distant topography. Each time the approach of my ship modified their course, their built-in sonar was quick to send them back on track.

At the bottom of the deepest trenches in the ocean the pressure exceeds one ton per square centimeter, and yet life is still to be found there. At the turn of the century Prince Albert of Monaco caught several hundred deep-sea fish in a giant trap set at a depth of 6,000 meters. The bathyscaphe saw fish and shrimp at a depth of 10,800 meters. How can life adjust to such pressures? It is still a bit of a puzzle. Although the compressibility of flesh is not much different from that of sea water, fairly primitive marine invertebrates seem to suffer permanent damage when compressed in the laboratory at 500 atmospheres (equivalent to 5,000 meters). Nevertheless, the same invertebrates abound in nature and can be found in good shape at much deeper levels.

A better understanding of the physiological effects of extreme pressures is vital to study tomorrow's techniques of very deep diving. Once again, nature may show us the way. Sperm whales are mammals, having lungs, bones, flesh, cavities, and well-developed brains. Yet they dive easily to depths of 1,000 meters and occasionally to 1,200 meters or more. We must learn more about the physiology of these sperm whales.

Many more peculiarities of the marine environment make it very different from ours. Gravity seems abolished. Fish and man enjoy apparent weightlessness. Since fish have cold blood, they have no calorie loss and thus need no energy to fight gravity. Food is needed almost solely for growth, and fish grow almost as long as they eat and live. In exceptional circumstances creatures can become exceptionally large. Some creatures—sharks, for example—cannot stop swimming and never sleep.

These brief remarks all point to the fact that the study of the

7

ocean encompasses all conceivable disciplines of science—physics, chemistry, biochemistry, radio chemistry, geology, geophysics, biology, microbiology, ecology, physiology, archeology, engineering, electronics, and so on.

There is no such science as oceanography. Oceanography is the global study of an environment. Because we now have a general picture of our planet, because we begin to realize how vast oceanography really is, we become aware of how futile it would be to study the oceans in the narrow frame of a nation. The oceans are an ideal field for cooperative studies and for international coordinated programs. Today steps to provide common financial resources and brains are in the process of being developed by the United Nations.

Until recently man and the sea have had a fairly difficult relationship. In the first period, which includes prehistoric times, the sea frightened mankind. It was a symbol of mystery, inspiring tales and legends, and was the home of monsters. Daring men —fishermen and navigators—tried to use the sea as a source of food or as a route for discovery and invasion. The risks involved were enormous. A few philosophers, such as Aristotle, began a systematic investigation of sea life, but they had only a small following.

The nineteenth century saw the birth of oceanography and the organization of the great scientific causes—Darwin on board the *Beagle,* Will Thompson with the *Challenger,* Prince Albert of Monaco, the German research ship *Meteor,* and many others. Primitive but ingenious instruments were developed that slowly unveiled the essential facts about the ocean depths. This period was one of an indirect involvement of man in the sea, which came just before World War II with the development of diving, exploration vehicles, and bathyscaphes, underwater photography, and television. A historical landmark was set when Jacques Piccard and Don Walsh in the bathyscaphe *Trieste* reached the deepest trench in the world near the Mariana Islands at 10,800 meters. Together with the sophistication of modern instruments, diving announces a new era when man will be able to settle as long as necessary on the bottom of the sea to perform any kind of work.

Manned undersea stations have already been in operation for periods of several weeks at depths of more than 100 meters and experiments have been conducted to depths of about 600 meters. In such deep stations specialized divers—called oceanauts in France, aquanauts in the United States—live for extended periods of time in the dry, but under pressure. They breathe a mixture of helium and oxygen, which is lighter than air. They swim out of the station to work, for example, in training operations, repairing pipes, or mining. They swim back inside to warm up, eat, rest, and sleep. The oceanauts' bodies are saturated with the gases they breathe, and they must be decompressed very slowly and gradually to avoid decompression accidents. This slow decompression is performed only once at the end of the operation. The original idea for these settlements came from Dr. George Bond of the U.S. Navy and was developed by my group in France with the Conshelf Station Program and in the U.S. Navy with Sealab Stations.

In France we now have a mobile and self-contained Conshelf Station in construction, which is capable of sailing from port without tender for several hundred miles, to settle for one week on the bottom of the ocean at the formidable depth of 600 meters, where four oceanauts will come out of the submarine station and will be able to work at those depths for several hours a day.

I publicly announced in London in 1962 another possible development of deep diving—the amphibious man, who will either be breathing a liquid or will not breathe at all, but will have his blood purified and oxygenated through special membranes by liquid chemicals. Such science fiction projects are now being very seriously studied and will enter the experimental stage before 1980. Tomorrow's amphibious man will be able to swim and work at depths of at least 1,500 meters, as well as climb very high mountains without oxygen masks. The practical or scientific applications of such developments in diving physiology and submarine technology are many and extremely important. They will allow geologists to work under the sea almost as well as on land and find clues to the early history of the earth. Undersea archeologists working methodically from Conshelf Stations will contribute to a better knowledge of man's own early history. Oceanaut biologists will be able to directly observe the strange behavior of marine creatures and better understand the structure of the food chain.

The public has often been misinformed about man's future uses of the oceans. Of course, the sea is a large potential source of food and minerals, but it is by no means a panacea. Improving fishing techniques—sonar, electric nets, fish pumps—will only lead to overfishing and the depletion of stock, which is already happening. However painful and costly, we will have to entirely abandon industrial fishing and turn to aquaculture. We will also have to increase the basic productivity of the sea. New families of drugs will also be extracted from marine creatures. Oil and minerals should be found in many areas, and reserves are probably larger than they are on land. But the cost of drilling and mining will increase considerably with depth and will be mainly justified by the shortage of the equivalent mineral on land. Although returns are, unfortunately, more obvious in the development of marine recreation facilities—as well as military defense and attack systems—floating airports, huge artificial islands, highways in tunnels or on floating stretches, undersea cable cars, restaurants, and institutes will eventually be built.

Perhaps the most important practical application of the marine sciences will be in climate control. The sea is the boiler and the condenser of a giant thermodynamic machine, the sun being the heat source. Evaporation and rain are the conveyors of fantastic amounts of energy. A better knowledge of these mechanisms would allow us to modify the weather in one part of the world by increasing or decreasing the evaporation rate in another part.

The development of exact and human sciences of the sea will automatically increase the fields of intellectual speculation and substantially raise our cultural level. Human beings have built their cultural and artistic heritage from their sensorial reactions to their own world ruled by gravity. Our intrusion into outer space and into inner space, where all subjective connections follow different patterns, will generate new sources of inspiration for the artists, the poets, and the philosophers. But however rich the prospects of exploitation of the oceans, however important the potential impact of the sea on our cultural and artistic commonwealth, we may soon have to deal with the problem of our very own survival. The sea is the inevitable end of the line for any kind of pollution—thermal, oil, bacterial, nuclear, or industrial—whether the pollution process leads directly into the sea, onto the land, or into the air.

It is a race against time for survival, a race between science, mass information, public wisdom on the constructive side; population increase, overspecialization, and industrial greed on the destructive side. In the outcome of this dramatic race to protect the oceans, all men are vitally concerned.

1 THE HISTORY OF OCEANOGRAPHY

George E. R. Deacon and Margaret B. Deacon

During the past few decades man's need to improve his scientific knowledge of the sea has led him to devote his energy and resources to the study of the oceans on an unprecedented scale. We have gained a better understanding of waves, tides, and currents, and of what goes on at great depths as well as at the surface of the sea. We have studied the interaction of oceans and atmosphere to improve our understanding of events in the atmosphere as well as in the oceans. We have learned much about the geological and physical processes that determine the nature and character of the sea floor. We know much about the temperature and salinity structure of the oceans and something of how its variations and the water movements help to control plant and animal life in the sea. As the over-all picture becomes clearer, we are in a much better position to apply our knowledge and experience to solve the urgent problems that arise in navigation, coastal and harbor engineering, meteorology, and the exploitation of marine fishery and mineral resources.

To determine how far back this scientific endeavor extends, or when the science of oceanography began is not an easy task.

The first stage in the development of our knowledge of the sea must have begun in the depths of time long before the dawn

The material for this chapter was largely taken from Margaret Deacon, *Scientists and the Sea, 1650–1900: A Study of Marine Science* (N.Y.: Academic Press, 1971).

of recorded history, when primitive man first took to the sea in boats to fish, trade, and fight. From the earliest times sailors of all lands gained a working knowledge of the sea and its moods from their day-to-day experiences. They saw the force of the waves, the set of tides and currents, and measured the depths of waters near their coasts, but they did not generalize about their knowledge, nor did they use it to develop their understanding of what they saw.

The scientists of ancient Greece and Rome tried to explain how the sea came to be as it is, why it remained at the same level—neither drying up nor overflowing; why it was saline whereas the lakes were fresh, why there were tides in the open ocean but not in the Mediterranean Sea. The questions they asked were too difficult and far ranging to be answered conclusively by the little knowledge at their disposal, and their discussions remained on a speculative plane in which rival theorists depended more on ingenuity in argument than on demonstration from fact to make their points. Aristotle remarked disparagingly of their efforts that "no theory has been handed down to us that the most ordinary man could not have thought of."

But Aristotle was not deterred from putting forward his own theory, and, as occasionally happens by some accident or chance insight, he outlined the most important principle of water exchange between the oceans and atmosphere. Aristotle reasoned that continual rainfall and river flow failed to raise the level of the ocean, because it was evaporated by the sun and condensed again as rain. There was no need to account for the appearance and disappearance of vast quantities of water, as the same water progresses through a continuous cycle from water to vapor and back to water again.

To organize the study of the sea on a scientific basis, the detailed knowledge of the sailors had to be combined with the speculative approach of the philosophers, and, as the sailors of the Renaissance began to extend their field of competence from the coasts of Europe to the oceans of the world, they became aware of gaps in their knowledge. The Elizabethan sailor Sir Richard Hawkins, after a narrow escape from a shipwreck, complained that:

> How to know the setting of the current from east to west in the main sea is difficult; and as yet I have not known any man, or read any author that hath prescribed any certain way to discover it.

The importance of a mastery of the oceans insured a place for this study in the revolutionary expansion of science that began in the seventeenth century. In Britain the men who took part in founding the Royal Society of London, with the expressed aim of improving natural knowledge, intended to be quite systematic in studying the ocean. They tried to measure its characteristics, not only at the surface but also in the depths, and faced the task of developing instruments that would record information and collect samples. They were genuinely curious about the depth of the oceans and the shape of the sea floor, and while better knowledge, for example, of the tides had immediate practical uses, they also believed that careful study would give them a better understanding of the forces that govern the ocean. In turn this would benefit the people whose livelihood depended upon the sea—and as they stated, would be "of good use both naval and philosophical."

One of the problems discussed in the Royal Society's circle was how to overcome the difficulties of using a lead and line in deep water when measuring the depth of the sea. They tried what was even then an old device—a weight and float joined by a catch that released the float as soon as the weight touched the bottom. They made experiments to find the velocity of bodies sinking and rising in water and found that water had sufficient resistance to produce a constant speed. By measuring the time for the float to return to the surface, the depth of the sea could theoretically be determined. At sea the new instrument, however, proved to be a failure. John Winthrop, the governor of Connecticut and son of the first governor of Massachusetts, reported that there could be no perfect trial of the instrument at sea because the motion of the waves unhooked the lead. Robert Hooke, who is better known for his work on barometers, microscopes, pendulums, and springs, developed an apparatus for finding depth by measuring the pressure at the bottom. He realized that the pressure would depend upon the temperature and salinity of the water and described instruments that would inform him about their changes.

The idea of finding out about temperature and salinity was new both for the surface of the sea as well as for the depths. Robert Boyle, who is better known for his law on the variation of the volume of a gas with pressure, was interested in both. Submarine temperature, he wrote, is a subject on which the classic authors are silent and about which philosophers seem not to have made any experiments because they lacked both the opportunity and the means to make them. With the help of sailors and travelers, and the newly developed thermometer and hydrometer, Boyle found that the surface temperature of the sea varied in accordance with the climate, being warm in the tropics and cold in polar regions, and that the salinity at the surface depended upon a balance between rainfall and evaporation. But even though Hooke had described a thermometer and water sampler for deep-sea research, and Boyle, from the reports of divers and swimmers, had some idea of what to expect, they were both unable to make these measurements. They knew about the widespread custom of cooling bottles of wine in the tropics by lowering them into deep water, but for the moment, the technical difficulties of exploring the depths of the sea and of getting sailors sufficiently interested seemed too great.

Attempts to explain the remarkable currents of the Strait of Gibraltar began to promote a better understanding of the variations in the density of sea water and its possible effects. It was generally known that water always runs into the Mediterranean Sea from the Atlantic Ocean and from the Bosporus as well as from many rivers; the problem was why the sea did not overflow and how it emptied itself of the water it visibly received. Today we have no difficulty in accepting the fact that much of the water is transferred to the atmosphere by evaporation, and that the remainder, made heavier by the salt from the evaporated water, flows out of the Strait of Gibraltar as an undercurrent. But in the seventeenth century John Greaves, the mathematician who wrote about the Pyramids, could still conjecture that perhaps it ran out through a hole in the bottom of the sea feeding subterranean channels. Sir Henry Sheeres, engineer of the mole at Tangier, while ridiculing such a suggestion did so only because of the philosophy that "Nature doth nothing in vain." It would be an idle supposition, he said, to think that so vast a quantity of water could be hurried into the Mediterranean for no other reason than to be hurried out again. Several scientists of the day tried to devise ways of demonstrating the presence of an undercurrent flowing out of the Strait of Gibraltar, and the Earl of Sandwich, who went to Portugal to fetch the bride of Charles II, was asked to let down a bucket from a boat to find whether there was a contrary motion near the bottom. The Earl did not manage to make the measurements, and the undercurrent remained uncertain until a current measuring drogue was let down from the HMS *Porcupine* 200 years later.

Combination of the philosophical with the naval approach was more successful in the study of the tides. Galileo had argued that tides are caused by the movement of the earth and had used tides as evidence of the rotation of the earth. John Wallis, one of the early fellows of the Royal Society, had elaborated upon Galileo's theory raising questions that called for more detailed observations at different parts of the coast. When these observations were made, they cast doubt on Wallis' predictions, but twenty years later they were used by Sir Isaac Newton to illustrate his theory of the effect of the principle of universal attraction on the tides, and this marked the beginning of modern tidal theory and practice.

About this same time the Italian scientist Count Marsigli was studying water layering in the Bosporus, where the current tends to flow toward the Mediterranean at the surface and in the contrary direction at the bottom. He had reached a clearer understanding of the possibilities of water exchange between regions of different density and could see the denser water from the Mediterranean forming an undercurrent below the fresher water of the Black Sea. Marsigli was also a pioneer in oceanic surveying and made a remarkably thorough survey of the Gulf of Lyons early in the eighteenth century, measuring its depths, temperatures, and salinities, tides and currents, and studying its flora and fauna. By then it was clear that the study of the sea required facilities larger than those usually available to private investigators, and Marsigli made the prophetic announcement that little could be done "unless some Prince orders for that purpose special vessels with suitable instruments."

The seventeenth-century scientists liberated the science of the sea from the limiting and rigid propositions of classical learning that had persisted without improvement through the Middle Ages. They advanced more realistic and flexible ideas and developed a picture of the oceans that is recognizable today. They recognized and made early progress along some of the lines that we still follow today and devised instruments similar to those used until the development of electronics. We might regard them as the founders of oceanography, but their work did not flourish as a separate scientific discipline. Interest continued, and travelers with a bent for scientific investigation made isolated observations and measurements, but they did not reach to the point of integrating the new discoveries into a unified, continuing discipline. The philosophers had not succeeded in persuading the sailors, and the vision of the unity of oceanic research and its useful application seemed to decay. Basic study was neglected, and its application was restricted to very obvious things such as diving and the freshening of salt water.

Then, as now, advances in the science of the sea depended upon progress in other sciences, and other environmental subjects had a lean time in the eighteenth century. Meteorology fared no better than the study of the sea, and perhaps fared worse because marine science was soon to reap great benefits from the remarkable advances in navigation that followed improvements in the accuracy of astronomical observations at sea and the development of the marine chronometer. World voyages such as those of Captain Cook demonstrated the value of the new methods and directed further interest to the oceans.

In spite of the loss of impetus in the late seventeenth century, there were a number of notable events. Edmond Halley, the British astronomer, made a voyage as far as the Antarctic ice-edge from 1698 to 1700, studying the trade winds and the earth's magnetism, and Count Marsigli published a notable work on the science of the sea in 1725. The Reverend Stephen Hales, vicar of the English parish of Teddington, best known for his experiments on plant physiology, invented a sea-gauge and persuaded Captain Ellis, master of a slave trader, to use it to make the first temperature measurements of the ocean at considerable depths in 1749. Benjamin Franklin found time to make a careful study of the stilling of waves by oil and to draw a chart of the Gulf Stream. The first deep sounding was made by Captain Constantine John Phipps during an Arctic expedition on which Nelson served as a midshipman. Laplace, among others, made an extensive contribution to the theory of the tides. Such advances were made by clever men engaged primarily in other work but who saw in the sea opportunities to extend or shed new light on existing inquiries.

In 1819 Alexander Marcet, a Swiss chemist working in London, made the remarkable discovery that although some parts of the sea were more salty than others, sea water contains the same ingredients all over the world and in the same proportions to each other, so that they differ only as to the total amount of their contents. This discovery proved particularly useful because if one of the substances in sea water, such as the chloride ion, is measured, the others, and the total salt content, can be computed. Marcet also made the important discovery that the volume of sea water continues to contract as it cools to its freezing point—unlike that of fresh water, which has a point of maximum density at about 4 degrees C. This is of great significance to the pattern of ocean circulation. It was clear by this time that the water at great depths in the tropical oceans was almost as cold as the surface water near the polar regions. Emil von Lenz, a physicist who sailed with Admiral Kotzebue on his second voyage around the world in 1823–1826, was aware that the great water pressure would affect the reading of a self-registering thermometer of the maximum and minimum type by compressing the bulb and forcing the index up the temperature scale. He obtained more accurate results by hauling water up from the required depth in a special apparatus, taking its temperature and making an allowance—carefully determined by experiment—for the gain in heat during the hauling operation. In this way he obtained remarkably accurate temperatures, a little above 2 degrees C at 1,000 fathoms. Sir John Ross obtained readings as low as −1.8 degrees C at the bottom of Baffin Bay by hauling up a large sample of bottom mud and taking its temperature.

Although it had been demonstrated by Lenz and Professor Parrot of St. Petersburg early in the nineteenth century that self-registering thermometers were seriously affected by pressure, and that sea water unlike fresh water did not have a point of maximum density at 4 degrees C, many of the subsequent world expeditions such as those of Dumont d'Urville, Wilkes, and Sir James Clark Ross, with all the learning of France, the United States, and Britain behind them, went to sea firmly believing that all the water in the depths of the oceans had a temperature of 4 degrees C. Their observations did not undeceive them because they used unprotected self-registering thermometers, which when lowered into water of 1 degree C at about 3,000 meters would come up reading 4 degrees C because of the error caused by pressure.

Such mistakes would not have been made if there had been a school of marine science, a body of men making the application of science to the sea their life's work, so that new discoveries and advances would not pass unnoticed. This degree of specialization was not reached in physics although in biology the turning point came fairly early in the nineteenth century. By 1850 marine biologists such as Michael Sars in Norway and Edward Forbes in Britain might well have been called biological oceanographers although the name oceanography was not introduced until the 1880s. The growth of marine biology in Edinburgh now tends to be attributed largely to the whaler William Scoresby, who after serving as mate on his father's ship commanded his own expedition and afterward studied at Edinburgh University under Professor Jameson. He was a keen observer who made remarkable contributions to geographical knowledge and undoubtedly turned the interest of Professor Jameson and his successors toward the sea. Forbes, Wyville Thomson, and eventually the *Challenger* expedition may well owe much to his enthusiasm and inspiration. It was because of this growing and continuous interest in the biology of the sea that the French, U.S., and British world expeditions were better equipped to study the plant and animal life of the oceans than to observe their temperature and salinity structure and to measure the currents.

Cooperation between philosophers and sailors followed Benjamin Franklin's study of the Gulf Stream. The remarkable temperature difference between the current and the coastal water was known as was the fact that the surface temperature in the coastal region was generally less over a shoal. Sir Charles Blagden, physician to the British army, as well as Colonel Williams, Franklin's nephew, Captain Strickland, and Captain Truxton, one of the first six captains of the U.S. Navy, wrote papers on thermometrical navigation, and other sailors, notably Captain Hamilton, also emphasized the variability of the current. At the same time Major James Rennell, a surveyor-general in Bengal, was collecting comprehensive information on all the principal currents of the North and South Atlantic Ocean and on the Agulhas current between the Indian and Atlantic oceans, and Marsden, Secretary of the British navy during the Napoleonic wars, divided the ocean into squares that still bear his name for the purpose of collecting systematic information for the use of the sailors.

A remarkable fillip to the systematic study of winds and currents was given by Lieutenant M. F. Maury when he was appointed Officer-in-Charge of the U.S. Navy's depot of charts and instruments. Already the author of a standard work in navigation, he found a vast amount of useful information in the logbooks of every voyage made by ships of the U.S. Navy. His activity was widely recognized as being beneficial to world shipping, and he was well supported in his efforts to set up an international conference on maritime meteorology, which was held in Brussels in 1853. The conference marked the beginning of meteorological offices in most of the maritime countries and of the systematic return of meteorological logs from merchant ships. At the same time the U.S. Coast Survey under its director, Professor Bache, a descendent of Franklin, was making detailed studies of the temperature and velocity structure of the Gulf Stream, which culminated in a remarkable series of velocity-depth profiles measured at anchorages along six sections across the current by Lieutenant Pillsbury in 1885–1889.

Franklin and Rennell, convinced that ocean currents were caused mainly by the winds, divided the currents into two classes, drift currents caused by the continued action of the wind, and stream currents formed as a result of the accumulation of water that must occur when a drift current meets an obstacle. But Arago, the French philosopher, believed that the cooling and warming of water in the north and south, together with eastern and western deflections caused by the earth's rotation, would be more important. Maury was of the same opinion, although he was inclined to admit that the grand circulation of the ocean caused by density differences would be modified by winds, rain, barometric pressure, evaporation, and even by the flora and fauna of the ocean. In England there was a bitter controversy between James Croll, who had made notable contributions to geological science, and W. B. Carpenter, who was a colleague of Wyville Thomson on several of the voyages inspired by the Edinburgh marine biologists. Croll would never admit that the density differences could produce appreciable currents in the ocean. Carpenter was somewhat more reasonable, being ready to admit that the wind would produce currents at the surface. The U.S. mathematician William Ferrel made an important contribution by taking a detailed account of the effect of the earth's rotation, and by reasoning that whatever produced the meridional water movements would form a pattern like the movements in the atmosphere, although more conspicuously gyratory in the oceans because of the land barriers. Ferrel's work is typical of the contribution of an expert who sees fallacies in a popular argument.

Although biological problems were more widely discussed, these were also not closely investigated at first before Edward Forbes, joined the Surveying Ship *Beacon* in 1841 to dredge for animal life in the Aegean Sea, and found that the number of different species found decreased with increasing depths. Forbes postulated that there would be an azoic zone, in which there was no life, at ocean depths below 300 fathoms. Just as the idea that the temperature in the depths of the ocean was 4 decrees C obsessed students of ocean circulation, the idea of an azoic zone —although there was already evidence against it—preoccupied biologists. In the end, however, increasing contrary evidence roused enough skepticism to promote more dredging in deep water, and all doubt on this question was removed in 1869 when Wyville Thomson brought up living creatures from depths greater than 2,500 fathoms. Protected thermometers were used on the same voyage, and the discovery that the bottom water of the Norwegian Sea was colder than −1 degree C also finally disposed of the mistaken ideas about ocean temperatures.

At about the same time the growing potential of submarine telegraph cables stimulated further interest in the deep-sea floor. Sir James Clark Ross had solved some of the problems of deep-sea sounding during his Antarctic expedition, using a line four miles long from an open boat held in position by another boat. In the United States Maury took a great interest in soundings and sent Berryman in the brig *Dolphin* to make the first successful line of soundings across the North Atlantic. On the next voyage of the *Dolphin* Maury used a device that released the sounding weight when it touched the bottom leaving only a light bottom-sampling device attached to the line. Before long, wire sounding lines, steam winding engines, and steam-driven ships made the task of sounding even simpler.

Growing interest in the deep sea and its life led, in 1872, to the round-the-world voyage of HMS *Challenger* that lasted three and one-half years and produced an unprecedented mass of observations in physics, chemistry, biology, and geology. The *Challenger* expedition is often regarded as the beginning of oceanography, perhaps because its sheer size tends to dominate the historical perspective. If not the beginning it was an important stage in the development of man's study of the sea: an effort on such a scale had never before been concentrated on the ocean. The *Challenger* was followed by important expeditions from Germany, the United States, Denmark, France, Italy, Norway, the Netherlands, and Russia, by the founding of institutions especially devoted to marine science, and by the notable activity of Prince Albert I of Monaco.

The establishment of permanent stations for the conducting of marine studies soon gained impetus from the need to carry out oceanographic investigations in support of research on fishing problems. Among the new bodies that were established to obtain more information were the Kiel Commission for the scientific investigation of the German Sea, the Scottish Fishery Board, and the United States Fish Commission and an International Fisheries Exhibition took place in 1883. With the rapid development of the fisheries that followed the introduction of steam, and the use of the otter trawl, in about 1895, the possibilities of overfishing increased the demand for research on the sea. In 1899 the King of Sweden invited representatives of the countries interested in the North Sea and Baltic fisheries to a conference that resulted in the founding of the International Council for the Exploration of the Sea in 1901.

The early development of the physics of the oceans owes much to the inspiration of fishery research. The migrations of fish, particularly the herring, were found to be related to the distribution of water masses and currents. This led to more extensive studies reaching from the Baltic Sea to West Greenland, and the inevitable discovery that the currents were linked to the North Atlantic circulation stimulated theoretical and practical studies on general oceanic circulation. The early work was dominated by interesting but qualitative approaches, such as that of Otto Pettersson, who believed that the main force driving Atlantic water toward the Arctic region was provided by the melting of ice. Pettersson was not mathematical enough to be able to carry his new and interesting ideas beyond rather diffuse physical reasoning, but theoretical physicists such as Sandstrom, V. W. Ekman, Bjerknes, and Helland-Hansen were soon drawn into the field, and in the following years, while they occupied chairs in theoretical physics, they worked actively on meteorological as well as oceanographical problems. This new activity was encouraged by rapid improvement in observations. The new reversing deep-sea thermometers were a great improvement on protected maximum and minimum thermometers, and the newly developed methods of determining salinity by titrating the chloride were more accurate and consistent than hydrometer readings. The relation of chemistry to temperature and salinity also came to be well understood. The work of the scientists of the Norwegian North Atlantic Expedition, and of Knudsen in Copenhagen, were particularly important, and fresh interest in the Arctic and Antarctic Ocean contributed to the activity of this period. Nansen and Helland-Hansen worked effectively in the north, as did Schott, Drygalski, Brennecke, and Rouch in the South.

The great activity of this period of theoretical oceanography was not sustained, but there was continuing work done in Bergen, Christiania, Stockholm, and Hamburg, and a new school was developing in Berlin. One of the highlights of the period before World War I was the oceanographic studies conducted by the German Antarctic Expedition in 1911–1912. In the brief reports posted home from the *Deutschland* during her outward voyage, Wilhelm Brennecke gave an accurate representation of the distribution of temperature and salinity in a vertical section from north to south through much of the Atlantic Ocean, which made all the previous work much more intelligible. The complete results of this expedition, published after the war, provided similar added enlightenment to the study of water conditions in the Antarctic Ocean. The next great effort also came from Germany in 1925–1927, when the research vessel *Meteor* secured accurate data from 14 sections across the Atlantic Ocean between the latitudes of 20 degrees N and 65 degrees S. Another notable expedition of the early postwar period was that of the Norwegian ship *Maud,* which spent five years fixed in the ice off the northeast coast of Siberia.

The *Meteor* expedition, like that of the *Challenger,* was followed by world expeditions from other countries. The *Discovery* investigations, starting in 1925, made a thorough study of the temperature and salinity distribution in the Antarctic Ocean, and a very comprehensive study of the plankton and its seasonal variations, particularly of the krill on which whales feed. Norway sent the *Norwegia* to the Antarctic. The round-the-world oceanographical expedition of the Carlsberg Foundation was the largest of several Danish expeditions led by Johannes Schmidt, who made the remarkable discovery that the Sargasso Sea was the breeding place of the European freshwater eels. The Netherlands made an extensive survey of the water conditions in the East Indian Archipelago from the ship *Willebrord Snellius.* The United States started her increasing activity with the *Atlantis* from Woods Hole, Massachusetts, and the *E. W. Scripps* from the Scripps Institution in La Jolla, California, as well as intensive work in the Pacific Ocean from the nonmagnetic ship *Carnegie.* Wust, one of the *Meteor* scientists, has called this era between 1925 and 1940 the era of national systematic and dynamic ocean surveys.

The interwar years were a period of active research into the life-history and growth of the principal food fishes of the northern hemisphere, particularly of northwest Europe, continuing and flourishing in what was perhaps the heyday of the International Council for the Exploration of the Sea. It was not, however, an outstanding period for theoretical oceanography, except in the study of tides. The work of the newly founded Liverpool Tidal Institute, and similar activity in the Deutsche Seewarte and the U. S. Coast and Geodetic Survey, were achieving remarkable improvements in the theory of tides as well as in the analysis and prediction of tidal levels. The biological collections of many of the earlier oceanic and Antarctic expeditions continued to appear, but the physicists working on ocean circulation seemed to be getting smaller returns from their observations: they began to need more advanced techniques, more accurate, continuous, and closely spaced observations, and more realistic theories before much more could be done.

World War II brought a new influx of theoretical and practical physicists, and since that time the effectiveness of oceanography has developed as never before. It began particularly in the United States and Great Britain as part of the war effort. The beginning was rather slow as new scientists began to be attracted to the study of factors that affected the performance of underwater acoustic devices, and it advanced very rapidly when they were given a fairly free hand to find out more about surface waves and the detailed structure of the sea floor. Their early results were scientifically attractive and promised applications to seagoing industry as detailed and reliable as those that make science essential to industry on land. Marine science then spread rapidly throughout the world. There were many world expeditions, first by Sweden and Denmark and then by the United States and the Soviet Union, but the greatest achievement was the development of new physical, geophysical, biological, and chemical techniques, and the gradual establishment of more realistic theories. Much of the best work was done by theoretical and practical men working together, using theory to plan the observations and the observations to check and extend the theories. This was often made more effective by joint action between laboratories interested in similar problems, sharing the planning, the observations, and the analysis, and integration of the data.

A number of new international organizations grew up to coordinate marine science. The International Council of Scientific Unions has a Special Committee on Oceanic Research to coordinate the work of the different scientific disciplines interested in marine research. UNESCO and FAO sponsor an Intergovernmental Oceanographic Commission, which is composed of governments ready to take an active part in joint programs. The International Geophysical Year promised useful contributions to world problems such as ocean circulation, variations in mean sea level, and long-wave activity in the ocean.

The International Indian Ocean Expedition of 1962–1963 brought a concentration of ships using the latest methods into a little known area. They compared their techniques and used them to gain much new information about the physics, geology, and biology of the ocean, and about methods of determining the length of time it takes the monsoon winds, which change every six months, to reverse the currents.

During the past ten years, geophysical exploration and commercial exploitation have spread rapidly across the continental shelves, and now look into the deep ocean. They have greatly increased the demand for marine technology. The greatest benefits from marine science in the next few decades are still likely to be the benefits that better knowledge and understanding of the waves, currents, water levels, interchanges with the atmosphere, plant and animal life, and submarine geology are likely to confer on existing industries and on existing applications of science to meteorology and pollution problems, but the more remote possibilities of exploiting the deep-sea floor seem increasingly likely to call the tune. By too sharply dividing off the deep and shallow seas into areas of national interest, countries run some risk of hindering the scientific study of the ocean, without which little progress can be made. There are still enormous problems, as well as new, unanswered questions—such as how to cope with marine pollution.

All this—the growth of oceanography from "little science" to "big science"—has taken place during the working life of marine scientists who are still active, and much more will be done in the years ahead.

2 THE BIRTH AND GROWTH OF THE OCEANS

Harold C. Urey

In discussing the origin and evolution of the oceans, it is necessary to discuss the oceans and the atmosphere together, because one is so dependent upon the other. We should also recognize at the onset that no one has succeeded in describing the earth's atmosphere without an enormous amount of observational data. Therefore, I shall present the evidence, as we know it at the present time, that helps us understand the early history of the earth, its oceans, and its atmosphere.

First, we will assume that the earth accumulated from solid objects similar to the asteroids and perhaps even larger objects such as the moon. It is contended that the earth could not have accumulated in its present form if any important amounts of the primordial gases of the solar system had been present in the neighborhood in which the accumulation took place because the solid objects and gases together would have been about as massive as Jupiter. It is very doubtful that there is any possible method by which the gases could have been lost from an object of that mass. Even if we were to assume that there was some solar effect that blasted many of the gases away, the earth might be left with about 5 per cent of its original mass present in its dense atmosphere. The gravitational field would then be that of our earth, and it would be difficult to remove these gases, particularly the ones having a higher atomic weight than hydrogen and helium such as water, neon, argon, or even krypton and xenon. There seems to be no answer to this problem except that the principal gases involved in the origin of the solar system and the planets were mostly swept away from the region in which the earth accumulated.

The age of the solar system, as judged by studies on the meteorites, must be at least 4.5 to 4.7 thousand million years. It seems difficult to believe that the meteorites acquired their structure at any time except at that very early age. At the present time, objects moving in orbits near that of the earth collide with the earth within 10 or 20 million years. If the earth were much smaller—if it had the mass of the moon or even less—the probability of collision would be much less. We will tacitly assume that such massive objects were present, and that they provided the centers for the accumulation of the planets.

Solid objects moving near the early earth, when it had reached approximately its present mass, would have collided with the earth at very high velocities, at least as high as the 11.2 kilometer/second escape velocity of the earth. Substances of the kind that compose the earth, colliding with the earth at this velocity, would create temperatures as high as 100,000 degrees Centigrade, sufficient to completely vaporize the object itself along with some material of the earth in the immediate neighborhood of the collision. In a short time after a collision of this kind, the resulting hot spot on the earth would have cooled down, water would have condensed, and produced a landscape perhaps somewhat like that we see on the moon today. After the passage of some time, a subsequent collision would produce another hot spot of this kind. This process would be repeated many times in the course of the accumulation. In the accumulation process, water would be buried in the rocks below the surface, and even such substances as the inert gases could be buried to some extent. But finally, when this accumulation process was essentially completed, the earth would have many craters scattered over its surface, and some amount of atmosphere—and probably water with some hydrogen, and some ammonium salts dissolved in it. Today we think that most of the water on the surface of the earth came from the earth's interior during geologic time, as a result of volcanic activity. It is therefore difficult to ascertain how much water was present on the surface of the earth during the terminal stage of its accumulation. In the past, I have assumed that perhaps 10 per cent of the water of present oceans was present as superficial water at that time. It is also of interest to ask how much of the other volatiles (such as nitrogen that is present in the atmosphere at the present time to approximately 800 grams per square centimeter [800 g/cm^2] of the earth's surface) was present in the initial stages after the accumulation of the earth. Superficial carbon to the extent of some 5,000 to 6,000 grams per square centimeter of the earth's surface is present on the earth at the present time, but how much of this was present at the beginning of the earth history? Again, we do not know. In the past, I have made the arbitrary assumption that perhaps as much as 10 per cent of the present volatile materials of the earth's surface was present at the terminal stage of the formation of the earth.

It is safe to conclude that the surface of the earth was a pock-marked surface similar to that of the moon. Water probably filled the earth's craters. Today, the surface of the earth is covered with great continental masses and very deep oceans. Geologists have demonstrated, I believe, that the continents are now growing and have probably grown in the past. This means that in the early history of the earth, there were probably no continents, only great craters some hundreds of kilometers in dimensions, filled with pools of water. Or perhaps, in the early history of the earth, there might have been seas as large as the Mediterranean Sea. One of the immediate results of this would have been that tidal effects that are now moving the moon away from the earth would not have been very effective. Hence, probably the movement of the moon from the earth was substantially less effective than it is at the present time. Of course, volcanic activity would have started very early in the history of the earth. It may in fact be that because of radio-active heating, the iron nickel of the earth's core melted and sank to the center of the earth, thus producing a very substantial amount of additional heat which melted the entire earth in its early history. The earth then solidified with the molten iron-nickel core at its center, with so-called dunitic-type rocks being formed above the core, and more acidic or basaltic-types being formed in the outer parts of the earth.

We would certainly expect that water would be present on the surface of the primitive earth, but in addition to this, other volatile substances must have been present—such as carbonaceous materials, nitrogen in the form of nitrogen gas of ammonia or carbonaceous nitrogen compounds. It seems very certain that there was no oxygen present. The earth is relatively low in oxygen with a large iron mass in its interior core. The meteorites are highly reduced, and there is every evidence that reducing substances such as hydrogen gas should have been present in excess amounts, and that oxygen could not be present.

The most important chemical process that took place during the early geologic time was caused by the escape of hydrogen from the high atmosphere of the earth. Being a very low atomic weight element, the mean velocity of hydrogen atoms is larger than that of any other element. This makes hydrogen the one element that can most easily escape from the earth. As hydrogen escapes by the decomposition of water, oxygen is left behind. As a result of this escape of hydrogen, the surface regions of the earth have changed from a highly reducing character with excess hydrogen present to an oxidizing character with an excess of oxygen present. During this process, if there were any substances on the surface of the earth that could have absorbed the oxygen, they would have done so. For example, the element carbon, if it were present in the early history of the earth, would have been changed from methane, which is CH_4, to elemental carbon or to carbon dioxide. My estimate is that this process during geologic time required the dissociation of some 9,000 grams of water per square centimeter of the earth's surface. In the same way, nitrogen being changed from ammonia to nitrogen gas, sulfur from sulfide to sulfate, and considerable amounts of ferrous iron in the low oxidation state to ferric iron in the highly oxidized state would have required very considerable amounts of oxygen. The total estimated in this way amounts to about 30,000 grams of water per square centimeter of the earth's surface. Some years ago it was observed that the heavy hydrogen concentration in the oceans is higher than that which comes from the interior of the earth at the present time. This could have come about by a fractionation of the hydrogen isotopes in their escape from the earth—the light hydrogen escaping more readily than the heavy hydrogen. But, if no heavy hydrogen escaped, about 14,000 grams of water must have decomposed per square centimeter of the earth in order to accomplish this change in the present oceans of the earth. Since this fractionation process was not perfect, it looks very much as though the loss of about 30,000 grams per square centimeter of water, or the equivalent of a layer 300 meters thick, is a reasonable estimate of the water that was dissociated into hydrogen and oxygen, with the light hydrogen and some of the heavy hydrogen escaping in order to produce the present oxidized state of the earth's surface. I think this is a fairly good estimate, although not highly precise of course.

At present, there is about one half part per million of hydrogen in the atmosphere on the earth. This hydrogen is not at all in equilibrium with the oxygen concentration of the earth, but it is probably being produced by the action of ultraviolet light on water in the high atmosphere of the earth. This means that hydrogen is escaping from the high atmosphere of the earth at the present time. Some years ago, I showed that the rate of escape of hydrogen from the earth is not determined by the temperature of the high atmosphere but by the rate of diffusion from the lower atmosphere to the high atmosphere. This rate of diffusion should be proportional to the concentration of hydrogen in the surface regions of the earth. With this amount of hydrogen, apparently in the course of geologic time only about 20 grams of water per square centimeter would be dissociated into hydrogen and oxygen, and the hydrogen would escape losing only about 20 grams of water per square centimeter, that is, less than one-thousandth of the amount that we have estimated to be required. There is evidence that the oxidizing atmosphere of the earth appeared approximately 2 billion years ago. I shall describe this evidence later. If this oxidation is to take place during the course of $2\frac{1}{2}$ billion years, then we must expect that the pressure of hydrogen was higher $2\frac{1}{2}$ billion years ago than it is now. I shall arbitrarily assume that the pressure had to be sufficiently higher to account for this, and this gives us about 1.5×10^{-3} atmosphere of hydrogen present in the early history of the earth. Of course, there is no evidence that the pressure of hydrogen was constant during all of this time, but we have no evidence to guide us in estimating what this concentration of hydrogen may have been. Taking this pressure of hydrogen in the primitive atmosphere of the earth up to 2 billion years ago, we can ask in what forms other volatile compounds existed during this period. First, there was no free oxygen in the atmosphere, and it is probable that nitrogen was not present as such. We can ask about the amount of ammonia that might have been present in the atmosphere if hydrogen were present. Hydrogen and nitrogen react very slowly at ordinary temperatures. In fact, in order to produce ammonia in chemical plants, we react nitrogen and hydrogen at very high pressures and high temperatures, but remember, we are interested in getting the job done quickly. It seems likely in the high atmosphere of the earth that nitrogen and hydrogen would react slowly to give ammonia, which would be transported to the surface of the earth. Being highly soluble the ammonia would dissolve in water. This process would go on until some approximate equilibrium process were present. If we make calculations from data that is present in the chemical literature, we find that nitrogen would be present almost entirely as ammonia dissolved in ocean water. I am assuming a tenth as much nitrogen in the surface regions of the earth as there is now, and a tenth as much water. If there were less water, the concentration of ammonia would be larger, but the probability of dissociation would also be greater. What can be said with confidence is that in the first $2\frac{1}{2}$ billion years of the earth's history, the atmosphere had little nitrogen in it, and the oceans contained the ammonium-ion. It is also possible that the ammonium-ion would be captured in the sedimentary rocks of the earth, and the pressure of nitrogen might then be something like a hundredth of an atmosphere.

The next element to consider is carbon. Would carbon be present as methane, as elementary carbon, or as carbon dioxide? Exactly similar calculations show that with the pressure of hydrogen of the magnitude that we are considering, the carbon would be predominantly present as methane in the early history of the earth rather than as carbon dioxide. It would seem, therefore, that the amount of carbon present as carbon dioxide would not be very great, and as far as I know, no large deposits of carbonates have been found in the oldest surface rocks of the earth. This may be a rather doubtful conclusion because of the improbability that such rocks would have been preserved over billions of years. But the evidence seems to point in that direction. We must remember, in discussing these subjects, that equilibrium situations do not always exist, and therefore that some carbon dioxide might be present. For example, the ultraviolet light in the high atmosphere of the earth might have produced some hydrogen peroxide; and this hydrogen peroxide, washed down to the surface of the earth by rains, would react with carbon compounds, probably to produce some carbonate. This would not be an equilibrium process. But substances that are not completely in thermodynamic equilibrium exist in the atmosphere at the present time. There is now some hydrogen, a little methane, and some oxides of nitrogen in our atmosphere. All of these are unstable under present conditions in the atmosphere. We can say that it was very likely that most of the carbon in the surface regions of the earth during its early history was present in a highly reduced form such as methane, CH_4, or formaldehyde, or similar forms. Water, carbon in the form of methane, and ammonia are the volatile substances that might have been present in the atmosphere with only trace amounts of oxygen, nitrogen, and carbon dioxide.

We should consider carbon dioxide a little more closely. At present it exists in the atmosphere to the extent of about three ten thousandths (.0003) of an atmosphere pressure. However, carbon dioxide will react with certain other rocks, for example, magnesium silicate; and thermodynamic calculations show that the pressure of carbon dioxide that would be in equilibrium with magnesium silicate, magnesium carbonate, and silicon dioxide would be about 10^{-5} of an atmosphere. That is less than what is observed at the present time. It is obvious that carbon dioxide as it exists in the atmosphere today is not in equilibrium since it would be removed if equilibrium were established. Its pressure would be reduced by a factor of about thirty-three from where it is at the present time. This would interfere considerably with the growth of plants as we know them. It is interesting, indeed, that this carbon dioxide, upon which plants depend and upon which therefore animals depend directly, is unstable, and hence, we are living in an unstable situation. If an equilibrium should be established, plant and animal life would decrease.

Other substances such as sodium chloride and sodium bromide that are found in the oceans are distinctly soluble substances. In fact, the chlorides and bromides are soluble except for compounds with rather rare elements such as silver. These substances do not exist in the atmosphere (except very temporarily in the neighborhood of volcanoes), but they do make up important substances in the oceans. A related compound, the fluorides (one of the so-called halides, along with chlorine and bromine), forms invaluable compounds in the form of calcium fluoride, and hence is not soluble in water, nor is it volatile. It is therefore found in the rocks of the earth and is not found in the oceans. Another set of compounds that exist in the oceans at the present time are sulfates and compounds of sulfur. These are also found in deposits in the form of calcium sulfate. A study of the thermodynamics of these compounds, as compared with others, shows that in the primitive conditions on the surface of the earth, sulfur should have been present as iron sulfide, if equilibrium conditions were established. It might also be that sulfur would be present as the element sulfur itself, as it is in certain parts of the earth at the present time. However, this would have been unstable in a reducing atmosphere, and it is unstable in an oxidizing atmosphere. Therefore, all sulfur deposits are thermodynamically unstable under all conditions. It seems likely that compounds of sulfur did not appear in the oceans until oxidizing conditions existed, that is, until there was free oxygen in the atmosphere. Of course, it is always possible that small amounts of such compounds were present even though they should not be on the basis of our equilibrium calculations.

In a situation in which we have great energy being expended, as it is in an atmosphere that is very far from being in equilibrium with the conditions we find on the earth because of light from the sun, then it is entirely reasonable, and is in fact a well observed situation, that some rare substances or small amounts of substances of this kind are present. Of course, this is true with respect to hydrogen and methane and the oxides of nitrogen in the atmosphere at the present time. Also, in the neighborhood of our cities, there are carbon compounds of various kinds; and in some places hydrogen sulfide and sulfur dioxide are present in the atmosphere in small amounts. All of these are unstable. The primitive oceans may have had small amounts of sulfates present. It is well known that ultraviolet light acting upon water, as for example in the high atmosphere, will produce hydrogen peroxide. Hydrogen peroxide will oxidize sulfides to sulfates and sulfites, and they will dissolve in water. Hence, these substances may have been present in the primitive oceans of the earth. It is to be expected that they would be present only in small amounts, and perhaps not in sufficient quantity to result in the deposition of calcium sulfate. In this connection, it would be very interesting indeed to know under what conditions calcium sulfate deposits occurred during the early history of the earth.

Thus far, we have been discussing simple elements and compounds—water, hydrogen, nitrogen, ammonia, sulfates, carbon dioxide, oxygen—but in addition to these simple compounds, we must expect that in the primitive oceans of the earth an enormous amount of carbonaceous matter of a very complicated kind was present—compounds of carbon, oxygen, hydrogen, nitrogen, and other elements such as those that are found in living organisms at the present time. At present, all such compounds that we meet generally have been through the bodies of living organisms, but this need not have been the case in the early history of the earth. Some of these compounds could have been present as a result of inorganic reactions of a slow and nonenergetic kind. With volatile compounds of carbon in the atmosphere, one could expect that ultraviolet light from the sun or electrical discharges would have produced many substances of a very complex character, such as those that may have been present and may have enabled living organisms to evolve. It has recently been demonstrated that indeed such chemical substances would be produced under such conditions, and they would be expected to react to give complicated carbon compounds that may have been, and probably were, the precursors of biological life on the planet. It might be noted that the early atmosphere of the earth could have been exceedingly opaque to light. If we look over our modern cities, particularly those in which petroleum refining operations or production facilities of any kind are prominent, we find that there is a dark, cloudlike atmosphere above such cities. In a primitive atmosphere of the earth in which carbon compounds were generally present, one might find that the atmosphere was nearly opaque to light, and the earth may have been an exceedingly gloomy place. Furthermore, the odor of the atmosphere (to us) would have been most unpleasant.

I think there is considerable evidence to indicate that an atmosphere containing free oxygen appeared about 2 billion years ago. This evidence comes from several bits of information. First, the great iron deposits of the earth appeared about 2 billion years ago, and this seems to have required a series of events of approximately the following kind. Iron was dissolved out of the mountainous masses by water and flowed down to lakes or bays of the oceans where plants probably converted the iron to a nonsoluble form. The particular compound that fits this description is what we call iron carbonate, which is slightly soluble (about as soluble as limestone) and would be washed

37

down from the mountains to the seas as calcium carbonate is at the present time, providing that there is a reducing atmosphere. If some biological organisms such as plants then oxidized this ferrous carbonate to the ferric form, which is one that makes up some of our important iron deposits, it would become highly insoluble in water, precipitate out, and give the great iron deposits on the earth. This is what we find in the great iron deposits of Venezuela, Scandinavia, the northern United States, and Canada, which were deposited about 2 billion years ago.

I have been discussing the atmosphere of the earth for the most part, and I shall now turn to the question of what the oceans were doing during this time. First of all, water had been coming from the interior of the earth through volcanic activity, and the oceans were slowly growing in size. Probably carbonaceous compounds and nitrogen were also coming from the interior, and perhaps the proportions of these substances were remaining approximately constant during this time. The atmosphere would be very dark, filled with carbonaceous compounds, and I would expect that the oceans were also filled with compounds that would give the water a very brown, dark appearance, anything but the clear oceans, streams and lakes that we admire today. Also, during this time, continents probably were growing in size because of great convection currents in the earth's mantle. Rocky material rose in the regions of the ocean basins and pushed the surface material toward the present continents. That is, the great oceans grew in size from the rather small lakes characteristic of the primitive earth until the present. About 2 billion years ago, oxygen appeared, and the relatively clear water resulted so that the pleasant situation, as it exists today, came forth.

There is an interesting situation that exists with respect to oxygen in the atmosphere. The presence of an oxygen atmosphere surely is caused by the activities of plants. For if water, nitrogen, and oxygen were allowed to react spontaneously without any activity of plants, the oxygen of the atmosphere would disappear because of the formation of nitrates such as are found in Chile and various places on the earth. It is interesting again that living organisms, as we know them today, depend first of all on excessive amounts of carbon dioxide in the atmosphere, which probably is maintained by volcanic activity pouring carbon dioxide into the atmosphere. At the same time, oxygen-loving animals and plants depend upon the oxygen supply that is maintained by the activity of green plants. Without these two situations, the present condition on the earth would be very different. The oceans would be a dark, murky color, and the atmosphere would contain no oxygen. The sort of plants and animals that would exist would be those that thrive upon reducing conditions, that is, the absence of oxygen and some appreciable concentration of hydrogen, methane, and ammonia in the atmosphere.

In this group of papers there are other discussions on the origin of life in the oceans, and I wish to emphasize, at this point, that it was the reducing condition in the atmosphere that was congenial to the origin of life. Under these conditions, that is, an excess amount of hydrogen in the air rather than an excess of oxygen, the complicated carbon compounds are possible. This was demonstrated a number of years ago by Stanley Miller in his doctoral dissertation at the University of Chicago. Much other work of this kind has completely confirmed the general conditions that were postulated. Living organisms of both the plant and animal variety have amino acids containing carbon, oxygen, and nitrogen, which form proteins that are very important substances for all living organisms, plants and animals—those living in reducing atmospheres and those living in oxidized atmospheres. In addition, it should be noted that all living organisms, from the simple to the most complex, have what are called nucleic acids, which are compounds containing so-called bases known as purines and pyrimidines. These bases owe their origin, under primitive conditions, to the existence of hydrogen cyanide, a substance that is highly poisonous to higher life at the present time. In addition to these bases, these compounds contain a sugar known as ribose, and finally they also contain a phosphoric acid group.

39

These nucleic acids are the punch card mechanisms by which hereditary qualities are transmitted, and are the substances that determine the character of the proteins produced in the bodies of these organisms. Furthermore, these proteins apparently determine the detailed character of organisms to a very large extent. Hence, in thinking of the origin of life, I think of oceans that contained compounds of this kind—amino acids, the so-called nucleic acid bases that probably are produced from hydrocyanic acid or compounds like it, phosphoric acid, and a special type of sugar. All of these must be present simultaneously, and the one depends upon the other. Life, as we know it, was produced in some way by an interaction between these compounds, and it looks very much as though the primitive oceans of the earth were the setting for chemical reactions of this kind. It might be, as has been suggested, that claylike substances served as catalysts for this process, although I think there is no certainty that this is the case.

It should be emphasized that an adequate source of energy is required for this process. Chemical reactions proceed spontaneously and produce a variety of new compounds only because they have energy stored in them, and there must be a source of this high energy. It is evident that the sun is the source of such energy at the present time, and I think we must conclude that it was the source at all times in the past. One of the important things that was taking place was the volatilization of compounds that were carried up into the atmosphere, and activated by ultraviolet light or electrical discharges. They fell in raindrops to the surface of the earth into the oceans where the chemical reactions took place, producing different compounds—some complex, others simple, such as methane. These were carried to the high atmosphere, activated again, and carried down into the oceans. This process was repeated many times and was an important factor in the production of life and the maintenance of living processes. This sort of thing must have taken place from the very beginning in the atmosphere of the earth and produced first the complicated compounds (probably the slowly reacting kind), later more complicated compounds, until finally the simplest of living organisms gradually evolved over the course of the billions of years that the earth has existed under the approximate conditions of temperature that we have at the present time. Ultimately living organisms, as we know them today, were produced.

To conclude, the most important phenomenon relative to the evolution of the oceans and atmosphere is the photochemical dissociation of water in the high atmosphere by ultraviolet light into hydrogen and oxygen, the escape of hydrogen from the earth, and the retention of oxygen and its reaction with the compounds of carbon, nitrogen, sulfur, and iron at the earth's surface. This influenced the chemical character of the atmosphere and oceans and promoted the origin of living organisms. Physically, the oceans have grown in size because of the growth of continents and the escape of water from the earth's interior. The atmosphere has changed from a murky, vile smelling one to a clear one with no odor at all. This murky ocean has become one teaming with living organisms all related to one another, some of whom have crept upon the land. We Homo sapiens are one variety of these creatures from the sea that have developed a brain that enables us to ask these interesting questions about the history of the earth extending back to 4.5 thousand million years ago.

3 CHEMICAL CYCLES IN THE SEA

Donald W. Hood

In the previous chapter, Harold C. Urey discussed the birth and growth of the oceans, in which he skillfully developed the early history of the oceans and suggested the probable mechanisms by which organic matter was first formed on earth. Resulting from these early beginnings, the simplest of organisms have gradually evolved during the course of billions of years into the complex biota that we now observe in our modern environment. The primitive ocean as discussed by Urey was low or devoid of oxygen; it contained inorganic salts and complex organic molecules, which provided the basis for life's early processes. During the evolution of complex life on earth, oxygen has accumulated through high altitude decomposition of water vapor and production of oxygen by photosynthetic processes until at the present time the atmosphere contains 21 per cent gaseous oxygen, and a proportionate amount of this is dissolved in ocean water. This provides a medium in both the atmosphere and ocean that is adequate to carry on the metabolic processes of organisms that require oxygen including all animals, most higher plants, and many, but not all, lower forms of life.

Chemical cycles, which now occur in the oceans, are, therefore, largely in an oxidized system. In some areas, however, conditions exist where the available oxygen has been used up because of the decomposition of organic matter at a sufficiently great rate such that a supply of oxygen from the atmosphere or from photosynthetic plants is inadequate and thus oxygen free (or anoxic) conditions prevail. In the oceans these areas are limited to such places as the deep waters of the Black Sea, the Curaçao Trench in the Caribbean Sea, many glacial fjords, and other environmental situations where the mixing between surface of the ocean and deep water is very slow.

The development of today's ocean occurred over a very long period of time and the building of conceptual hypotheses of the oceans has engaged scientists and philosophers since the beginning of scientific literature (and evidence from past cultures suggests that ancient people were similarly occupied). There is a trend of continuing questions and attempted answers in the literature of oceanography that are still of major concern to modern scientists. Some questions that are still pertinent include:

1. Is the ocean becoming saltier?

2. Has the volume of the ocean changed markedly during geological time?

3. What are the phenomena that control the chemical composition of the ocean?

4. Has the chemical composition changed through time?

As early as 1715 Edmund Halley, an important philosopher of his day, suggested "the ocean itself is becoming salt and we are thereby furnished with an argument for estimation of the duration of all things from observation of the increment of saltiness in the water." He considered the interactions between the earth and the ocean during all of geological time to be the same as he observed them in 1715. He regretted, for instance, that the ancient Greeks and Romans had not measured the salinity of the sea so that the increase of saltiness over some 2,000 years could be used in an extrapolation technique to estimate the time at which the salt content of the ocean was zero. This early hypothesis of the earth's oceans was extremely simplified from what we consider today to be the "real world." He thought that small changes of saltiness could lead to estimates of the duration of all things. He assumed a linear extrapolation from the beginning of the oceans to the present. Using modern values for saltiness and taking the annual input of dissolved solids by the world's rivers, we find that it would take about 20 million years to accumulate the total ocean salt. But what must be true if 20 million years is the age of the oceans? First, it must be assumed that the annual rate of introduction of salt per year has either been constant over geological time or represents an average value of a variable rate. Second, the dissolved solids, once introduced to the ocean, must remain there. Both of these assumptions are probably wrong, particularly the second. Certainly, the process of sedimentation in the ocean indicates that the second assumption cannot be valid.

In 1899 Joly, using the element sodium rather than total salt, computed the age of the ocean to be 80 to 90 million years. His data was based upon the fact that sodium, one of the major elements in sea water, remains in solution in the water, thus avoiding the sedimentation problem. However, it is known that a substantial amount of sodium in river water is derived from salt aerosols that are formed by winds and evaporation over the surface of the sea and then fall as rain over the land and finally return to the river system by means of runoff. Adjusting the Joly hypothesis for cyclic sodium gives an age of 200 million years. Finally, using similar reasoning a period of about 700 to 800 million years was computed by allowing for the marked lowering concentrations in dissolved solids in river waters during flood times. All of these estimates are the result of modifications that do not change the basic original Halley model or its underlying assumptions. None has provided for sedimentation.

All of the models based on sodium depend upon the uniqueness of sodium, which is not evident from our knowledge of the behavior of ionic solutions of sodium salts. If computations based on sodium are reliable, then it follows that computations using data for the other major dissolved elements—magnesium, calcium, and potassium—should yield the same age as that obtained from sodium. If not, the differences must be explained in terms of a chemical or geochemical process. However, the age of the ocean was found to be 23 million years based on magnesium, 1.3 million years based on calcium, 700 million years based on sodium, and 10 million years based on potassium. These differences could be reconciled by noting that these elements may be unique in their geochemical behavior. However, this assumption requires a major revision of what we now believe the over-all behavior of the ocean to be. Thus we are forced to produce a new theory. Recently, the older models have been reconstructed to incorporate known differences and similarities in the chemical behavior of elements. This system has the following important properties: chemical reactions occur during weathering of the land masses, in the transit of water into the sea, and finally during the aging of sediments. The composition and quantity of sea water cannot be accounted for by assuming the weathering of igneous rocks to be the sole source. We know that the ocean contains massive quantities of volatile constituents in excess of the amount that could have been produced by weathering of igneous rocks including water, sulfur compounds, the halogens, boron, and carbon. These so-called excess volatiles are accounted for by the fusion of the earth's interior, a process that is now going on and has been going on throughout geological time. In addition, small quantities of matter are being added to the ocean from outer space. The processes of addition to or removal of these volatiles from the ocean is assumed to be in equilibrium, an assumption for which there is experimental verification. This means that the rate of addition of material by river water is about the same as the rate with which the same kind of material is removed by sedimentation and evaporation. (A significant quantity of the material carried to the sea by rivers is cyclic salt, a part of which is then deposited on land and finally back to the sea as river constituents.) Most of the chloride in river waters and significant fractions of sodium and sulphate have been shown to be cyclic. Thus, river water composition is not a measure of erosion or weathering. Chemically unreactive elements will remain in solution in the sea for a longer time than reactive elements. Reactive elements, which readily enter into reactions that produce solid phases, will be removed rapidly by sedimentation processes. This difference in the chemical activity immediately accounts for differences in residence time of different elements, difference in relative composition of river water and sea water, and the spacial distribution of some elements in sediments.

We now realize that the age of the ocean is not computable from the observations and theories discussed thus far. We can, however, learn something about the behavior of specific elements in the oceanic environment. We can compute an element's residence time in the ocean, that is, the average time an element remains in the ocean before being removed by some process. Elements with short residence time are highly active chemically. Those with long residence time are relatively nonreactive. As for the actual age of the ocean, we now believe from measurements and computations based on the radioactive decay of naturally occurring elements that the ocean is almost two billion years old.

Thus far, I have mentioned mainly the metallic elements sodium, magnesium, calcium, and potassium. These cationic elements, coupled with the anions chloride, sulphate, bicarbonate, and bromide, comprise what are commonly known as the major components of sea water. These eight elements were found by the classical work of Dittmar, a Scottish chemist working on the *Challenger* samples collected throughout the world, to have *fixed ratios* in sea water, no matter where the samples were collected. This relationship has come to be known as the "constancy of composition concept," and many of our methods for measuring salinity, density, and physical-chemical properties of sea water have been based on this concept. While small deviations have been shown to occur from the constancy of composition concept, these are usually of minor significance and are only of importance when the most exacting oceanographic studies are made.

Although 99.7 per cent of the salt in the ocean is made up of the 8 major components, chemical oceanography would be a dull subject, indeed, if the other 0.3 per cent, consisting of approximately 80 elements, were not present. These trace components, with concentrations of between 1 ppm for fluoride down to gold and other rare heavy metals in concentrations of about 1/1000th part per billion, have attracted much scientific attention. In this group are the nutrient or fertility elements that are necessary for the growth of plants. The plants, mostly microscopic, are, of course, the primary producers of organic energy for the ocean's biota. The compounds of phosphorus, nitrogen, and silicate; the trace metals manganese, copper, zinc, molybdenum, iron, and cobalt; along with some trace organic components, an adequate supply of carbon dioxide, and sunlight constitute the necessary ingredients for plant growth. All of these biologically active materials are subjected to processes that cause different concentrations in different water layers. Organic matter formed by photosynthesis in surface layers sinks under the force of gravity to depths where it is decomposed, thus releasing the nutrient elements. Organisms selectively use many of the sea water components so that the constituents suffer a kind of fractionation. Biological fractionation is distinct from any that may result from water circulation, yet the over-all effects of biological fractionation are conditioned by the growth and movement in the water. Organisms effect the constituents of sea water both by synthesis and decomposition. The passage of elements from the water through living organisms and back to the water is determined by the biomass cyclic system, assimilation being termed energy fixation or photosynthesis and degradation being termed mineralization. The photosynthetic processes usually occur in the top 100 meters of the sea surface, known as the euphotic zone. Degradation may occur in sinking organisms all the way to the bottom of the ocean. However, most of the degradation of organic matter occurs above the first 1,000 meters of the ocean. Below these depths the organic matter remaining is resistant to oxidation and may remain at these depths unutilized for many thousands of years.

The cycle of nutrient elements is complex. The longest studied, and probably the best understood, of these nutrient elements is that of phosphorus. Phosphorus is not only important to the structure of the skeleton or organisms but is a required element for energy conversion and transfer in all biological systems. The major input of phosphorus into the ocean is from land run-off, which constitutes about 15 million tons per year,

47

a relatively small amount in terms of the total ocean content of 110 billion tons. Phosphorus in the sea is present largely in the form of inorganic phosphorus known as orthophosphate. In surface waters during the sunlit periods of the year, the microscopic plants known as phytoplankton utilize inorganic phosphorus for their growth requirements. Some of the organisms are consumed by predators or die and decay in the surface waters at which time the phosphorus is recycled to the surface water reservoir; however, a certain fraction of these organisms sinks below the euphotic zone and is there decomposed by bacteria. In the deep water some of the phosphorus precipitates as the mineral apatite, a calcium fluorophosphate mineral, similar to that from which phosphate fertilizers are derived. The annual precipitation of apatite is about equal to the annual delivery of phosphorus to the sea by the rivers. During photosynthetic processes surface water is depleted from inorganic phosphorus to the point where further biological growth is not practical. In the Atlantic Ocean and adjacent seas, phosphorus is thought to be the most frequently limiting nutrient.

The intricate details of the phosphorus system in the sea are quite complicated, since only part of the cycle is known. One of the difficulties is that analytical methods do not exist to determine orthophosphate in sea water at the low levels approaching that at which a limitation of growth occurs. Although phosphorus does occur in some organic forms, the exact chemical compounds composing this fraction are not known.

To better understand the phosphorus cycle in the oceans, it is necessary to increase our knowledge of ocean current systems. The classical example of the effect of currents on the concentration of phosphorus in ocean waters is that of the interaction between the Mediterranean Sea and the North Atlantic Ocean. In this exchange, the North Atlantic loses surface water to the Mediterranean Sea and gains high salinity Mediterranean water that passes out over the sill in the Straight of Gibraltar. This high salinity water is low in phosphorus as compared to other waters of equal depth, thus providing an intermediate layer in the Atlantic Ocean at a depth of approximately 1,200 meters of phosphate depleted water. Thus, an understanding of the phosphorus distribution in the North Atlantic requires not only an understanding of the biological processes occurring but that of the ocean current systems that are dominant.

Enrichment of the surface water with phosphorus or other nutrient materials occurs in areas of upwelling, a phenomenon brought about by persistent offshore trade winds, which are particularly pronounced along the West Coast of North and South America, Africa, Europe, and India. Similar upwellings occur in boundaries between the equatorial currents and in regions of island arcs such as the Aleutian Islands, where deep water is brought to the surface because of tidal energy and topographical features.

Phosphorus in shallow basins and estuaries and even in the ocean depths is much more concentrated in the sediments than in the overlying water. In shallow bay regions, such as along the coast of Texas, the sediments may be 100 times as rich in phosphorus as the overlying water. When such sediments lie under a stable strata of water, the exchange between the sediments and the water depends upon the oxidized state of the ionic forms of iron in the sediments forming compounds with phosphorus. Oxidized iron or ferric iron forms insoluble ferric phosphates that remain in the sediments as long as the overlying water contains sufficient oxygen to maintain this oxidative state. When reducing conditions occur, the ferric iron is converted to ferrous iron, which forms soluble ferrous phosphate, which is then released to the overlying water. In the open ocean, however, it is probable that the concentration of phosphorus in the water column is controlled by the solubility of apatite or calcium fluorophosphate, the common form of phosphorus in deep-water sediments at the seawater-sediment interface.

On a worldwide basis the major nutrient factor limiting the growth of phytoplankton in sea water is most likely the amount of nitrogen present. The nitrogen cycle in the sea is very complex. Despite the fact that gaseous nitrogen in the atmosphere and dissolved in sea water is chemically very stable, nitrogen in the sea readily responds to a multitude of biological reactions

49

and hence occurs in any one of nine different oxidation states, the lowest being that of ammonia, NH_3, the highest that of nitrate ion, NO_3^-. The highly reduced substances consisting of ammonia and organic nitrogen compounds are commonly the end products in nitrogen assimilation by marine plants or bacteria and represent about 35 per cent of the total nongaseous or combined nitrogen in the oceans. However, molecular or gaseous nitrogen is the most abundant form in the sea and amounts to about twenty times the entire amount of chemically bound nitrogen. The more highly oxidized forms of marine nitrogen are nitrite and nitrate, the latter comprising about 65 per cent of nitrogen's nongaseous form. Since nitrate is the terminal oxidation state of nitrogen in the sea, in this highly oxidized environment nitrate can originate only from oxidative processes, which presumably occur at rather constant rates for the oceans as a whole. The inorganic nitrogen in combined form is utilized by marine phytoplankton and certain bacteria for primary production; however, following a bloom of these organisms it is not uncommon for these algae populations to reduce the concentration of nongaseous nitrogen in the surface water to values below detection limits. Atmospheric precipitation, currents in the ocean, continental drainage, and the migrations of marine animals that excrete nitrogen compounds, all play important roles in the supply and distribution of nitrogen compounds.

The modern geochemical theory postulates that most of the nitrogen in the hydrosphere evolved as free nitrogen and ammonia from primitive earth as a result of radiogenic heating of elements, such as uranium, thorium, and potassium. This heating would have occurred about 5 billion years ago. During the subsequent 100 million years the primordial ocean is presumed to have evolved. Throughout geologic time the major fraction of nitrogen is believed to have entered the atmosphere through volcanism. It is believed, as described by Urey, that the early, lifeless ocean contained no oxygen and low acidity, and that most of the combined nitrogen was in the reduced chemical form of ammonia. The appearance of life on our planet depended upon early synthesis of complex nitrogen containing molecules that are vital constituents of all living material. Some of the earliest recognized fossils included the blue-green algae of Rhodesian limestone, which originated in shallow, continental seas about 2 billion years ago. The photosynthetic mode of existence of these organisms provides evidence that the biological oxidation of the atmosphere and the ocean began at an extremely early date. It is considered by most investigators that the evolution of the nitrogen cycle, the evolution of life, atmospheric oxygen, and the ocean appear to have developed concurrently.

For many years it has been known that many nitrogen compounds reach the ocean through atmospheric precipitation. Nitrogen occurs in the atmosphere predominantly in molecular form but it also occurs as organic compounds and as ammonia, nitrite, nitrate, and nitrogen oxide. It has been frequently postulated that atmospheric electrical and photochemical activity lead to the fixation of nitrogen as ammonium or nitrate since these are found in rain water. This subject has been carefully reviewed and it is concluded that atmospheric ammonia is derived from the decomposition of organic matter as largely absorbed onto dust particles. Perhaps only minor quantities of nitrate originate from lighting fixation compared to those derived from the oxidation of ammonia in the atmosphere. If this is the case, the ammonia and nitrate of the atmosphere must both correspond with stages of the cycle and are not products of nonbiological fixation. Nitrogen fixation in agriculture has traditionally been encouraged by activities of nitrogen-fixing bacteria. Similar fixation in the marine environment has received little attention, and the extent of such biological nitrogen fixation in the sea awaits a more detailed evaluation. We do know that two of the blue-green algae are capable of nitrogen fixation and are very common in tropical seas.

Denitrification processes are those processes that involve biological reduction of nitrate or nitrite to either nitrous oxide or free nitrogen. A wide variety of organisms within the sea and sediments are involved in reactions of this type but only under low oxygen or oxygen-free conditions. Such situations exist in the sediments in certain oxygen-free basins and may occur in intermediate depths over the broader Pacific and Indian oceans where the dissolved oxygen content between 150 and 500 meters approaches zero. The importance and the formation of nitrogen by the denitrification process in the sea remains somewhat obscure. However, the subject may well have important geochemical implications bearing upon the balance of nitrogen gas in the atmosphere. It is estimated that at the present rate of terrestrial fixation, nitrogen gas from the atmosphere would be exhausted in about 200 million years.

The utilization of the several fixed forms of nitrogen dissolved in ocean water by photosynthetic plankton algae is of considerable ecological interest. It appears that all marine algae capable of utilizing inorganic nitrogen can use ammonia and most of the common forms can use ammonia, nitrite, or nitrate. When all three nitrogen sources are available simultaneously, ammonia is often used preferentially, possibly because for the same energy increase algal cells can assimilate more nitrogen from ammonia than from nitrite or nitrate.

Ammonia is often the only form of available nitrogen measurable in the surface layer of the sea during certain seasons of the year. Thus, it appears that nitrate is the reserve supply of the oxidized state of nitrogen in the sea, while nitrite is an intermediate product, and ammonia is the most important source of nitrogen for photosynthesis. The oxidation of ammonia to nitrite or nitrate, commonly referred to as nitrification, is not well understood either biologically or chemically. In general, however, nitrate represents the terminal oxidation stage for deaminated nitrogen and, therefore, is the most abundant form of combined nitrogen in the sea. The direct utilization of organic nitrogen by the photosynthetic plankton has been recently observed. This capability, largely found in a group of organisms, called dinoflagellates, may be a partial explanation for the succession of phytoplankton species in the ocean surface waters and for the occurrence of algae blooms such as the red tide.

The quantitative exchanges effecting nitrogen distribution in the sea can be summarized as follows:

1. The available nitrogen in the sea amounts to 100 times the annual requirement for primary production.

2. The nitrogen requirements for primary production exceed the annual contributions of combined nitrogen from river drainage and precipitation by about 125-fold.

3. The estimated renewal time for the amount of fixed nitrogen present in the ocean is about 12,000 years.

4. The total fixed nitrogen contribution from nonmarine sources far exceeds the amount lost in sediments. Hence, assuming steady state conditions, the difference can be attributed to denitrification.

5. Without denitrification the annual deposition of nitrogen in the sediments would deplete the atmosphere of molecular nitrogen after about 200 million years.

Silicon is also an important nutrient to many organisms in the sea in that it forms the solid structure of the silicic flagellates, diatoms, some radiolarians, and sponges. Its concentration varies more than in any other element in the ocean. In the surface of the ocean or in shallow seas it may be undetectable and reaches 4 ppm in the deep waters of the Pacific and Indian oceans. In the Atlantic Ocean the concentration of silicon is about one-half of this value. The concentrations found in ocean water, even in the depths of the Pacific Ocean, is much less than what would be expected for waters in equilibrium with the solid sediment composed of amorphous silica, diatom tests, or even quartz. This lack of equilibrium concentration constitutes one of the more interesting geochemical problems in the ocean. It appears to be tied to a number of factors, the most important of which, probably, is its utilization in the skeleton parts of microorganisms in which many of the organisms may have 65 per cent of their body weight in the form of silica dioxide. Secondly, it may be precipitated by aluminum and utilized in the formation of silicate minerals, particularly that of magnesium aluminum silicates, and third, it may be absorbed to other sedimentary materials and deposited on the ocean floor. To show that this equilibrium with respect to the solubility of silicate in the oceans exists, one need only suspend ocean sediments in sea water for a period of a few days and the concentration of dissolved silica will reach values in the range of 100 ppm. It thus appears that the silicate minerals composing the shells of organisms to which sea water is exposed are protected from solution either by the presence of organic coatings or by failure of the water and solid particles to interact from lack of contact. The latter can be the result of the formation of silicate colloids, which provide an electrolytic layer surrounding the particle, thus shielding it from interaction with water molecules.

While the form of silica present in the skeleton material of organisms is usually in the SiO_2 form, the organisms can only extract silica from the ocean water when in the form of silicic acid, H_4SiO_4.

Although much work has been done on the actual mechanism of deposition of silica as the skeleton of organisms, this mechanism is not yet understood. It does appear, however, that there is an organic phase involved in which silicic acid reacts with organic components of the cell and is finally deposited as SiO_2 intermingled with layers of organic material. Since silicic acid concentrations become depleted in surface oceans under conditions of high productivity (where they are converted to the silica of skeleton solution of this silicious material) this is a vital part of the nutrient cycle in the sea. (Most of the evidence concerning the rate of solution of silica dioxide is circumstantial. In a study by Cooper of the Plymouth Laboratory in England, in which estimates of photosynthetic production from oxygen evolution and from consumption of carbon dioxide, phosphate, or nitrate agreed well, similar production values obtained from silica consumption were less than 0.1 of these amounts. This discrepancy could be explained if the silicious plants contained only 0.1 of the phytoplankton, but it was suggested that more probably the silica passed through the life cycle ten times in one season. The herbivores, consumers of the silicious plants, have little requirement for silica and, therefore, the element would be excreted unused. If this secreted silica is readily dissolved, it becomes available again for growth of diatoms. However there is still no direct evidence of the rate of solution of diatoms in sea water.)

Thus we see that the cycling of nutrient elements in the ocean (phosphorus, nitrogen, and silica) is fairly complicated and not fully understood. The cycling of the trace metals, dissolved gases, and organic matter is perhaps even more difficult to understand fully, but work is going on to gain this understanding. To emphasize the importance of this understanding, let us concern ourselves with the plague of mankind—pollution.

Today we are very much concerned about the pollution of our environment. This has become one of the most critical issues relating to our continued existence on this planet. The by-products of man's activities, which may directly effect the ocean environment, consist of the nutrient elements, solid wastes of all kinds and description, radioactive isotopes and trace metals, by-products of massive organic synthesis, conglomerates, insecticides, terrestrial debris and the like. In face of this serious difficulty, it is somewhat comforting to note that man has in the ocean environment a potential aid for his disposal problems, particularly those that are readily metabolized such as most human and organic wastes. If we were to apportion the total ocean to the number of human beings on earth, each man, woman, and child would have approximately a volume of ocean 1-square mile in area and 500 feet deep, as his personal property. This volume of water is probably capable of supplying his food, his water, and his environment for adequate waste disposal. As of now, man is incapable of efficiently collecting the production of the sea because it is too diffuse and is also unable to distribute his wastes so that dilution is adequate for proper metabolism and mixing. To accomplish this we must better understand the ocean environment, its mixing and transport processes, the mechanisms of the many chemical cycles of elements and compounds in the oceans, the rates at which these cycles operate, and the ultimate end products. Understanding the physical, chemical, biological, and geological phenomena of the ocean coupled with man's ingenuity in harnessing this medium to his own use is probably the most scientifically important effort needed in the world today if man expects to enjoy a long and affluent existence on his planet, the earth.

4 THE MARINE CHEMISTRY OF CARBON AND ITS ROLE IN OCEANOGRAPHIC RESEARCH

Wallace S. Broecker

Were the importance of carbon to ocean chemistry determined by its abundance in sea water, it would not even make the first team. When 1,000 grams of sea water are evaporated to dryness, about 35 grams of salt remains. Of this carbon makes up only 2/100 of one gram. Despite its rather lowly abundance, carbon still assumes the dominant role in studies of ocean chemistry. One reason for this is that carbon is the most abundant constituent in living organisms and living organisms are responsible for virtually all of the chemical differences that have been observed from place to place in the sea. Another is that the keystone to studies of the rates of mixing in the sea is the distribution of a naturally produced radioisotope of carbon, C^{14}. Finally, man's most abundant pollutant of his air-water environment is the carbon dioxide gas generated by the combustion of coal, oil, and natural gas. This chapter will describe the role that carbon plays in the enormous oceanographic research effort that currently occupies the attention of so many scientists.

Let us set the stage for this discussion by reviewing some of the key points regarding the geochemistry of the element carbon. Geochemistry is primarily a study of cycles that control the distribution of elements among the various geologic realms. These realms include the atmosphere, the ocean, sedimentary rocks, and so forth. There are three such cycles involving the element carbon that concern us.

The first of these is the sedimentary cycle. Each carbon atom in the earth's surface layers spends most of its time locked up in sediments in the form of either calcium carbonate, precipitated largely by marine organisms, or as resistant organic residues produced by all plants and animals. Only a very small fraction of its time is spent drifting through the ocean in ionic form. Carbon inventories show that for every 100 atoms of this element currently entombed in sediments only 1 atom enjoys the freedom offered by the sea. Those atoms now lucky enough to be in the sea have, however, served their share of time in sediments. Observation of the rates at which calcium carbonate and organic residues are currently accumulating in sediments on the sea floor suggests that about one-millionth of the carbon in the ocean is being removed each year. At this rate there would be no carbon left in the sea a million years from now. However, the erosion of ancient marine sediments that have been lifted above sea level by the slow but persistent upheavals of the earth's solid skin add an amount of carbon to the ocean each year very nearly balancing that being lost to oceanic sediments. Although carbon atoms are continually being cycled between sediments and the ocean, the amount of carbon in the ocean (and in the sediments) has probably remained nearly constant during at least the last 1,000 million years of the earth's history. On the other hand, the identity of the atoms present in the ocean at any given time will be quite different.

The durations of residence in these two realms are revealed by the relative amounts of carbon present. Since the sediments contain 100 times more carbon than do the oceans, we know that a given carbon atom will spend 100 times longer in the sedimentary than in the oceanic realm. The life cycle of any given carbon atom must then be roughly as follows. In the ocean 1 million-year stints are separated by 100 million-year incarcerations in sediments. During the past 1,000 million years the average carbon atom has, presumably, made about 10 trips into the ocean. Each time it is spewed from some river mouth and drifts about until captured by $CaCO_3$ fragments or organic residues destined for storage in sediments.

While in the oceans, carbon atoms participate in two more

geochemical cycles of interest. The first of these involves transfer between what we can, for convenience, describe as the warm
water sphere and the cold water sphere of the ocean. Most
waters in the ocean are cold; just one to three degrees above
o degrees centigrade. Only a thin skin of water a few tenths of
a meter thick, extending from about 45 degrees N to 45 degrees
S, ever gets warm enough for bathing. This state of affairs is
the result of the greater density of cold water. High density
waters formed by cooling in the polar seas sink and spread toward the equator under the skin of water warmed by the sun.
Separating the two water types is a gradational zone, which is
referred to as the main oceanic thermocline.

The major chemical differences observed in the oceans are
between its warm and cold waters because the remains of some
plants and animals living in the warm surface water sink under
the influence of gravity into the underlying cold water. Here
they are eaten by the hungry inhabitants of the deep and most
of their constituents are released back into solution. Thus, organisms cause a transfer of carbon and, of course, other elements
as well, from the warm to the cold realm of the ocean. This
transfer leads to the enrichment of the cold ocean realm with
carbon.

Not all the carbon in the sea ends up in the cold water for
the same reason that all the carbon on the earth's surface does
not end up in sediments. Carbon exported in particulate form
from the warm to the cold waters is continuously returned by
physical mixing. At present, cold water contains, on the average, 20 per cent more dissolved carbon than does warm water.
This has probably been the case for at least the last several million years. For each 100 units of carbon given up by warm waters
by physical mixing with the cold, 120 units are received in return. The extra 20 units received by the warm waters are the
ones fixed by organisms and sent back down as particles. In
other words, for every 120 units of carbon the warm waters receive from physical mixing, 100 are exported by mixing and
20 by sinking particles. The time scale of this mixing, as we
shall see, is such that a given carbon atom remains in the cold

water sphere 1,000 years before receiving a warm vacation, and in the warm water sphere about 30 years before returning to the cold abyss.

The life of a carbon atom is hence rather bleak. Of the 1 million out of 100 million years it is free to drift through the oceans, only about 30,000 years are spent in warm, sunbathed water. This small interval represents the aggregate of about one hundred vacations each of 30 years duration.

Each time a carbon atom does reach the warm surface, it faces one of two fates, transfer by surface currents to the polar regions where it is cooled and sent back to the deep sea, or fixation by photosynthesis followed by sinking into the deep sea.

Carbon is also a constituent of the atmosphere, where it is present mainly in the form of carbon dioxide gas. The amount of carbon in the atmosphere is only 1 per cent of the amount in the ocean. The cycle of carbon dioxide between the ocean and atmosphere is the last of the three of which we must be aware. As a result of chemical reaction with water, carbon dioxide can be transformed into ionic form. In this way at the air-sea interface carbon atoms are traded between the surface ocean and atmosphere. Since the warm-water layer blankets about 85 per cent of the sea surface, only a small part of this exchange occurs between the polar exposures of the cold-water sphere and the atmosphere.

The exchange of carbon between the atmosphere and oceans somewhat complicates the picture of the oceanic cycle we have just discussed. A third path for carbon transfer between the cold and warm ocean becomes available. In addition to the physical mixing of the water and the sinking of the remains of organisms, we now have the possibility that a carbon atom existing as bicarbonate in the warm ocean could be transformed to CO_2 gas and escape to the atmosphere. It could then return to the cold sea in the polar oceans and return to the bicarbonate form. The reverse path could, of course, also be followed. This atmospheric path between the warm and cold water spheres proves to be more than a curiosity. It creates a major uncertainty in mixing rates calculated from radioactive data.

Once in the atmosphere the average carbon atom bounces about for about five years before it is once again ensnared by the sea. During their flight these atoms have the possibility of becoming fixed into organic material by the photosynthetic activity of terrestrial plants. Although most of the organic matter so produced is quickly oxidized and the carbon returned to the atmosphere as CO_2, a small fraction goes into resistant compounds that survive oxidation and are eventually carried to the sea where they become incorporated into deep-sea sediments.

So much for the complex and intertwined geochemical cycles of ordinary carbon. Let us turn our attention to the radioactive variety known as C^{14}. Unlike most carbon atoms that exist indefinitely, the average C^{14} atom has the geochemically brief lifespan of only 8,000 years. C^{14} atoms are continually being spawned in our atmosphere by the collision of cosmic rays with atmospheric nitrogen. The carbon atoms made in this way are radioactive. The component of eight neutrons is too great to remain in harmony with the six protons present in the nucleus. Spontaneous emission of an electron eventually remedies this instability by converting the C^{14} atom back into nitrogen.

Let us consider where a C^{14} atom might travel during its 8,000-year lifespan. Born in the atmosphere, it soon becomes a CO_2 molecule and loses its identity among the myriad of normal CO_2 molecules that inhabit the atmosphere. From this point until the electron emission terminates its existence, it acts just like its stable carbon brothers.

Assuming that it does not become temporarily ensnared by a plant, our C^{14} atoms will drift about in the air for about five years before being captured by the sea. In most cases this capture will occur in the warm surface water. Once in the warm water realm the atom could be transferred via mixing or via a sinking particle into the cold water. After about 1,000 years in this major carbon reservoir it would reappear at the surface and commence another cycle. Thus, in the 8,000 years of its life, a C^{14} atom would have time to make several visits to each part of the ocean-atmosphere-biosphere system. Since the average carbon atom circuits the sea for a million years before becoming incorporated into the sediment, only about 1 in 100 C¹⁴ atoms will suffer this fate. Those few that do, however, spend the rest of their days in the sediment.

Now the fact that in their lifetimes, C¹⁴ atoms are able to make several traverses of the ocean-atmosphere system would imply that they become fairly well mixed with ordinary carbon. This is true. However, real differences in the ratio of C¹⁴ to ordinary carbon do exist. Atmospheric carbon has about 5 per cent more C¹⁴ per unit carbon than does carbon from the warm water sphere. These differences are the result of the time required for carbon to traverse the system. As C¹⁴ moves from the atmosphere to the warm ocean and on to the cold ocean, radioactive decay takes its toll. In fact, the way we know that the average CO_2 molecule remains for about five years in the atmosphere before entering the ocean and that once in the cold water sphere a carbon atom remains about 1,000 years before returning to the warm water sphere is from these observed differences in the ratio of C¹⁴ to normal carbon. If, for example, the atmospheric and oceanic carbon were mixed ten times more rapidly than they are today, we would not be able to detect a difference between the ratio of C¹⁴ to ordinary carbon in atmospheric and warm ocean carbon. If the average water parcel remained in the deep ocean for 5,000 rather than 1,000 years, the C¹⁴ deficiency in cold ocean carbon relative to atmospheric carbon would be far greater.

Those few radiocarbon atoms that become trapped in the sediments are of considerable interest. By measuring the C¹⁴ content of carbon extracted from various depths in the sedimentary column, it is possible to determine the rate at which the sediment is accumulating. Although the average life of a C¹⁴ atom is 8,000 years, a given atom may by chance survive a much longer time or succumb much sooner. The disappearance of the C¹⁴ atoms trapped in the sediments is such that the number of atoms present drops by a factor of two each 5,700 years. Thus that level in the sediment for which the ratio of C¹⁴ to normal carbon is one half that for the uppermost sediment must have been formed

5,700 years ago; that level with one quarter ratio of the C^{14} to normal carbon 11,400 years ago, and so forth. This radiocarbon method of dating, of course, depends upon the assumption that cosmic rays have been generating C^{14} at a constant rate for many tens of thousands of years. In this case, the number of C^{14} atoms in the system at any one time will also have remained constant. Experimental checks of this assumption made by carrying out radiocarbon age determinations on materials whose age is known by tree ring counting or by some other radioisotope method suggest that, whereas this constancy has not been exact, the deviations have not been large enough to affect these uses in oceanographic research.

Having reviewed some of the important aspects of the geochemistry of the element carbon, let us turn our attention to two important long-term research goals of the oceanographer in which carbon chemistry plays an important role. In both cases an understanding of the geochemical cycles of carbon is essential.

The first of these involves food. As the population grows man looks more and more to the sea as the source for this food. The desirable varieties of fish are hunted with an ever increasing intensity. Processing techniques, permitting the use of protein from currently underused portions of the catch, are under development. But a long-term look at the situation suggests that, just as our prehistoric ancestors turned from hunting and gathering to agriculture, we will have to begin to think of ways to "farm" the sea. The two basic approaches seem likely. One will be the exertion of ecologic influence on the sea in such a way that the more desirable creatures prosper at the expense of the less desirable. Such programs are already well underway in many of the world's fresh water systems. However, as this is a problem for the biologist rather than the geochemist, let us turn to the second approach. It involves increasing the over-all productivity of the sea in much the same way a farmer increases the productivity of his land by fertilization. Today the over-all productivity of the ocean is limited by the availability of the elements phosphorus and nitrogen. The warm water sphere is almost devoid of these two essential elements. The same particulate transport phenomenon that gave rise to a 20 per cent enrichment of carbon in cold water relative to warm water causes a 10 to 100-fold enrichment of nitrogen and phosphorus in cold relative to warm water. Between 90 and 99 per cent of the amounts of these elements brought to the warm water by mixing are incorporated into organisms and sent down in particulate form. As these two elements are absolutely essential to organisms, the productivity of organisms in the oceans is limited by the rate at which they are made available.

Conceivably we could fertilize the ocean as we fertilize the land. Nitrogen and phosphorus could be converted to the proper form in chemical plants and then added to the water. On an oceanwide basis this would be prohibitively expensive. The return could not nearly balance the cost. Most of the fertilizer would end up in particles that would sink to the deep sea where they would remain for 1,000 years. We would be literally dumping our precious fertilizer into the deep sea. Instead, man must consider the possibility of accelerating the rate of mixing between the warm and cold waters of the sea. Doubling this rate would, of course, bring nitrogen and phosphorus to the surface at twice the present rate and would, presumably, double the productivity of the oceans. Man would then be merely making much more effective use of the fertilizers already "buried" in the deep sea.

Currently no one knows whether, let alone how, the rate of mixing in the sea could be changed. We are not even certain as to how this process operates. Our effort in the next decade must be to gain an understanding of how the system works and to make a computer analogue of the system. Once this is accomplished, man can tamper with the computer analogue of the ocean and see what sorts of things might alter its rate of mixing. Eventually we may hit on a safe and practical way to fertilize our ocean. One step in this process is now being planned.

The distribution of stable carbon and of C^{14} in the world's ocean have been mapped in only certain areas and with only limited accuracy. Most oceanographers believe that much is to be learned about the manner in which our ocean mixes by more extensive and accurate surveys of the distribution of these properties. Oceanographers at various laboratories in the United States are currently planning a joint program to map the chemical and radiochemical properties of the ocean along three traverses from the Antarctic to the northern limits of the Indian, Pacific, and Atlantic oceans. This so-called geochemical ocean section study, GEOSECS for short, will have as its major objective the definition of those properties that can aid in unraveling the manner in which the warm and cold waters of the sea mix. Carbon, of course, will head the list of elements to be studied.

The second research goal meriting mention is that aimed at the prediction of the fate of the carbon dioxide produced by man's combustion of chemical fuels. Although CO_2 does not present any threat in the quantities produced by man to our medical welfare, it does pose a potentially serious threat to our climate. It is well known that the CO_2 and water vapor in the atmosphere retard the loss of heat by absorbing infrared light. The result is a higher temperature for the earth's surface than would be the case in the absence of these gases. By adding CO_2 to the system, man is altering his global climate. The question is how this will affect areas that now lie on the borderline of habitability. Slight changes in the moisture budget in certain desert areas would have profound effects on the inhabitants. Likewise, small changes in temperature would greatly alter the situation in the northern regions of North America, Europe, and Asia.

The problem of predicting these effects is twofold. The first is basically a meteorological problem. How will the climate of the earth change for given increments of CO_2? Here again the key lies in computer analogues of the earth's global weather systems. Once the climate of the earth can be reasonably well modeled in the laboratory, the effect of various changes can be evaluated. Of course, the success of any such model depends strongly on a detailed knowledge of all the processes going on in our atmosphere and oceans. Much of this knowledge is yet to be obtained.

The second problem connected with this prediction is geochemical. What is the fate of a given increment of CO_2? How rapidly will it be removed to the oceans, the biosphere, and the sediments? Here we encounter the geochemical cycles discussed previously. We must know in detail how the excess carbon will distribute itself among the various available reservoirs and the rates at which this transfer will take place.

From our present rather primitive knowledge of the system, the prediction has been made that 60 per cent of the CO_2 generated to date remains in the atmosphere. The remaining 40 per cent has been absorbed by the ocean. The living biosphere and sedimentary realms have not taken up a measurable amount of the manmade CO_2. If man continues to increase his fuel consumption at the current rate of 5 per cent per year, then the distribution between these two reservoirs will not change appreciably. As of today the CO_2 content of our atmosphere must be about 10 per cent higher than it was at the beginning of the Industrial Revolution. By the year 2000 it will be twice as high as it is today.

Some scientists have pointed to the $CaCO_3$ in ocean sediments as a long-range neutralizer of manmade CO_2. The idea is that as the CO_2 content of the ocean increases, the $CaCO_3$ in the sediments will be attacked and dissolve. This solution will continue until the CO_2 has been largely converted to ionic form. Were this to happen, the 60–40 distribution of manmade CO_2 between atmosphere and ocean would shift strongly in favor of the ocean, greatly alleviating the atmospheric pollution problem. What little is known about this process suggests, however, that significant reaction will not even begin for fifty or so years. This is because those areas of the ocean floor containing $CaCO_3$-rich sediments are either covered with water that is highly supersaturated with this mineral or so remote from the surface that a long time will pass before the CO_2 reaches it. Moreover, once reaction commences, the rate at which neutralization would proceed is not at all known.

So we see that man's understanding of the oceanic chemistry of carbon is essential to understanding the fate of the CO_2 that threatens to cause significant changes in our climate.

This brief discussion provides a bit of insight into the role of the element carbon in marine chemistry. Further, we have seen that these researches bear on important problems that affect us all. They happen to be vast and difficult problems, not the kind that any one man or even one generation of men can solve. Little by little the pieces of the gigantic puzzle begin to fit together. Observations must be made and remade. Theories must be proposed, often to be discarded when better ones come along. Long periods of seemingly slow progress are suddenly rewarded by significant breakthroughs. Gradually man moves toward an understanding of his surroundings. With this understanding will come the capability to care for our environment, to foresee abuses of our environment, and, hopefully to improve our environment. The scientist, if given the chance, will lay the groundwork for such progress, but it is up to each one of us to make sure that his government gives the scientist the support he needs and that his government uses the knowledge so gained to achieve long-range benefits to mankind rather than short-range political objectives.

5 MARINE MANGANESE MINERALS

Edward D. Goldberg

Pouring into the world's oceans each year are billions of tons of dissolved and suspended solids that have been weathered from the continents. The entry of these materials, carried primarily by the rivers, is complemented by a precipitation of substances to the sea floor, some unchanged from their chemical forms on the continents. On the other hand, new solids form from the dissolved substances in sea water, some as parts of the living organisms of the oceans, others by direct interactions between the materials in solution. Perhaps the most publicized and clearly the most studied of these substances are the black marine ores that contain the ferromanganese minerals, more popularly known as the manganese nodules, which have stirred a good deal of interest both among scientists and the general public as a potential source of such heavy metals as copper, cobalt, and nickel.

Manganese nodules were first observed about 100 years ago during the globe-circling *Challenger* expedition from England. Since that time they have provoked many theories as to their origin and significance. Their potential usefulness as metallic ores was not considered initially because they were so inaccessible—lying four to five kilometers beneath the surface of the oceans. In the past twenty years an explosive growth has taken place in the number of studies on these materials—investigations to consider their geographic distributions, chemical and physical characteristics, and potentials as heavy metal resources.

Originally, the ferromanganese minerals were considered as

deep-sea deposits, but recent surveys have shown that they build up at very shallow depths, below 10 meters of water. They are found in all oceans as well as in such shallow seas as the Barents, White, Kara, and Baltic. In the Firth of Clyde, they form on living mollusks. However, most samples are collected from depths between 4 and 5 kilometers, the average depths of the oceans.

These minerals are found over vast areas of the sea floor. About 25 to 50 per cent of the southwestern Pacific basin is covered with the ferromanganese minerals, as determined by bottom sampling and bottom photographs. The Blake Plateau, off the southeastern coast of the United States, an area of about 5,000 square kilometers, has continuous pavements of these substances, averaging 7 centimeters in thickness. A very rich deposit bands the North Pacific from the equator to just north of Hawaii. William Menard of the Scripps Institution of Oceanography suggests that the total expanse in which the nodules are concentrated is of the order of 13 million square kilometers. The total area of the oceans and adjacent seas is about 360 million square kilometers. Thus, the area of extensive coverage is about 3½ per cent of the sea floor.

These ferromanganese accumulations occur in a wide variety of sizes. The micronodules, which are buried within the sediments, range up to several millimeters in their longest dimension, and very large concretions are as much as several meters in diameter. The largest reported nodule had a weight of 850 kilograms.

The nodules are often composed of concentric shells built up about a nucleus that might consist of almost any solid material —commonly, bits of volcanic pumice, a shark's tooth, the ear-bone of a whale, accumulations of sediment, or shell fragments form the central core. These accretions take a variety of forms, including ellipsoidal or spherical shapes, either as individuals or grapelike clusters; crusts or pavements ranging in thickness from millimeters to centimeters; and flat discs or tubes. Their shape often follows the contours of their nucleus; some are near-perfect spheres.

Encrustations of these minerals upon slabs of volcanic debris or consolidated sediments are quite common in the eastern Pacific Ocean. Thicknesses of up to 11 centimeters have been measured. Nearly all outcroppings of rocks in the open ocean appear to be painted with the oxides of manganese and iron.

MINERALOGY

Two aspects of the compositions of ferromanganese minerals in the ocean are of special interest: their mineralogies and their chemistries. Both considerations are distinctly related to a marine origin, and yet these minerals have similarities to precipitates that occur on the continents.

The ferromanganese accretions contain both minerals that precipitate from sea water and solids that have come from the continents, from volcanoes, or from the remains of organisms. The sea water precipitates are primarily oxides of iron and/or manganese. Two of these are of major importance. Birnessite, a manganese dioxide, is similar in chemical composition to substances often used in dry cells. A second important building block is todorokite, which consists of alternating sheets of manganese dioxide and manganese hydroxide, the latter layer containing a considerable number of "guest" metals, most notably iron. Often oxides of iron are found dispersed throughout these accumulations.

Embedded in the ferromanganese minerals are continentally and volcanically derived solids such as quartz, feldspars, and micas, as well as the very small clay minerals that can become occluded in the growing structures. These materials constitute about one-quarter of the weight of the accretions.

Several scientists have recently found that the mineralogy of the ferromanganese minerals shows a depth dependence with the todorokite being the prevalent deep water form, while birnessite occurs predominantly in deposits below 3,500 meters or less of water. Furthermore, we have learned that the guest elements are determined by their mineralogy. High concentrations of lead and cobalt are associated with birnessite and thus are more commonly observed in shallow waters. Both lead and cobalt can have chemical forms similar to manganese dioxide, the chemical formulation of birnessite, and this association is sensible. Copper and nickel, on the other hand, seem to prefer an association with todorokite and hence are more abundant in nodules formed in deep waters. Thus, both the mineralogy and chemistry of the ferromanganese precipitates appear to have a depth dependence and to be indicative of the amount of overlying water at the time of their formation.

CHEMICAL COMPOSITION

The chemical compositions of the ferromanganese accretions are unique and unlike any material found on the continents. While oxygen constitutes about 50 per cent by weight in most accumulations and is the most abundant single element, the chemical characteristics of the accretions are determined by the concentrations of the metals. Manganese is usually the most abundant metal and often has a content of between 20 and 25 per cent; iron is somewhat less abundant with an average value close to 15 per cent.

Three metals with very low concentrations in sea water—cobalt, nickel, and copper—normally have contents in the minerals between $\frac{1}{10}$ and 1 per cent, but all of these metals can achieve levels of several per cent. Since the first analyses of the *Challenger* samples, hundreds of additional assays have been made, which have permitted empirical relationships between these metals to be developed. For example, copper and nickel are directly related to the manganese contents. More sophisticated analyses in which elements could be analyzed in the different ferromanganese minerals indicate that cobalt is enriched in the birnessite phases while nickel, copper, zinc, magnesium, barium, sodium, and potassium could replace manganese ion in the todorokite. Although there are changes as much as a factor of ten in the concentrations of a metal going from one geographical location to another, there is a remarkable uniformity in the compositions of the various shells of a given nodule.

The two principal organic compounds identified thus far in the nodules are pyrene and fluoranthene, which also happen to be the two most abundant compounds of hydrogen and carbon in sea water. The high surface areas of the nodular materials, ranging up to hundreds of square meters per gram of material, could, through the process of absorption, remove these organic materials from sea water. On the other hand, at the present time we cannot exclude the possibility that these materials were produced by organisms living on the nodules or even involved in their formation.

The ferromanganese minerals also accumulate remarkable amounts of the radioactive element thorium from sea water. Thus radioactive age determinations can be made on their various layers and their rates of accumulation can be measured.

FORMATION HYPOTHESIS

A variety of hypotheses have been proposed to explain the formation of the ferromanganese minerals, and each year new ideas or modifications of older theories appear. Even before the official *Challenger* report announced the discovery of these minerals, their existence was well known to the scientific community and several theories on their origin had been proposed.

There are three general classes of theories to explain the formation of these minerals: The first involves volcanic or hot spring activity to furnish the source for the manganese or iron; the second invokes biological intermediaries such as bacteria to convert the dissolved substances in sea water to insoluble minerals; a final group of hypotheses suggests that deposition of the ferromanganese minerals results from direct inorganic chemical reactions in sea water.

The involvement of volcanic activity was especially attractive to John Murray, one of the codiscoverers of these minerals on the *Challenger* expedition. He noted their frequent association with volcanic debris on the sea floor and suggested that the decomposition of manganese-rich eruptives was an important source for this element. Other investigators have suggested that submarine springs, containing manganese in solution, which forms manganese dioxide upon contact with sea water containing dissolved oxygen gas, furnished an alternate mechanism. This concept is favored by some Japanese investigators who have found a high density of sea-floor manganese nodules and crusts in the vicinity of the Fuji volcanic zone, an area where manganese-rich solutions may flow into the oceans. Indirectly, volcanic activity may be involved in the mineral build-up. Several workers have proposed that volcanic material settling through the water column acts as nucleation centers for the extraction of dissolved forms of manganese and iron from sea water.

Another group of scientists has proposed that biological agents form these minerals. Bacterial oxidation of manganese is the basis of many such theories. Some investigators have claimed to have isolated bacteria that either cause the disappearance of dissolved manganese from sea water or that precipitate manganese oxides. One scientist has suggested that the foraminifera, microscopic animals living both in the upper layers and on the sea floor, could extract manganese and iron from sea water, and upon their death release these two metals to produce the marine ores, following collection upon a suitable nucleus. Recent findings of high organic contents of the minerals have developed a renewed interest in the involvement of living creatures in the formation of these substances.

A third group of scientists, not tempted by volcanic or biological agencies, have held the belief that the formation of these ferromanganese minerals can be explained purely in chemical terms in which dissolved oxygen gas in sea water interacts with dissolved manganese to precipitate manganese dioxide. Sea water is the reservoir for all of the chemical reactants.

All three groups of theories have their supporters, and the scientific literature remains an arena for their consideration.

In order to try to understand how the manganese minerals might be formed, we may consider some of the characteristics of the chemical reactions that occur within the oceans.

First of all, the chemical reactants are often in very low concentrations. Sea water contains the two principal metals in these minerals, iron and manganese, in concentrations of hundredths of a part per billion. Sodium and chloride, the two main components of sea-water salts, have concentrations of about 10 million parts per billion. Yet the iron and manganese achieve concentrations in the nodules of 10 to 20 per cent—an enrichment of a billionfold. This is a most remarkable phenomenon.

The guest elements, such as cobalt, nickel, and copper, have values in the minerals between .01 and 1 per cent, yet in sea water their concentrations are around a part per billion. Thus they are enriched to the order of a millionfold over the surrounding water environment. The very rare radioactive element in sea water, thorium, is amassed 100 millionfold over its aqueous surroundings. Thus, the extraction efficiencies of the process or processes forming these minerals are very high.

Complementing the extremely low concentrations of the chemical reactants are the extremely long times required to accumulate discernible amounts of the minerals. Whereas a chemist in a laboratory considers a chemical reaction to have a reasonable speed if it takes place during a work day, slow if it takes place over longer periods, and rapid if the rates must be measured by electronic techniques, the ferromanganese minerals in the deep-sea deposits accrete at rates of millimeters per million years or about a layer of atoms per year. Perhaps this is the slowest rate of a chemical reaction ever measured by man. Faster rates by the order of 1,000 or so have been observed with the ferromanganese minerals accumulating in shallow deposits. A coating of iron and manganese oxides was found about a naval shell fragment off the coast of San Diego with a thickness of 2 to 3 centimeters. Since shells of the type had been in use for about fifty years, the rate of accumulation must be around 5 centimeters per 100 years. In deep waters, however, geological time periods of thousands to millions of years are required to form observable coatings of these minerals, whereas in coastal areas veneers can be acquired in a year or so.

Finally, marine chemical reactions usually occur at phase discontinuities—sites at which the sea water encounters a material other than itself—the atmosphere, the sediments, or the surfaces of marine organisms. Such different materials can provide either a source or a sink for the reactants or products of chemical reactions. For example, in chemical processes where electrons are exchanged, a solid surface can act both as a source and a sink—providing the electrons at one stage in the reactions and accepting them in another stage. In such a case its composition and structure are not altered. Such a substance is known as a catalyst.

A catalytic role may be played by the nuclei about which the ferromanganese minerals form—a sink for the electrons removed from the manganese in going from a dissolved state to the manganese dioxide and a source of electrons for the dissolved oxygen gas. After receiving the electrons, the oxygen can combine with hydrogen to become water. Following the build-up of some initial layers of the ferromanganese minerals, perhaps the reaction becomes autocatalytic—the nodular material itself becomes a source and sink for electrons.

We can gain an insight into manganese mineral formation by examining this electron exchange in somewhat greater detail. First, let us compare the states of manganese in sea water and the solid phases. In sea water manganese exists as a manganous ion, a form differing from the metal by the loss of two electrons. That is, manganese in sea water is in a higher state of oxidation than manganese metal. The form of manganese in the ferromanganese minerals is in an even higher oxidation state than the dissolved manganese in sea water; it has lost four electrons from the metallic state, or two electrons from the solution state. Thus we define the process as one of oxidation where manganese going from sea water to the solid phase loses two electrons.

How is this brought about? The electrons must be transferred to another substance, an oxidizing agent, in this case probably oxygen gas. But most probably this exchange takes place at a third body or site. At such a place, oxygen gas, which consists of two atoms of oxygen, is converted to single atoms of oxygen, which have a greater ability to receive electrons than the molecule. Thus the site essentially absorbs oxygen gas and the manganous ion and releases the products manganese dioxide and water.

What type of surfaces can produce this reaction? Iron oxides and manganese oxides have long been noted as having the abilities to provide sites for the uptake of oxygen gas and presumably its dissociation into atoms. Since these surfaces remain unchanged during the ensuing reaction, they are catalysts. Thus, the association of iron oxides with the ferromanganese minerals is not surprising. The iron oxides can act as surfaces for the reaction to take place.

But as the ferromanganese minerals build up, they themselves can act as catalysts for this reaction. Hence, if the reaction products can catalyze the reaction (that is, break oxygen molecules into atoms and allow manganous ions to give up two electrons to them), the reaction is then said to be autocatalytic.

ENVIRONMENTAL INDICATORS

The ferromanganese minerals can now be viewed as a marine precipitate indicative of a chemical system containing dissolved oxygen gas—an oxidizing environment. There are also other chemical systems in the oceans that are devoid of oxygen gas—the so-called anoxic or anaerobic waters. In such zones the dissolved oxygen gas is consumed in the combustion of organic matter produced by the plants and animals of the sea. Oxygen depletion in marine waters is associated with high biological productivity, for the greater the production of organic matter by photosynthesis in surface waters, the greater is the amount of oxygen needed to burn it at the surface or adjacent deeper waters.

But then this question may be raised: Why "manganese nodules"

—why not "platinum nodules" or "zinc nodules" or "titanium nodules"? Two characteristics of the element manganese provide the answer. First, manganese exists in crustal rocks on the earth in a reduced state, the manganous state, which can go readily into solution upon the weathering of the rock. This is the same dissolved manganese that we find in sea water. However, this state is theoretically unstable and in the presence of oxygen gas should form the solid, oxidized form, manganese dioxide. Very few other metals enjoy this situation: weathering from crustal rocks to soluble states, the transportation by the rivers to the oceans, and oxidization by the dissolved oxygen gas in the oceans to an insoluble solid phase.

The second characteristic of manganese that may explain "Why manganese nodules" is that it is the most abundant element that has these characteristics. Lead, cerium, and cobalt perhaps fall into this category, but they are much less abundant in the oceans and in surface rocks than is manganese. But all three of these elements are markedly and strongly enriched in manganese nodules compared to sea water, just as is the manganese. For example, cobalt has a concentration in sea water of about $\frac{1}{20}$ that of nickel, whereas in the ferromanganese minerals nickel and cobalt are equally abundant. Yet nickel cannot be precipitated from solution by interaction with oxygen as can cobalt. The simultaneous enrichments of lead, cobalt, cerium, and manganese in the minerals are indicative of oxygen-containing waters.

TERRESTRIAL COUNTERPARTS

The weathering of manganese from surface rocks with the subsequent formation of manganese dioxides through interaction with oxygen is quite widespread and occurs in continental areas to produce products similar to the ferromanganese minerals of the deep sea. For example, exposed surfaces of stones and outcrops in deserts become coated with a veneer of manganese and iron oxides, the so-called "desert varnish." The formation of this material is also a weathering process in which there is a solution, transportation, and deposition of manganese and iron from the host rock upon which the coating forms. As in the marine processes, elements such as cobalt, lead, copper, nickel, and barium are in abundance. Also the rates of formation of these very thin coatings, usually less than $\frac{1}{10}$ of a millimeter, are extremely slow. Hundreds of thousands of years may be necessary in certain cases to produce observable varnishes, while in others only twenty-five years appears to be required.

More extensive, however, are the manganese dioxide ores formed either by the descending or ascending waters of the earth's surface. Because of the wide variety of environments through which the waters rise or fall, an interpretation of the mineralogies and guest elements becomes an extremely complex problem. This contrasts with the marine environment, which is clearly more homogenous with respect to the composition of the sea water solution, providing the sources of materials of the ferromanganese accretions. Hence, there are clear chemical differences between the land and marine forms. For example, tungsten, arsenic, antimony, and germanium are often quite high in continental manganese dioxides, whereas they are virtually absent from the marine forms. On the other hand, nickel and cobalt are higher in the sea-water deposits.

One quite interesting deposition of manganese oxides occurs in drainage tiles in agricultural areas. Where the tiles are above the water table, the percolating waters, containing oxygen, can cause the deposition of manganese oxides. Where the tiles are below or in the water table, the waters are usually devoid of oxygen and no manganese oxide deposition takes place.

VERY OLD DEPOSITS OF THE MINERALS

An axiom of environmental scientists is that the key to the past may be found in the present. An examination of a phenomenon occurring today on the earth's surface tells us what may have happened in past epochs. From western Timor in the East

77

Indies there are reports of the ferromanganese minerals occurring in Cretaceous sedimentary deposits on land. These deposits, around 100 million years old as determined on the basis of numerous shark's teeth, fish teeth, and bones of organisms that lived during this time period, have the ferromanganese minerals in the forms of finely disseminated small grains in red shales, similar to the micronodules, of manganese nodules, of slabs and flat concretions, and of veneers on rocks.

All of the experimental work done on these materials suggests a very close similarity with the ferromanganese minerals depositing today in the deep oceanic areas. The nodules are 1.5 to 5.0 centimeters large and spherical in form. They are predominantly manganese dioxide, perhaps indicating that they precipitated at intermediate depths, if we can assume that this mineralogy does reflect the height of the overlying water layers.

Although the nodules lacked the concentric banding that is often found today, one showed a nucleus that may have been a small chambered animal shell. The micronodules, 2 to 3 millimeters in diameter, with nuclei of fish debris, are in good agreement compositionally with recent nodules, particularly with respect to such minor components as nickel, cobalt, copper, lead, zinc, and molybdenum. The sediments in which these micronodules were imbedded are chemically and mineralogically similar to the recent deep-sea clays of the Pacific and Indian oceans.

This is the only well documented case in which the ferromanganese minerals can be used to tell us about past environments. Clearly, these materials were deposited in seas containing dissolved oxygen gas most probably at intermediate depths. No evidence for an association with volcanic material was found.

A PUZZLE

One unsolved problem concerning the ferromanganese nodules is their very existence on the surface of the deep ocean sediments. The rates of accumulation of oceanic bottom sediments are of the order of millimeters per thousand years, about a thousand times faster than the accumulation rates of the concretions that build up in units of millimeters per million years. Then, why are not all of the manganese concretions buried within the sedimentary column?

We really do not have an adequate answer for this query. It is made even more difficult when we realize that the nodules are more dense than the surrounding sedimentary materials.

Perhaps bottom-dwelling organisms constantly nudge the concretions, maintaining them at the water-sediment interface. Organisms are very often photographed in the vicinity of the nodules and can clearly burrow around these rocks.

Or again, it may be bottom currents moving the nodules about, keeping them from burial by maintaining them in motion. But both of these mechanisms are purely speculative. The curious problem of the concentration of nodules at the sediment surface still remains a mystery of the sea.

AN INTERNATIONAL MARINE RESOURCE

The past 100 years since the discovery of the ferromanganese minerals on the sea floor has been a period of exploration in which their distribution, modes of occurrence, chemical, physical, and geological characteristics have been studied. We may now be initiating a period of exploitation of these substances; perhaps it will come in ten years, perhaps in fifty years. But the millions of tons of the materials on the floor of the world's ocean are tantalizing many students of natural resources with the economics of their potential recovery. Most investigators have concerned themselves less with the manganese, which itself is probably not worth mining, than with the associated copper, nickel, and cobalt. Some authorities, such as Kenneth Emory of the Woods Hole Oceanographic Institution, point out the tremendous problems involved in recovering multikiloton amounts annually from depths of four to five kilometers. He states, "Possibly, the manganese nodules with their associated metals represent a resource which just now is out of our grasp in terms of economics, but they may be worth mining sometime in the distant future."

The million tons of ferromanganese nodules on the sea floor can in principle become a source of cobalt, copper, or nickel that could satisfy the present use rates of these metals for the next century of millennia. Where today the annual world production of nickel is about 500 tons, William Menard of the Scripps Institution of Oceanography has computed that there is 50,000 times as much nickel in the manganese nodules of the top meter of sediments in the Pacific Ocean. Similarly, the world production of cobalt of 20,000 tons per year is matched by a 100,000 fold greater amount in the ferromanganese nodules from the top meter of Pacific sediments.

With such a resource, what is holding up the extraction of these valuable metals from the sea? Possible mining techniques such as suction dredges would require a vast investment of capital that today cannot be justified by real shortages of the minable metals or by the problems that will clearly arise when we first attempt their retrieval from the deep sea.

The ferromanganese deposits of the world's ocean in general may be considered an international resource. Since at the present time it is difficult to assign national sovereignty of the deep-sea floor to bordering nations on a rational geological or geographic basis, the world is left with artificial guidelines. Kenneth Emory of the Woods Hole Oceanographic Institution has suggested that the 1,000-meter contour might reasonably circumscribe all presently exploited sea-floor resources and many potential ones for the bordering nations. Such a concept leaves the bulk of the ferromanganese deposits out of the control of individual nations. Perhaps, the United Nations or some other international group might exercise control over these potentially important marine ores. Emory suggests that "tax revenues, if any, could serve to defray costs of administration with excess revenues being distributed to land-bound nations that otherwise might not share in the possible future wealth of sea-floor resources."

It is possible that the first development of this deep-sea resource may be initiated by one of the smaller countries of the world which lacks its own continental resources of these metals and may invest the required large sums of money to mine the ferromanganese minerals from the sea. As the demands for increasing amenities of life are made by increasing populations, the deep-sea minerals appear more and more attractive for use by man.

6 TRACE ELEMENTS IN THE OCEANS

Karl K. Turekian

The major elements comprising the dissolved salts in sea water are relatively few in number. For all practical purposes, we can think of sea water as a solution of constant proportions of sodium chloride, potassium chloride, magnesium sulfate, and calcium bicarbonate. Together with a few additional elements this group comprises about 12 per cent of the total number of naturally occurring chemical elements in sea water—the remaining 88 per cent are present in such small quantities that they are difficult to determine by simple analytical techniques. These elements, which are called *trace elements,* range in concentration from an upper level of several parts per billion to concentrations of less then one part in 10,000 billion! The concentration of elements in sea water and streams is given in Table 6-1.

In the 1920s the great German chemist Fritz Haber decided that of the trace elements in sea water, gold should be extractable on an economically profitable basis. He based his decision on some early determinations of the concentration of gold in sea water, which indicated that gold might be present in sea water at levels of about one part per billion. Even at this low concentration it seemed that the extraction of gold from sea water could be an economically rewarding venture and the supply of gold would be virtually endless. A gold concentration of one part per billion in sea water corresponds, on the average, to 4 million grams of gold for every square kilometer of ocean area. Since the area of the oceans is roughly 4 million square

TABLE 6–1

The Composition of Sea Water (salinity = 35 parts per thousand)
and Streams (salinity = 120 parts per million) in
Micrograms per liter

Atomic number	Element	Sea water	Streams
1	Hydrogen	1.10×10^8	1.10×10^8
2	Helium	0.0072	*
3	Lithium	170	3
4	Beryllium	0.0006	*
5	Boron	4,450	10
6	Carbon		
	(inorganic)	28,000	11,500
	(dissolved organic)	500	*
7	Nitrogen		
	(dissolved N_2)	15,500	*
	(as NO_3^-, NO_2^-, NH_4^+, and dissolved organic)	670	226
8	Oxygen		
	(dissolved O_2)	6,000	*
	(as H_2O)	8.83×10^8	8.83×10^8
9	Fluorine	1,300	100
10	Neon	0.120	*
11	Sodium	1.08×10^7	6,300
12	Magnesium	1.29×10^6	4,100
13	Aluminum	1	400
14	Silicon	2,900	1,350
15	Phosphorus	88	20
16	Sulfur	9.04×10^5	5,600
17	Chlorine	1.94×10^7	7,800
18	Argon	450	*
19	Potassium	3.92×10^5	2,300
20	Calcium	4.11×10^5	15,000
21	Scandium	<0.004	0.004
22	Titanium	1	3
23	Vanadium	1.9	0.9
24	Chromium	0.2	1
25	Manganese	0.4	7
26	Iron	3.4	(670)
27	Cobalt	0.39	0.2
28	Nickel	6.6	0.3

TABLE 6–1 (cont'd)

Atomic number	Element	Sea water	Streams
29	Copper	0.9	7
30	Zinc	5	20
31	Gallium	0.03	0.09
32	Germanium	0.06	*
33	Arsenic	2.6	2
34	Selenium	0.090	0.2
35	Bromine	67,300	20
36	Krypton	0.21	*
37	Rubidium	120	1
38	Strontium	8,100	60
39	Yitrium	0.013	0.7
40	Zirconium	0.026	*
41	Niobium	0.015	*
42	Molybdenum	10	1
43	Technetium	Not naturally occurring	
44	Ruthenium	0.0007	*
45	Rhodium	*	*
46	Palladium	*	*
47	Silver	0.28	0.3
48	Cadmium	0.11	*
49	Indium	*	*
50	Tin	0.81	*
51	Antimony	0.33	1
52	Tellurium	*	*
53	Iodine	64	7
54	Xenon	0.047	*
55	Cesium	0.30	0.02
56	Barium	21	10
57	Lanthanum	0.0034	0.2
58	Cerium	0.0012	0.06
59	Praseodymium	0.00064	0.03
60	Neodymium	0.0028	0.2
61	Promethium	Not naturally occurring	
62	Samarium	0.00045	0.03
63	Europium	0.000130	0.007
64	Gadolinium	0.00070	0.04
65	Terbium	0.00014	0.008
66	Dysprosium	0.00091	0.05
67	Holmium	0.00022	0.01
68	Erbium	0.00087	0.05

TABLE 6–1 (cont'd)

Atomic number	Element	Sea water	Streams
69	Thulium	0.00017	0.09
70	Yterbium	0.00082	0.05
71	Lutetium	0.00015	0.008
72	Hafnium	<0.008	*
73	Tantalum	<0.0025	*
74	Tungsten	<0.001	0.03
75	Rhenium	0.0084	*
76	Osmium	*	*
77	Iridium	*	*
78	Platinum	*	*
79	Gold	0.011	0.002
80	Mercury	0.15	0.07
81	Thallium	<0.01	*
82	Lead	0.03	3
83	Bismuth	0.02	*
84–89 and 91	(Polonium, astatine, radon, francium, radium, actinium, and protactinium)		
90	Thorium	<0.0005	0.1
92	Uranium	3.3	0.04

* No data or reasonable estimates available.

kilometers, the total gold reservoir would be over 10 million million grams!

Haber's acceptance of this reported gold concentration, which was the basis of his reasoning, was understandable since all the gold brought to the sea by streams derived from the weathering of continental rocks should easily accumulate in the oceans because gold forms a very soluble complex with chlorine—the dominant nonmetal in the oceans.

After many unsuccessful attempts to extract gold from sea water, Haber decided that the concentrations that had been reported must be too high. Subsequent determinations showed that the concentration of gold in sea water is actually about 5 parts per 1,000 billion, or about a factor of 1,000 lower than the previously accepted value. This eliminated the prospect of the economic exploitation of gold from the sea.

Haber's work, however, raised the question: what factors control the levels of concentration of trace elements in the oceans? The oceans apparently are not behaving as a simple repository for metals brought to it by the streams throughout the history of the earth. A balance between input and output was obviously determining the levels of concentration of the elements in the sea.

To answer this question, accurate determinations of the concentrations of the trace elements are required. Since the time of Haber's studies, increasingly sensitive and accurate methods for analyzing sea water for trace elements have been developed. With the data presently available to us, although it is still far from satisfactory, certain answers are possible.

The overwhelming observation with regard to the chemistry of trace elements in sea water is that the concentrations of many of the trace elements are indeed far lower than would be expected if the oceans were saturated with them. Of the few elements that are close to their saturation concentrations, thorium and the rare-earths such as lanthanum and cerium appear to have their concentrations mainly controlled by the phosphate concentration since highly insoluble phosphate compounds are formed by these elements. Manganese, iron, and aluminum are also close to their saturation concentrations because of the highly insoluble oxides that they form in sea water. It is not surprising then to find these elements, whether injected naturally or formed by radioactive processes, easily transported to the sediments from sea water. Their passage times through the water to the bottom are rapid in the open ocean.

Normal sea water, because of its composition, actually enhances the concentration levels to be expected of certain trace elements. Many of the elements such as gold, silver, lead, and mercury form extremely strong complexes with the charged chlorine atoms (or ions) in sea water. These complexes are very stable in solution and thus increase the solubility of these elements. Another type of enhancement of solubility is seen in the case of uranium, which forms a highly soluble complex with the carbonate present in sea water. In addition, chromium and molybdenum form highly soluble chromate and molybdate ions in normal sea water.

Knowing the general properties of sea water—its major elements, its salinity, its acidity, and its oxidation state—we can estimate the solubilities of most of the elements in sea water. In most cases the observed concentrations are considerably lower than expected from this solubility data and the measured supply rate of streams. Why, then, are the concentrations maintained at such low levels?

Several mechanisms have been suggested: (1) adsorption on particles; (2) biological removal; and (3) the effect of near-shore and anoxic (or oxygen-free) environments.

Fine-grained sediments of the type reaching the ocean floor (mainly clays) are typical of materials that can act as sites for the removal of certain elements by adsorption. Despite this fact, the role played by adsorption of trace elements on clays in the sea is probably not of great importance in lowering the concentration of the trace elements. The reason for this can be seen if we trace the history of a clay particle derived from the land. The particle, produced by weathering and erosion, has been in intimate contact with fresh waters during the weathering process or during stream transport. Adsorption of trace elements from such a dilute solution is expected to be high. Adsorption experiments in the laboratory simulating clay particles in streams verify this as does the experience from nuclear reactors where cooling water spiked with radioactive tracers is in contact with stream sediments downstream from the reactor. However, when these particles encounter sea water, the tendency is to *release* the trace elements that were adsorbed rather than to adsorb more trace elements. The reason for this is the massive competition for adsorption sites by the major elements in sea water such as sodium, magnesium, potassium, and calcium. Hence, on the basis of laboratory and field experiments we would expect particles brought to the oceans to actually release trace elements rather than to adsorb them.

Biological removal has often been invoked for the mechanism of modifying the trace-element composition of sea water. This argument is based on the trace-element analyses of marine organisms. When a comparison of the concentration of a trace element in an organism is made with an equal volume of sea water, it is almost always found that a massive concentration has been achieved by the organism. The highest degree of concentration by organisms is found for phosphorus because organisms require phosphorus for all their life functions including growth and reproduction. More than 10,000 liters of sea water must be stripped of phosphorus to provide the phosphorus found in a small fish! It is not surprising then that surface waters quickly become depleted in phosphorus, and were it not for the continuous resupply of phosphorus-rich deep waters by upwelling, surface ocean life would soon be terminated.

If we compare the trace-element enrichment in organisms relative to phosphorus enrichment, the trace-element enrichment is invariably considerably less. For instance, the cesium-to-phosphorus ratio in an organism is less than the ratio in surrounding sea water. From this viewpoint many trace elements are actually discriminated against relative to phosphorus.

The bearing of this discussion on the problem of how to remove trace elements from sea water is that most of the phosphorus extracted from the sea by organisms is returned to the sea by degradation processes in the food chain of the oceans. Since most of the phosphorus in the open ocean is recycled, one would expect very little of the trace elements—already discriminated against relative to phosphorus by the organism—to be removed from sea water to the deep ocean bottom by this process.

It thus appears that we are forced, by elimination, to find the solution to our puzzle in near-shore and anoxic marine environments.

Before we proceed further, we must define the qualities of near-shore and anoxic environments that make them different from the open ocean environment. The dominant characteristic of near-shore and anoxic environments is that in both the rate of dissolved oxygen utilization in a part of their system is more rapid than the supply rate. In anoxic environments such as fjords, the deep parts of the Black Sea, and the deep parts of some oceanic regions of intense upwelling and high surface biological productivity, the oxygen is completely depleted at depth. This is either because the flood of organic debris falling from the surface is more than enough to use up the oxygen supplied to the deep water by large-scale circulation processes, or because the stratification of the water prevents any sort of efficient overturn and aeration of the deeper waters. These anoxic waters are characterized by a complete absence of fish. Further biologic usage of organic material derived from the surface water is effected by sulfate-reducing bacteria, which produce hydrogen sulfide, to in turn cause the appearance of high concentrations of sulfide ions and the lowering of the oxidation state of the water.

In this environment the chemical properties of sea water are totally different from that in the previously discussed larger open-ocean environment. Where manganese and iron have low solubilities in open-ocean oxygenated sea water, their solubilities in anoxic environments increase dramatically and relatively high concentrations of these elements have been found in the deeper parts of the Black Sea and in the fjords. On the other hand, chromium is changed from its primarily oxidized state, which is highly soluble, to the reduced state, which precipitates effectively as an oxide. Uranium and molybdenum are also removed effectively from the water into the sediments.

In modifying the trace-element composition of the open oceans, the hundreds of thousands of miles of coastal areas of the world are quantitatively more important than the deep anoxic basins. The near-shore estuarine environments are not themselves anoxic since the circulation there is generally too rapid to significantly deplete the oxygen in the water; nevertheless, the sediments underlying the water are very rich in organic material and the oxygen in the interstitial waters of the sediment is quickly used up by organisms living in the mud. Further degradation of organic material in the sediment takes place by the action of the same sulfate-reducing bacteria that are found in anoxic basins.

89

During low tide in some areas at which disturbances by man or weather have occurred, the escaping hydrogen sulfide from mud flats can be detected by its characteristic odor. Generally, however, most of the hydrogen sulfide reacts with the ever present iron oxide, derived mainly from weathered minerals, to form iron sulfide, which gives these environments their characteristic black color.

If trace elements are transported in some manner to the bottom of an estuarine basin, the subsequent decay and release of metals is effected in a totally different context from that in the open ocean. The metal encounters a high concentration of sulfide or senses a reducing environment. The effect is strong enough to cause even the most soluble metals in an open-sea water environment—silver, gold, lead, and mercury, for example —to be precipitated as highly insoluble sulfides.

Organisms provide the mechanism for the transport of trace elements to the bottom in the relatively shallow water of the near-shore environment. Thus although biological transport is not the likely mechanism for removing most trace elements in the open ocean, it plays the fundamental role of providing the elements to the reducing sulfide-rich environment of the near-shore estuarine environment.

We then conclude that for many of the trace elements, the concentration level in the open ocean is maintained by processes active in the volumetrically insignificant part of the oceans—the near-shore and anoxic basin environments.

We have tried to consider mechanisms. It will be useful now to describe in general terms what happens to the trace elements in the ocean. Without considering the actual method or site of removal of a trace element, we can calculate an index of the element's reactivity in the ocean, called the *mean residence time,* which is obtained by dividing the total amount of a particular element dissolved in the oceans by the rate of supply of the element by all the streams of the world to the oceans. The use of this index implies that the rate of removal of the element from solution just equals the rate of supply—that is, a steady state condition is maintained in the oceans. The physical significance of the mean residence time is that it represents the average length of time that an atom of the element remains in the ocean before it is removed. Statistically, after a length of time equal to about five mean residence times has elapsed, virtually none of the original atoms of the element remain in the ocean—having been replaced by new ones from land.

The major elements such as sodium, magnesium, and calcium have mean residence times between 1 and 100 million years. The trace alkali metals—lithium, rubidium, and cesium—have mean residence times of about 1 million years. Most of the other trace elements have mean residence times of about 10,000 to 100,000 years. The marked exceptions are elements such as thorium which have mean residence times of much less than 100 years.

We have now seen that the most probable locale for the modification of the trace element composition of the oceans occurs in near-shore environments and that we can calculate an index of reactivity for a trace element in the oceans that we have called the mean residence time. There are several applications for these generalizations in understanding the oceans and their response to trace elements.

1. Since we know that the oceans circulate with mean residence times for deep waters of about 1,000 years, it is evident that the closer the mean residence time of the element is to this value the more likely will there be regional variations of the trace element concentration in the oceans. Such variations will be imposed on the water mass locally as the result of supply or removal, and may be useful as tracers of water masses much as a dye or a radioactive tracer.

2. In a related manner, artificial spikes of certain elements into the open ocean may be used for tracing water movements. This, unfortunately, is likely to be a by-product of the increasing pollution of the atmosphere with lead and mercury from industrial chemicals such as lead tetraethyl found in gasolines or mercury-bearing insecticides. Increases of lead and mercury in the surface layers of the oceans have already been reported. The lead concentration of the surface waters of the Mediterranean Sea

is already a factor of 10 to 100 higher than that of deep water. Mean residence times of the order of 10,000 years indicate that the effects will not be easily reversed. This high solubility of lead and mercury in ocean water because of chloride complex leads us to expect their levels to increase continuously as man continues to pollute his ocean environment with these elements. The significance of this long-lived pollution of mankind, fortunately, is not lost to some farsighted scientists.

3. In a similar application, predictions about the fallout of Sr^{90} and Cs^{137} can be made by measuring the distribution of stable strontium and cesium. Both of these elements have a fairly homogeneous distribution in the oceans both geographically and with depth, indicating that the transport of their radioactive isotopes should be primarily by bulk water transport that is typical of large-scale circulation. The role of biological transport is confined, if important at all, to shallow depths. This is borne out by a general restriction of Sr^{90} and Cs^{137} to the top 400 meters of sea water except in areas of strong sinking of surface waters. Biological transport of cosmic ray-produced silicon-32 and carbon-14 to depth, however, has been demonstrated as the dominant mode of supply of these nuclides to the deep oceans.

4. The fate of industrially supplied metals to estuarine environments can be determined by measuring the distribution of trace elements in the estuary, and comparing the rate of supply from the open ocean and streams with the rate of loss back to the open ocean. In one such study in Long Island Sound the results appear to show that despite the strong industrial supply of nickel, cobalt, or silver from factory effluents into streams debouching into Long Island Sound, the concentrations of these elements in the waters leaving the Sound is no greater than in the waters entering the Sound and is possibly actually lower. This is compatible with the idea that the estuaries are one of the best sites for the modification of the trace-element concentrations of the oceans.

5. The experience gained from the study of the trace elements, especially in near-shore environments, may add insight

into what may be expected of the radioactive nuclides released by coastal nuclear power reactors. There is no doubt that the number of power reactors located along sea coasts and on major rivers will continue to increase. The behavior of the radioactive isotopes released by these reactors may be simulated by the behavior of the natural stable elements. Hence by following the behavior of trace elements in near-shore environments we can make predictions about the probable fate of the reactor-produced radioactive isotopes. Using this knowledge, a more intelligent deployment of the reactor and management of its effluent may be effected.

Let us return again to the matter of the economic exploitation of sea water for chemicals. Is there any hope for the utilization of the vast quantities of elements dissolved in sea water on an economically competitive basis relative to land resources? Unfortunately, the answer for the main part is negative.

At the present time the main nonbiological chemical products obtained from sea water on a commercial basis are sodium chloride, magnesium, and bromine. Sodium chloride, which is a bulk product necessary for the production of sodium hydroxide and hydrochloric acid, is mined from large land deposits in many places. The only way in which sodium chloride, obtained by the evaporation of sea water, can compete economically with that obtained from land mining is in the existence of natural evaporation basins with an easy access to processing plants. Such a combination appears to have been attained by using a portion of the Bahamas platform as an evaporation pan and shipping the salt obtained to the processing plants on the northeast coast of the United States. The Gulf Stream flowing north from the Bahamas eases the transportation costs.

Magnesium and bromine are obtained from sea water in several plants along the coast at the present time, but it is significant that brine deposits from land sources are currently being more aggressively developed than the sea water sources. The problem of proximity to large sources of the power required for the extraction of these elements is another primary consideration in restricting the use of sea water as their source.

Magnesium can also be obtained from the sedimentary rock, dolomite—a calcium magnesium carbonate. If the demand for magnesium becomes great enough, the feasibility of its commercial recovery from the ubiquitous dolomite deposits will undoubtedly be demonstrated.

It is clear then that under special conditions some of the major components of sea water have been mined commercially although they face the tight competition with these raw materials obtainable from land deposits.

The same constraint is operative in the mining of metals from sea water. At the present time, all of the trace elements are more efficiently recoverable from land deposits than they are from sea water. But, if there were no more easily mineable land resources, I believe that we would still find it economically more sensible to exploit the almost barren land deposits rather than sea water.

Every trace element is present in higher concentrations in the continental crust than in sea water. The average concentration of uranium in rocks is three parts per million whereas it is present at levels of only three parts per *billion* in sea water. Similarly, the average concentration of cobalt in continental rocks is twenty parts per million whereas it is present in sea water at less than one-half part per billion. Since the average density of a continent is about three times the density of sea water, the concentration per volume instead of mass is proportionately greater in continental rocks.

The use of sea water as an ore is advantageous only if the metal can be extracted at least 1,000 times more efficiently from sea water solution than from solid rocks. The likelihood of this does not seem to be great. A few acid-leaching experiments on rocks in the extraction of uranium, for instance, or the cyanide complexing extraction of gold and silver, indicate that it is possible to conceive of ingenious methods of extracting metals from rocks even at low concentrations if the occasion demands. Similar experiments of economic importance are generally lacking or have proven to be unsuccessful when sea water analogs are used.

The only prospect of metal mining from sea water economically, if there is any at all, lies in the specific extraction of an element during the processing of the sea water for other purposes, such as desalination or the cooling of coastal nuclear reactors.

But here another competitor emerges. Stream waters have trace-element concentrations that are not markedly different from that of sea water, and where there are differences it is not unlikely that some river or another has the same concentration for a particular element as sea water. One cannot help but wonder that if a procedure for processing sea water could be developed for a particular trace element, it would probably be even more efficient for use on stream waters. A river could be made to flow through the proper processing plant more easily than sea water, and fresh water is free of the interference effects of the $3\frac{1}{2}$ per cent dissolved salts present in sea water. It thus seems that if one were to extract metals from natural water, some stream waters would be better candidates for this process than the average ocean water.

I have tried to examine the present status of studies on trace elements in the oceans. It is clear that we have come along a different path than that of economically exploiting the oceans for the dissolved metals as envisaged by Haber. Indeed, except for the major elements in sea water, it is not likely that the sea will ever compete with land resources for any of the metals. Any new schemes for economic extraction of metals from the sea will be as doomed as Haber's program for extracting gold from the ocean. The only possible exception is uranium, which is present at a level of three parts per billion, but only time will tell if even this element might not be more easily obtained from the source rocks on land. The study of trace elements in sea water, fortunately, does not receive its justification from the potential of metal mining from sea water. Instead its role is primarily in understanding the nature of large-scale oceanic processes and predicting and monitoring the effects of manmade chemical modifications of man's oceanic environment.

7 THE ORIGIN AND GROWTH OF THE OCEAN BASINS

Frederick J. Vine

Geologists have traditionally studied rocks exposed at the earth's surface and of necessity, therefore, have studied those on the land. Similarly, geophysicists have probed beneath the surface of the earth to determine the thickness and structure of the continental crust. Their findings reveal the dominance of vertical movements during the formation of the continents. Waterlain sediments now outcropping many thousands of meters above sea-level, uplifted plateaus, and downwarped sedimentary troughs all point to the importance of vertical movement. Such studies have also shown that rocks of all ages can be found in continental areas, some 3,000 to 4,000 million years old, almost as old as the earth and solar system itself, and probably representing a very primitive crust.

More recently *marine* geologists and geophysicists have been unraveling the history and structure of the two-thirds of the earth's crust that is covered by deep water. They have discovered that the deep ocean floor has a fabric that implies large-scale horizontal movements during its evolution. In addition, it now seems probable that no part of the deep-sea floor is more than 200 million years old. Thus this two-thirds of the earth's outermost skin has been formed within less than 5 per cent of geologic time.

The recognition of these fundamental differences between the continents and ocean basins has only come about within the past few years. It derives from the findings of that branch of oceanography known as marine geology and geophysics. Needless to say, it has produced a revolution in thinking within the whole of earth science.

Prior to World War II, very little was known about the deep-sea floor; even its topography was poorly documented. However, with the development of the continuous depth sounder during the war, and its subsequent improvement, details of submarine topography have been steadily revealed. But even today we have a much more detailed picture of the far side of the moon than we have of the ocean floors.

We have learned that the ocean basins are dominated by the great midocean ridges or rises. These volcanic mountain chains are thousands of kilometers in width, tens of thousands of kilometers in length, and at their crests rise to 2 to 3 kilometers above the flanking abyssal plains. If the water of the oceans were drained away, this world-encircling ridge system would be revealed as the most spectacular topographic feature on the earth's surface. This system runs down the whole length of the Atlantic from the Eurasian Basin of the Arctic, through Iceland and the Azores, to Ascension Island, Tristan da Cunha, and Bouvet Island in the South Atlantic. It then turns east and runs southeast of Africa and into the Indian Ocean, where it links up with the second major length of the system running from the Red Sea and the Gulf of Aden, across the Indian Ocean, south of Australia, and thence across the south and east Pacific to the Galapagos Islands and the Gulf of California. Only the western Pacific is without a ridge at the present time; but here there is evidence of a former rise that has subsided. This has been named the Darwin Rise in honor of Charles Darwin, who, more than 100 years ago, postulated that the atolls of the western Pacific were indicative of subsidence.

Another major structural and topographic element on the ocean floor is the fracture zone. These linear features are typically expressed by narrow ridges and troughs at right-angles to the midocean ridges and offsetting the ridge crests. The distance by which the ridge crest is offset varies from a few kilometers to as much as 1,000 kilometers. A third oceanic structure with a

97

pronounced topographic expression is the marginal trench or island arc system. Many of these trenches or arcs are convex toward the ocean basin and, with the exception of the Indonesian Arc in the Indian Ocean and the Caribbean and Scotia arcs in the Atlantic Ocean, all of these features border the Pacific Ocean. Examples are the Aleutian, Japan, Marianas, Tonga-Kermadec, and Peru-Chile trenches, all of which are typically 3 to 4 kilometers deeper than the adjacent ocean floor. (Figure 7–1 illustrates these three oceanic structures.)

It is now apparent that the ridge crests, fractures, and trench systems are characterized by other physical phenomena in addition to their topography. For example, earthquakes occur at shallow depths along ridge crests and associated fractures. Often these earthquakes, which originate at all depths up to ten to twenty kilometers, are concentrated in the cross-cutting fractures, and along these fractures between the points on the ridge crest that they offset. Trench systems are also characterized by earthquake activity but here, in contrast to the ridge crests and fractures, the earthquakes occur at all depths up to a maximum of approximately 700 kilometers. In addition, the distribution of the foci of these earthquakes is rather specific and important. They tend to occur on a plane dipping at about 45 degrees to the landward or concave side of the trench and intersecting the earth's surface on the landward wall of the trench. Thus the deeper focus earthquakes occur beneath points hundreds of kilometers landward of the trench itself. (Figure 7–2 shows recent earthquake activity.)

The crest of the mid-Atlantic ridge is marked by active or geologically recent volcanic activity, for example on Iceland, in the Azores, Ascension Island, Tristan da Cunha, and so on. Beneath the sea floor, probes that measure the temperature gradient and thermal conductivity of the sediments reveal that the flow of heat from the earth's interior is also high over all submerged parts of the midocean ridge system. This anomalously high heat flow is thought to reflect submarine volcanism. Volcanic activity also occurs within the island arc systems typically at 100 to 200 kilometers landward of the trench, but much of this

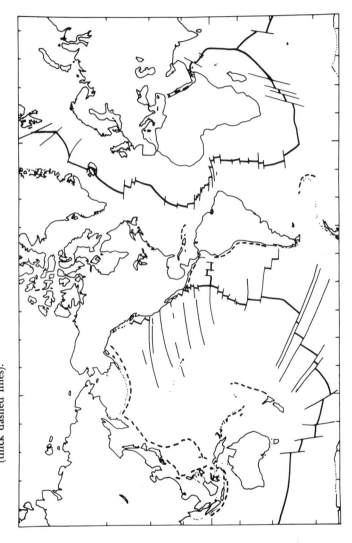

FIGURE 7-1.

Summary of the three main structural and topographic elements within the deep ocean basins: the mid-ocean ridge crests (indicated by thick solid lines), the transverse fractures (thin solid lines), and the marginal trenches (thick dashed lines).

FIGURE 7-2.

Summary of recent earthquake activity. The earthquake belts outline aseismic, quasi-rigid areas or "plates" bounded by the ridge crests, faults, trench systems, and zones of compression. The six major plates are named. Spreading rates at ridge crests are indicated schematically and vary from 1 centimeter per year per ridge flank in the vicinity of Iceland to 6 centimeters per year in the equatorial Pacific.

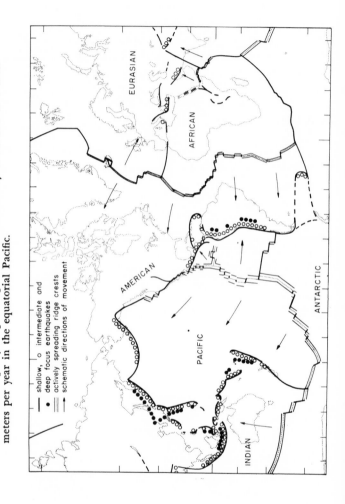

material is chemically different from that extruded and intruded at ridge crests.

The first ridge crest to be studied in detail was that in the north Atlantic, where the topographic crest is marked not only by earthquake epicenters and high heat flow but also by a general lack of sediments, a central valley or rift, and a pronounced disturbance in the earth's magnetic field. This disturbance, or "anomaly," in the earth's magnetic field is an enhancement amounting to 1 or 2 per cent of the total intensity and occurs over a distance of 10 to 20 kilometers, usually coincident with the central valley. Subsequent investigations of other parts of the ridge system showed that a pronounced magnetic anomaly is characteristic of virtually all ridge crests but that the central rift is only well developed in the Atlantic and northwest Indian oceans.

One of the earliest and most fundamental discoveries of marine geophysicists was made by the use of a refraction seismic technique. In the early 1950s this technique was successfully adapted for use in the deep sea for the first time, and it revealed that the oceanic crust is remarkably thin—a mere 6 or 7 kilometers in thickness compared to the 35 kilometers or more typical of continental areas. Sound waves traveling immediately beneath the crust, in continental or oceanic areas, have velocities indicative of the dense, very basic material thought to form the earth's mantle, a layer of material nearly half an earth radius thick and comprising 68 per cent of the earth's mass.

By the late 1950s two other distinctive features of the thin oceanic crust had become apparent. Magnetometers, first developed and towed behind aircraft during World War II in an attempt to detect submarines, were now being towed behind research ships to record magnetic disturbances over the ocean basins. In this way the central magnetic anomaly over ridge crests had been discovered. In the late 1950s a magnetometer was towed by the U.S. Coast and Geodetic Survey Ship *Pioneer* throughout a very detailed survey in the northeast Pacific Ocean. This survey revealed a remarkable "grain" of magnetic anomalies running approximately north-south and interrupted and offset by east-west fractures just as a ridge crest is offset by such fractures. However, whereas the east-west fractures have a topographic expression, neither depth sounding nor seismic reflection profiling reveal a correlation between bottom or subbottom topography and the north-south magnetic anomalies. These linear anomalies are quite unlike the magnetic anomalies observed over the continents and are now known to be typical of most oceanic areas.

The second distinctive feature of oceanic crust had been suspected for some time from the study of oceanic islands but was now confirmed, although modified, by the study of solid rocks dredged from the ocean floor. All of these rocks are basalts, or simple derivatives of basalts, comparable to those extruded on Iceland or Hawaii. In addition, the rock types extruded by the characteristic island arc volcanoes are absent from the ocean floor. Continental basalts are very similar to those of the deep-sea floor but in contrast form only a very small proportion of the continental crust.

Thus the preliminary findings of marine geologists and geophysicists gave every indication that the structure and composition of the earth's crust beneath the oceans is much simpler than that of the continents. Did this necessarily imply a simpler history? The late Harry Hess of Princeton University decided that it did, and in 1960 he postulated that the thin oceanic crust is very closely related to the earth's mantle, being derived from it by partial melting and simple chemical modification. Moreover, Hess suggested that this crust is constantly being created from the mantle at midocean ridge crests and resorbed back into the mantle in the trench systems. The immediate implications of this simple and bold concept were fantastic. If, as Hess maintained, oceanic crust was being formed at ridge crests at a mere 1 centimeter per year per ridge flank, the resulting sideways "spreading" would be sufficient to form the whole of the Atlantic basin within the past 200 million years, less than one-twentieth of geologic time (Figure 7–3). In terms of the earth's history, the ocean basins become young, short-lived features and the seemingly permanent continents are passively drifted apart and together by spreading ocean floors.

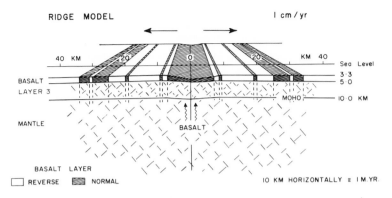

FIGURE 7-3.

Cross-section through a mid-ocean ridge crest illustrating spreading, as postulated by Hess, and the formation of "avenues" of normally and reversely magnetized crust resulting from intermittent reversals of the earth's magnetic field, as suggested by Vine and Matthews. The reversal time-scale for the past 3.5 million years has been incorporated into the diagram.

For most earth scientists Hess' idea was too startling and imaginative, and for several years it was largely disregarded. However in 1963 D. H. Matthews and I, both then at Cambridge University in England, suggested that if one accepted Hess' concept of sea-floor spreading, one might at least have an explanation for the rather distinctive and puzzling magnetic anomalies observed at sea. Our idea was dependent upon three conditions: (1) that new oceanic crust forms at and spreads away from ridge crests, (2) that the earth's magnetic field reverses its polarity intermittently as spreading occurs, and (3) that the permanent, or "fossil," magnetism retained by oceanic basalts is appreciable. We pointed out that if these conditions were met then as new crust forms at ridge crests and the basalts cool beneath their Curie temperature, they will acquire a fossil magnetism aligned with the current direction of the earth's magnetic field. As spreading occurs and the earth's field reverses, "avenues" of crust will be formed, magnetized in alternating normal and reverse fields. We were then able to show that the magnetization contrasts between these avenues might be sufficient to produce the central magnetic anomaly recorded over ridge crests and the linear anomalies of the northeast Pacific.

103

Thus to use a graphic, although unfortunately slightly inaccurate, analogy we converted Hess' conveyor belts of oceanic crust into giant tape recorders; two tapes running out in either direction from a single recording head at each ridge crest.

In 1965 J. Tuzo Wilson, University of Toronto, formulated an additional concept within the framework of sea-floor spreading (Figure 7–4). He noted that if the flanks of the ridges are spreading apart, then the offset of the ridge crests along the crosscutting fractures might well remain fixed with time, in which case movement between adjacent blocks of crust would be confined to that part of the fracture zones between the offset points of the ridge crests. Moreover, the sense of movement along this active length of the fracture or fault would be opposite to that implied by a classical sense of faulting in which the offset of the ridge crests would increase with time and earthquakes would occur along the whole length of the fracture. Wilson named this and other types of fault that were possible within the concept of sea-floor spreading "transform faults."

Hess' idea is clearly compatible with the earthquakes, volcanic activity, and lack of sediments at midocean ridge crests. Together

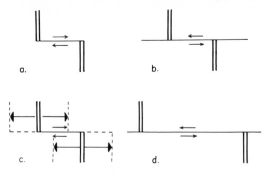

FIGURE 7–4.

A ridge-ridge type of "transform" fault formulated by Wilson within the framework of sea-floor spreading (a. and c.), compared with a "transcurrent" fault (b. and d.). The ridge crest is indicated by the parallel bars, and the active trace of the faults by the thin solid line. Note that the active length of the fault trace and the sense of movement along it are different in each case and that with renewed activity the offset of the ridge crest across a transform fault does not change.

with the extensions suggested by Wilson, Matthews, and myself, it made very specific predictions about the age of the ocean basins, the configuration of magnetic anomalies about ridge crests, and the nature of faulting and the distribution of earthquake epicenters along transverse fracture zones. Clearly as new data became available these hypotheses could be tested.

The first breakthrough came late in 1965 and early in 1966 in connection with the magnetic anomalies. In 1963 it was still debatable as to whether the earth's magnetic field had reversed at all in the past. However by 1965 painstaking measurements of the age and magnetic polarity of geologically recent lava flows from many different parts of the world showed that all flows of the same age had the same polarity. By sampling many such flows of different ages it was possible to construct a reversal time-scale for the past few million years. Early in 1966 this time-scale received striking confirmation from studies of the "fossil" magnetism of deep-sea sediments. Where the top few meters recovered by corers consisted of a complete sedimentary record for the past few million years, it was found that precisely the same sequence of reversals was preserved.

Thus armed with a reversal time-scale and new magnetic anomaly data it was possible to reexamine our idea. Interpreted literally, it implied that the disturbances in the earth's magnetic field should be symmetrical about ridge crests and correlatable with the reversal time-scale. Depending upon the value and constancy of the spreading rate, the correlation with the time-scale might or might not be apparent. The earlier data obtained along isolated profiles in the Atlantic and northwest Indian Ocean had never shown any obvious symmetry, but a very detailed aeromagnetic survey of the Reykjanes Ridge southwest of Iceland, which became available in 1965, did show rather convincingly for the first time linear magnetic anomalies paralleling the ridge crest (Figure 7–5). At about the same time it became apparent that anomaly *profiles* in the Pacific Ocean also displayed a remarkable symmetry and reproduced the reversal time-scale in every detail. The reason for this discrepancy between the Pacific and Atlantic and Indian Ocean profiles was

FIGURE 7-5.

(Top) Summary diagram of magnetic anomalies recorded over the Reykjanes Ridge. Areas of positive anomaly (enhancement of the earth's magnetic field) are shown in black. The straight lines indicate the topographic crest of the ridge.

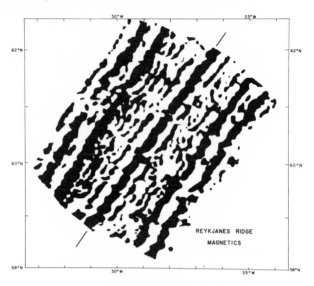

(Bottom) The location of the Reykjanes Ridge and the area of the top figure. The 1,000-fathom submarine contour is shown, together with the 500-fathom contours for the Rockall Bank.

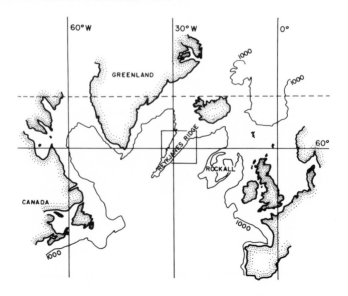

soon apparent. Using the reversal time-scale and a constant spreading rate it is possible to simulate Atlantic and northwest Indian Ocean profiles by assuming a rate of 1 to 2 centimeters per year per ridge flank. In the Pacific, however, one has to assume rates of 3 to 6 centimeters per year with the result that the record is much more boldly written.

Thus in 1966 these new magnetic results provided compelling evidence for sea-floor spreading and enabled us to assign spreading rates to all parts of the midocean ridge system for which magnetic data were available. The predicted pattern of magnetic anomalies is observed over all ridge crests with the exception of two areas: in the Arctic and to the southeast of South Africa. It is concluded that these ridges are either essentially dormant or spreading at a very slow rate.

In the early 1960s the United States set up a World-Wide Standardized Seismograph network and by 1966 results from this network enabled L. R. Sykes of the Lamont-Doherty Geological Observatory, Columbia University, to obtain greatly improved epicentral determinations and focal mechanism solutions for earthquakes occurring on ridge crests. These confirmed that the distribution of earthquake epicenters followed the crest or central valley of the ridges and the fracture zones between the offset points of the ridge crest. Away from the fracture zones, the larger earthquakes have tensional characteristics implying extension of the crust. Along the fracture zones they yield the sense of movement predicted by Wilson's "transform fault" hypothesis and only possible within the context of spreading.

The analysis of the magnetic anomalies and earthquakes which characterize ridge crests provided striking confirmation of Hess's first postulate that oceanic crust is continuously being formed in these settings. Needless to say it prompted an intensive investigation of Hess's second proposal—that oceanic crust is currently being destroyed at the same net rate in the trench systems (Figure 7-6).

Superficially there is very little evidence of compression of the crust in the trench systems or a piling up of oceanic sediments as one might expect. Many near surface structures are in fact

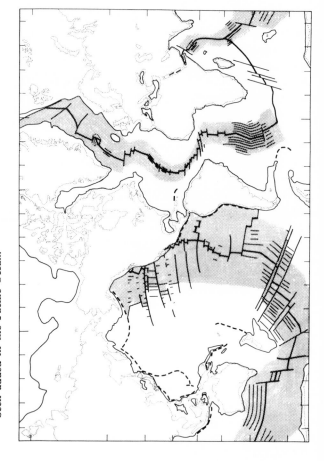

FIGURE 7-6.

Provisional attempt to delineate areas of continental and oceanic crust. Within the ocean basins areas of correlatable linear magnetic anomalies are summarized by means of 10-million-year "growth" lines paralleling the ridge crests. Oceanic crust thought to have been formed within the Cenozoic (the past 65 million years) is shaded, and a 65-million-year growth line has been added in the Pacific Ocean.

tensional in character. However, recent seismological studies of both shallow and deep focus earthquakes reveal crustal movement and structure at depths that are compatible with a downgoing slab of ocean crust and uppermost mantle as predicted by Hess. The upper surface of this slab would appear to be marked by the plane of earthquake foci extending downward and landward of the trench at an angle of about 45 degrees. Beneath this, seismic waves originating from the deeper focus earthquakes reveal an anomalous region in the upper mantle that has been interpreted as a cold rigid plate of oceanic crust and upper mantle being thrust down into the hotter and less rigid mantle at depth. In addition the larger shallow focus earthquakes on this plane give focal mechanism solutions implying that the oceanic crust is being thrust under the continents or island arcs.

It is now apparent that the sea-floor spreading concept can be reformulated in terms of current earthquake activity. Most earthquakes occur within very restrctied belts on the earth's surface essentially on the midocean ridge crests, in the island arcs and young fold mountain systems, and along certain faults linking these features. Between these comparatively narrow zones of earth movement there are vast inactive, undeformed areas, especially within the ocean basins. Thus to a first approximation one might think of the earth's outer skin in terms of a number of rigid plates in constant relative motion. Their boundaries are defined by ridge crests along which crust is being created, trench systems and mountain chains in which crust is being destroyed or compressed, and faults along which crust is translated without change in its surface area.

Thought of in this way, it is possible to analyze the geometry of these plate movements since the rate and direction of relative movement at ridge crests is defined by the magnetic anomalies and fracture zones. This is no trivial matter because one is dealing with a spherical geometry and finite movements. However, preliminary analyses of this type have met with considerable success and should enable us not only to assess the rates of crustal shortening and destruction in mountain and trench systems, but also to gain a better understanding of the distribution and cause of earthquakes. This in turn may lead us to that ultimate and elusive goal—earthquake prediction.

For all its clarity and compatibility with sea-floor spreading we must not lose sight of the fact that historically recorded earthquakes give us only an instantaneous picture of earth movements in terms of geologic time. One might justifiably ask therefore: what evidence is there that spreading has been operative for a significant proportion of geologic time and has formed the whole of the ocean basins as Hess originally suggested?

The most compelling and specific evidence for spreading prior to the past few million years again comes from the magnetic anomalies. The same sequence of anomalies away from ridge crests is recorded over the flanks of the ridges in all ocean basins. The distinctive sequence of linear anomalies first observed in the northeast Pacific in the late 1950s has now been recognized on either side of the East Pacific Rise in the South Pacific, on both sides of the Mid-Atlantic Ridge in the South Atlantic, and in part to the south of Australia and in the Indian Ocean. Because of their symmetry about ridge crests and worldwide correlation it now seems inconceivable that these anomalies could be generated by any process other than a combination of spreading and reversals of the earth's magnetic field.

As yet the widely recognized sequence of anomalies has only been traced up to the continental margins in a few areas, for example, in the extreme North Atlantic and to the south of Australia and New Zealand. However, it now seems probable that all the deep ocean basins were formed by spreading, as Hess envisaged, and with the acquisition of more detailed magnetic surveys the whole history of their growth should be revealed. Attempts to assign ages to the magnetic anomalies, and hence to the underlying oceanic crust and to the implied geomagnetic reversals, predict that the continuous sequence of anomalies recognized to date corresponds to about 75 million years of crustal and reversal history and that in all probability no part of the deep ocean floor is greater than 200 million years old. However, such predictions are inevitably based on linear extrapolations of spreading rates deduced at ridge crests and based on the reversal time-scale for the past few million years. Clearly such an extrapolation implies a progressive increase in the thickness of sediments and the age of the oldest sediments and rocks as one moves away from ridge crests.

The 1960s saw the development of the seismic reflection profiler at sea and this together with deep-sea corers enabled marine geologists and geophysicists to study the variation in thickness and age of deep-sea sediments. In all cases the age and distribution of sediments is found to be consistent with the predictions based on the magnetic anomalies. However, some scientists in this field believed that rather abrupt changes in sediment thickness on ridge flanks in all ocean basins indicate intermittent rather than continuous spreading. Continental geologists also favor intermittent spreading because the record of earth movements and volcanic activity on the continents seems to be intermittent with long periods of quiescence.

Thus until recently there was some doubt about the ages assigned to the magnetic anomalies on the basis of continuous spreading. However in 1969 the results of the first phase of the Joint Oceanographic Institutions Deep Earth Sampling program (JOIDES) brought final proof of the spreading hypothesis and the magnetic time-scale. Sponsored by the U.S. National Science Foundation and carried out by Global Marine's special drill-ship *Glomar Challenger,* this deep-sea drilling program obtained deep samples from thirty-one sites in the Atlantic Ocean and fifty-three sites in the Pacific Ocean. At many sites the whole of the sedimentary column was penetrated and basalt beneath the sediment layer was recovered. In no case did the age of the sediments conflict with that predicted by the spreading hypothesis and, on Leg III in the South Atlantic, a succession of holes drilled across the Mid-Atlantic Ridge at 30 degrees, and beneath the previously dated magnetic anomalies confirmed the magnetic time-scale in a remarkable way. The age of the oldest sediment encountered in each hole, that is, that immediately overlying the basalt basement, was directly proportional to the distance of that hole from the ridge axis. Moreover, the implied rate of spreading is 2 centimeters per year, precisely the rate assumed in deriving the magnetic time-scale.

Thus, within the past few years, oceanographers have established that the present ocean basins are comparatively young features of the earth's surface, which are constantly changing their shape as the continents drift apart and together. The hypothesis of "Continental Drift" was formulated more than fifty years ago, notably by the German meteorologist Alfred Wegener who postulated that a former supercontinent, "Pangea," had been rifted and drifted apart within the past 200 million years or so, thereby forming the Atlantic and Indian Oceans and encroaching on the Pacific, precisely the gross picture that has emerged from the much more recent study of the ocean basins. However, most geologists and geophysicists rejected Wegener's ideas on the grounds that there was insufficient evidence and no plausible mechanism. Even a few years ago the majority of earth scientists did not believe in continental drift.

Clearly the events of the last few years have wrought a revolution within the earth sciences. At last there is a simple and unifying framework on which to hang the whole of geology and geophysics and the detailed and exciting implications for all branches of earth science are only just beginning to be developed.

One of the biggest questions now facing us is what determines the positions of the upwellings in the earth's mantle that produce drift and spreading away from ridge crests. Another is whether there was drift and spreading prior to 200 million years ago. This latter problem should tax the ingenuity of earth scientists for some time for unfortunately the most clearcut record of earth history—that written in the ocean basins—is not available for that period of geologic time.

8 THE OCEAN SEDIMENTS AS KEYS TO THE PAST

John Ewing

Marine geologists are primarily concerned with mapping the shape of the sea floor and discovering the structure of the rock layers that lie beneath. Marine geologists, like land geologists, are historians who have a particular interest in those rocks containing fossil organisms, which record the history of the ocean basins. These fossils, which to geologists are equivalent to the old manuscripts studied by historians, give evidence of conditions in the distant past. They are found in deposits that geologists call sediments, as distinguished from igneous rocks that were originally molten. Sediments can vary in their nature from a very soft deposit, such as river silt, to a very hard material such as the limestones of the Alps. Because of the importance of sediments to the marine geologist, this discussion will include a review of the techniques and equipment used for mapping and sampling sedimentary layers in the deep ocean, some of the things that have been learned about the composition, distribution, transportation, and deposition of deep-sea sediments, and some of the discoveries made in recent years about the history of the ocean basins.

EQUIPMENT AND TECHNIQUES

The first development in the study of the sea bed that might properly be considered a breakthrough was the continuous-

The work described here was made possible through support by the Office of Naval Research and the Ship Systems Command of the U.S. Navy and by the National Science Foundation.

recording echo sounder that came into widespread use shortly after World War II. An echo sounder indirectly measures water depth by recording the time required for acoustic pulses, generated near the sea surface to be reflected from the sea floor back to the surface. The recording mechanism automatically converts the echo time to a depth scale and produces a profile of the sea floor topography on a moving chart as the survey ship proceeds along its course. Millions of miles of echo sounding traverse have now been recorded, particularly during the past two decades, and reasonably good maps have been produced for most of the major oceanic areas. These maps show that the floors of the main ocean basins lie 4,000–5,000 meters below sea level and that the borders of the basins are formed by the shallower continental margins and by large submarine mountain ranges that have been named midocean ridges because in many places they lie midway between the neighboring continental blocks. Topographic profiles from a midocean ridge crest toward a continent typically show extreme roughness near the ridge crests, somewhat more subdued relief on the ridge flanks, and generally diminishing roughness toward the continents. There are extensive flat plains in some areas, broad regions of hills or mountains in others. We now know that the smoother topography in the abyssal plains and near the continents corresponds to a thicker sediment cover that totally or partially obscures the roughness of the underlying basement rocks.

The desire for a convenient way of measuring sediment thickness in the oceans stimulated the development of another type of echo sounder, commonly called the continuous seismic profiler. This device is different from other echo sounders principally in the frequency of acoustic energy employed. The profiler utilizes acoustic pulses in the frequency range generally below 100 Hz. Low-frequency sound propagates through water and through most sediments with very little attenuation; therefore, the seismic profiler records echoes not only from the sea floor but also from interfaces below the sea floor—such as the interface between the sediments and the basement rock or interfaces between sediment layers of different composition or different degrees of lithification. With a seismic profiler at his disposal, the marine geologist now acquires not only morphologic but also stratigraphic data. That is, he measures not only the *shape* of the sea floor but the stratification and structure of the underlying layers of sediment as well. It is true that the marine geologist observes only "acoustic stratigraphy," not real stratigraphy, but he nevertheless learns far more than the shape of the sea floor. He observes that the sediments are several kilometers thick in some places, almost entirely absent in others. He notes that at some levels within the section the sediments are highly stratified, as evidenced by many reflecting interfaces; at other levels no reflectors are observed, indicating a zone of homogeneous material. He notes that some interfaces are much more efficient reflectors than others, indicating a greater contrast in the physical properties of the sediments, such as density, and presumably corresponding to a significant change in the sedimentation conditions. He notes that some reflecting interfaces can be mapped over distances of hundreds or thousands of kilometers. Many of these reflectors correspond to a fossil sea floor—the bottom of the ocean at some time in the distant past. Now the marine historian's interest is really aroused. What can he learn about the stratigraphy of these sediments? How long ago was it that a particular interface was the sea floor? What type of sediment was being deposited then—the same as at present, or a different type? What is the difference between the sediments above and those below the interface to cause it to reflect sound waves?

These questions can be answered only by obtaining and studying samples of the sediment. If the reflector in question is within a few tens of meters of the sea floor, it may be possible to sample it with a sediment corer. A core sample up to 30 meters long is obtained by simply driving a tube into the bottom, usually with the aid of a large weight. When the tube is withdrawn, a valve at the bottom retains the sediment inside, so a vertical section of sediment is recovered whose length is equal to the depth of penetration of the core tube. Coring devices of various design have been used for many years, and much has been learned about deep-sea sediments through the study of the core samples. However, when we consider that typical deep-sea sediment deposits are usually hundreds of meters thick, it is obvious that the core sampler will recover only the topmost, and youngest, sediment unless we can identify exceptional sites for coring. Fortunately we have the seismic profiler to assist us in finding such places. Subbottom reflecting interfaces, which typically may be buried under hundreds of meters of younger sediment, have been traced with the seismic profiler to points of outcrop on fault scarps or in erosional channels. There they can be reached by the core sampler. It is by no means an easy task to lower a coring device 5 kilometers through the water from a drifting ship and make contact with a specific point on the bottom; nevertheless, until quite recently, all of our knowledge of the older deep-sea sediments has been acquired through coring and dredging of outcrops. Approximately a year ago, a program sponsored by the National Science Foundation of the United States was initiated to drill several holes in the Atlantic and Pacific oceans entirely through the sediments, recovering samples at as many levels as possible. The program has been eminently successful and is discussed by Mel Peterson in the next chapter.

SEDIMENT DEPOSITION

How are the sediments useful in deciphering the history of the oceans? One might imagine, for example, that an average rate of sediment accumulation could be established, from which it would be possible to calculate the geologic age of a certain interface simply by measuring the thickness of the sediment above it and dividing by the accumulation rate. Unfortunately, the task is not that simple.

In some parts of the oceans, one centimeter of sediment may represent the accumulation of a million years; in other places it may represent the accumulation of only one year. In the first case, it would be reasonably safe to assume that the sample consists almost entirely of clay and came from a deep place, distant from continents or islands, and probably from the middle latitudes. In the second case, the core would probably have been recovered from a position near a well-drained continent and would consist mainly of sand and silt. In most core samples, the average accumulation rate would fall somewhere between these extremes, and 1 centimeter would represent between 1,000 and 10,000 years accumulation. Why is the rate of sediment accumulation so variable? For several reasons—some obvious and others not so obvious. Few people will be surprised that sedimentation rates are high near continental margins, particularly those margins where large rivers enter the sea. A river such as the Mississippi or the Amazon discharges as much as a cubic kilometer of sediment each year. Although the major part of this sediment comes to rest near the foot of the continental slope, large quantities may be transported thousands of kilometers from the source by underwater avalanches or turbidity currents, and by strong movement of the bottom water. In some areas, large quantities of terrestrial material are supplied to the oceans by glaciers or by volcanoes. Although the study of terrestrially derived sediments is an important part of marine geology, another type of sediment, derived from the ocean itself, is far more useful in the study of historical geology. These sediments consist of skeletons of plants and animals that lived and died in the sea. In deep-sea sediments, the remains of the minute forms of plant and animal life are by far the most abundant and, therefore, the most useful. These tiny creatures, known as plankton, in contrast to larger free-swimming fishes, cannot swim or otherwise significantly propel themselves through the water, so they generally die in about the same part of the ocean where they originated. Their skeletons then become part of the sediment. Although there is some form of planktonic life everywhere in the ocean, the population density is widely variable. Some forms are sensitive to water temperature and all are highly sensitive to the concentration of nutrients in the photic zone, that is, the upper 100–300 meters of the sea where sunlight can penetrate. In the open sea the nutrients are supplied principally from the deeper water, so the abundance of life is closely related to the upwelling of nutrient-rich deep water. Almost continual upwelling occurs in many parts of the oceans, and it is in these areas that the largest concentrations of biogenic sediments are found. Therefore, just as there are principal source areas of sediment derived from the land, there are also principal source areas of sediment derived from the overlying water.

The plankton create their skeletons by secreting calcium carbonate or silica from the sea water. The most common secretors of calcium carbonate are the coccolithophorids (microscopic plants) and the minute animals known as foraminifers and pteropods. Common silica-secreting plants are diatoms and silicoflagellates, and the most plentiful animal that secretes silica is the radiolarian. The skeletal remains of these planktonic forms are common constituents of deep-sea sediments, but the concentrations are widely variable. For example, a core sample, or a section of it, may consist almost entirely of the remains of diatoms. We know of such deposits on continents, usually called diatomaceous earth, and often used as a material for filtering. In the sea we call similar deposits diatom ooze. We also find zones of radiolarian ooze, pteropod ooze, and coccolith ooze. More commonly, instead of finding a pure biologically derived sediment, we find the planktonic skeletons mixed with sand, silt, or clay in varying proportions. Many cores contain no biogenic material at all, but consist entirely of sand, silt, or clay, particularly the latter.

This does not indicate that no life existed in these waters, although it may well indicate a low population density. The absence of planktonic skeletons may simply be an indication that the sediments were deposited in such deep water and at such a slow rate that the calcium carbonate or siliceous remains were dissolved in the sea water before they could be preserved by burial. In broad areas of the Pacific Ocean, for example, particularly in the middle latitudes where biological productivity is low and where the water is very deep, we usually find only clay and altered volcanic material in the core samples. Near the equator and in the high latitudes we may find some planktonic remains, even in very deep water, because productivity of the surface waters is high enough—therefore, sedimentation rates are high enough—that some calcium carbonate or silica is buried before it dissolves. Thus we see that the amount of biogenic material preserved in deep-sea sediments may vary widely with geographic location (because productivity varies geographically) and with water depth (which determines the amount of solution of the skeleton). We can also be reasonably certain that time has played an important role. We do not know enough about historical oceanography to know how much conditions in the sea have changed through geologic time to affect the deposition of the biogenic sediments, but the changes have probably been significant.

SEDIMENT AGE DETERMINATION

Why are we so interested in the preservation of planktonic skeletons? Because the presence of a fossilized skeleton of a particular species often indicates the *age* of the sediment in which it is found. The evolution of several genera and species of the larger planktonic forms, foraminifera and radiolaria, have been well studied by paleontologists, and these have for some time been used as stratigraphic indicators. The minute phytoplankton forms are similarly useful, particularly the coccolithophorids and dinoflagellates. Not only does the relative abundance, or absence, of the various species indicate the age of the deposit in which they are found, but also much can be learned about oceanographic or climatic conditions prevailing at the time of the deposition. Some of the planktonic forms apparently preferred the warm waters of tropical or subtropical latitudes; some have adapted to the colder waters of the high latitudes. The cooling of the oceans during major glacial epochs has in some cases caused the extinction of some species; in others it has caused major evolutionary changes. For example, temperature changes associated with the Pleistocene glacial stages have caused some species of foraminifera, such as *Globorotalia truncatulinoides,* to reverse the coiling direction in the construction of their shells (Ericson and Wollin, 1968). Thus we see the importance of the preserved skeletons of plankton. If a core sample contains a sufficient number of fossil remains, paleontologists can determine its age and sometimes, in addition, determine something about the environmental conditions prevailing during that age.

What if the sediment sample contains no fossils—can we determine its age? It is possible sometimes if certain radionuclides are present. For example, if a sufficient amount of carbonaceous material is recovered, the age of the sample may be determined by measuring the amount of remaining radiocarbon. This technique is useful for ages up to a few tens of thousands of years. There are other techniques utilizing the properties of other radionuclides that are widely used in the dating of continental rocks. At present, it is questionable whether these same techniques can be accurately applied to the dating of oceanic sediments, but there is not much doubt that accurate techniques can be developed.

Quite recently a third method of dating sediments has been discovered. This method depends, in turn, upon recently obtained evidence that the earth's magnetic field has reversed itself many times. A few years ago, the history of these reversals was determined with relatively good accuracy for about the last 3.5 million years by measuring the age and polarity of magnetization of volcanic lavas on land (Cox, et al., 1968). These field reversals have also left a record in the ocean sediments. During the deposition of fine-grained sediments the magnetic particles align themselves with the existing field of the earth, like so many compass needles. Later deposits, coming to rest under the influence of a reversed magnetic field, will be aligned in a reverse direction. Thus, a vertical section of sediments, such as we obtain with a core sampler, will be magnetized in a certain direction in parts of its length and magnetized in the reverse direction in other parts. If the pattern of magnetic-field reversals observed in the core sample corresponds to a recognized part of the pattern of earth field reversals, we know the age of each section of the core, even if it contains no fossils. A large number of core samples have been studied in this manner, the age of the sections containing magnetic-field reversals being compared with the age determined paleontologically. Not only has the history of field reversals, originally determined from lava flows, been verified, but it has now been significantly extended by studies of oceanic cores to 10–12 million years (Foster and Opdyke, in press). We can probably look forward to the time when the history of field reversals will be extended much farther, and the techniques of "magnetic stratigraphy" will be even more valuable. Already we are depending heavily upon this technique to provide dates of deposition of unfossiliferous sediments and to permit accurate determination of rates of sedimentation, particularly in areas of very slow deposition.

HISTORY AND DEVELOPMENT OF OCEAN BASINS

With these tools and techniques, what have marine geologists learned about the history of the ocean basins by studying the sediments? A year or two from now, it will be possible to give much better answers, because more of the data from the deep-sea drilling program will have been studied and disseminated. Even now, however, there are some significant answers. For example, even though intensive efforts have been made to sample the deepest layers by coring and dredging outcrops, and more recently by drilling, we have recovered sediment no older than Upper Jurassic (160 million years old). There is good reason to believe that deeper drilling may reach sediments appreciably older, but unless sedimentation was extremely slow during the earlier geologic periods, it seems unlikely that deposits older than about 200 million years will be found in the oceans. (We must remember that sediments ten times older than this are known on the continents.) A possible exception may be the western part of the north Pacific Ocean, which, according to our present evidence, is the oldest part of the ocean's floor. This suggests, of course, that all parts of the ocean's floor may not be of the same age. If this is true, which parts are older? There is a clear answer to this question if we talk about the Atlantic and Indian oceans (probably also the Arctic Ocean). The midocean ridge system approximately bisects these oceans, and our sampling has recovered only very young sediments near the ridge crest, whereas progressively older sediments are found as we move farther away from the ridge toward the continents. There seems to be little doubt that the floors of these oceans are relatively young in the center and older near the continents. We may recall that the variation in thickness of the sediment layer follows the same pattern—thin sediments on the ridge, thickening toward the continents. Although the pattern is more complicated in the Pacific Ocean, because the midocean ridge system there is not really a median ridge, we find, as in other oceans, only young sediments on the ridge crest—progressively older sediments at increasing distance from the ridge. What does this pattern of sediment accumulation signify? By itself, it might signify that for some reason, difficult to imagine, no sedimentation occurred in the middle of the ocean basins during early geologic times—or it might signify that the older sediments were buried by lava flows as the midocean ridges were built up. Most earth scientists now believe, however, that the ocean floors are not static; instead, large plates of the earth's outer rigid shell have long been in motion relative to each other. New crust, created at the midocean ridges, where crustal plates are separating, slowly moves outward and eventually is thrust back into the earth's interior in the deep-sea trenches. According to this theory there are no old sediments near the crests of midocean ridges because the crust is new. The older sediments found nearer the continents lie on older crust. The *very* old oceanic sediments, and the crustal rocks on which they were deposited, have long since disappeared into the earth's interior, perhaps to reappear as andesitic volcanics. Or perhaps some of the old sediments were scraped off the oceanic crust as it was thrust under the continental margins or island arcs and now constitute thick belts of metamorphosed sedimentary rocks on the landward sides of the deep-sea trenches. This concept of "sea-floor spreading," which is described in Chapter 7 by Frederick J. Vine, has strong support from other geological evidence and from paleomagnetic and other geophysical evidence. Our present knowledge of the age and distribution of oceanic sediments seems to be explained most satisfactorily in terms of this important concept.

What other information have we obtained from ocean sediments about the geologic history of the oceans? A few specific observations will serve as examples.

As mentioned earlier, some areas of the oceans are much more fertile than others for the growth of plankton and hence produce an abundance of biogenic sediment. One such area of relatively high fertility is a belt about 1,000 kilometers wide in the equatorial Pacific Ocean. Strong currents generated and controlled by the prevailing winds, the rotation of the earth, and other geographic and oceanographic factors cause a substantial amount of deep, nutrient-rich water to be brought up and mixed with the surface water in a strip lying approximately between 5 degrees north and 5 degrees south latitudes. Studies of sediment core samples show that the recent deposition closely follows the productivity pattern indicating that most of the planktonic skeletons fall to the bottom at about the same latitude where the animal or the plant lived. However, if we consider the accumulation of several tens of millions of years of deposition, we find that the axis of the belt of thick sediments does not lie exactly along the equator, but instead is a few degrees to the north. It is entirely possible that the over-all level of productivity in this part of the ocean has changed with the passage of time, but there is little reason to believe that the productivity *pattern* has changed. In other words, we would expect that biogenic sediments would always have accumulated faster at the equator than they would a few degrees north or south of the equator. If this is so, how do we explain the fact that the total accumulation has resulted in the pattern that we observe? There appear to be two possible explanations: one, that the axis of rotation of the earth, and consequently the equator, has shifted a few degrees during the time of deposition of the sediments, or two, that the equator has not shifted but the crust has been moved relative to the equator by sea-floor spreading. In reality, both processes may have been involved, but sea-floor spreading has probably been more important than polar wandering. Most of our evidence indicates that for most of the past 30 million years, during which time most of the sediments in this area were deposited, the sea floor was being moved approximately westward—perhaps in a direction slightly south of west. If this movement had not been nearly parallel to the equator, it is probable that no recognizable sediment belt would have accumulated. The shifting of the belt toward the north of the equator apparently began about ten million years ago, at which time several lines of evidence suggest that a major reorientation, and possibly a change of speed, occurred in the sea-floor spreading over much of the earth.

Deep-sea drilling in the Atlantic Ocean has shown that a prominent and widespread reflecting interface that has been mapped by seismic profiling is the top of a sequence of radiolarian chert beds of Middle-Lower Eocene age (M. Ewing, et al., 1969; Peterson, et al., 1970). The sediments above and below these very hard beds are very little different physically from the soft, recently deposited sediments. Does the presence of these chert beds simply indicate that there were periods exceedingly favorable for the growth of radiolaria? Did the chert form from the radiolaria skeletons shortly after deposition or only after burial? Why, in most places, were no chert beds formed in the younger sediments? We cannot yet answer these questions, but they surely will be answered after more investigation. Although of great geological interest, the chert beds have proven to be a serious practical problem in our other studies because they are very difficult to penetrate with the drill and in many places have prevented the sampling of deeper layers.

Another observation of considerable interest is the discovery, by seismic profiling, of large dome-shaped structures in the deep basin of the Gulf of Mexico (J. Ewing, et al., 1962). These features, which are large masses of material that appear to have thrust their way upwards into overlying stratified sediments, have been proven, by drilling, to be salt domes (M. Ewing, et al.,

1969). The salt is believed to be about 150 million years old, about the same age as that found offshore and onshore around the margins of the Gulf. It has been thought generally that salt can deposit from sea water only in shallow seas with restricted circulation. The salt in the Gulf of Mexico basin now lies about 6 to 7 kilometers below sea level. Is it possible then that salt can be deposited in a deep basin, or does this evidence indicate that the Gulf of Mexico basin has subsided 6 to 7 kilometers since Jurassic time? Similar domed structures have also been found in the Mediterranean Sea and in several marginal areas of the Atlantic Ocean.

A final observation about the deep-sea sediments concerns the possible effects of reversals of the earth's magnetic field on the planktonic community and, hence, on the geologic record in sediments. It is rather well known that changes in the temperature of the sea have caused extinction of some planktonic species. Recent studies appear to indicate some correlation between extinction and magnetic field reversals (Hays and Opdyke, 1967). The correlation is not perfect; that is, some species that disappeared soon after a field reversal had survived earlier reversals. Therefore, it would appear that each field reversal does not create the same effect and that the extinction is not a direct result of the reversal but instead is a result of some related environmental change. In one instance, it has been noticed that a reversal of the earth's magnetic field coincided with a gigantic shower of meteorite particles, tektites, that fell over a large area of the Indian Ocean and Australasia (Glass and Heezen, 1967). Whether any of these correlations will prove to be significant and meaningful, or simply coincidental, will surely be answered by further work in this new area of geological research.

These are just a few of the observations that have taught us something about the structure and history of the ocean. The search for more knowledge has been expanding rapidly in the past few years, and it is reasonable to expect that the search will be increasingly more rewarding in the next few years, particularly in view of our recently acquired capability of deep-sea drilling.

References

Cox, A.; Doell, R. R.; and Dalrymple, G. B. 1968. Radiometric time scale for geomagnetic reversals. *Quart. Jour. Geol. Soc. London 124:* 53–66.

Ericson, D. B. and Wollin, G. 1968. Pleistocene climates and chronology in deep-sea sediments. *Science 162:* 1227–1234.

Ewing, J. I.; Worzel, J. L.; and Ewing, M. 1962. Sediments and oceanic structural history of the Gulf of Mexico. *J. Geophys. Res. 67:* 2509–2527.

Ewing, M.; Worzel, J. L.; Beall, A. O.; Berggren, W. A.; Buckry, D.; Burk, C. A.; Fischer, A. G.; and Pessagno, Jr., E. A. 1969. Initial reports of the deep sea drilling project. National Science Foundation 1.

Foster, J. and Opdyke, N. Upper Miocene to recent magnetic stratigraphy in deep sea sediments. *J. Geophys. Res.,* in press.

Glass, B. and Heezen, B. C. 1967. Tektites and geomagnetic reversals. *Nature 214:* 372–374.

Hays, J. D. and Opdyke, N. D. 1967. Antarctic radiolaria, magnetic reversals, and climatic change. *Science 158:* 1001–1011.

Peterson, M. N. A.; Edgar, N. T.; Cita, M.; Gartner, Jr., S.; Goll, R.; Nigrini, C.; and von der Borch, C. 1970. Initial reports of the deep sea drilling project. National Science Foundation 2.

9 SCIENTIFIC DRILLING IN THE DEEP OCEANS

Melvin N. A. Peterson

Since August 1968, the United States of America has been supporting a project of scientific drilling into the sediments and rocks of the deep ocean basins. The main purpose of this drilling is to recover samples of sediments from deep beneath the ocean floor in order to study the age and history of development of the ocean basins.

This drilling project is supported by the United States National Science Foundation and receives guidance and backing from a group of five oceanographic institutions in America known as JOIDES, the Joint Oceanographic Institutions for Deep Earth Sampling. These are the Scripps Institution of Oceanography at the University of California; Lamont-Doherty Geological Observatory at Columbia University; Woods Hole Oceanographic Institution; the Institute of Marine and Atmospheric Sciences at Miami; and the University of Washington. The Scripps Institution of Oceanography in California has the responsibility of managing the project.

The scientific program was developed by the JOIDES institutions working through a panel structure composed largely of geological scientists from the United States as well as from the rest of the world. From across the nation and throughout the world, well-known scientists have helped bring this remarkable scientific effort to the high level of success that it has already achieved.

The drilling and coring, or sampling, is done from a specially designed drilling ship named the *Glomar Challenger,* which is

122 meters long and has a displacement of 10,500 tons. A drilling derrick, which extends about 60 meters above the water, was placed on this drilling vessel.

The *Glomar Challenger,* which was built by Global Marine, Inc., a drilling company in Los Angeles, California, was named in honor of her builder and also for the original HMS *Challenger,* on which the British scientist Sir Wyville Thomson led the first major oceanographic expedition out of Portsmouth, England, almost one century ago. Thus far, *Glomar Challenger* has set a record that is a credit to the historic ship after which she was named.

After a little more than one year of drilling operations, almost 5 kilometers of core have been recovered from deep beneath the surface of the sea floor. Some of this material has been recovered after penetration of more than 1 kilometer. The drilling operations can take place in water almost 6 kilometers deep.

This achievement stands as a great advance over prior efforts to sample the ocean floor. In the past the normal methods of obtaining samples of sediments from beneath the deep sea were simply to penetrate and recover samples with an open pipe dropped into the soft sediment, or to dredge by means of a wire line and bucket. Most of these samples were taken from within a few meters of the surface of the sediment; only rarely were samples obtained from deeper than 30 meters in the sediment. With the new technology of the *Glomar Challenger,* it is now possible to recover sediment from throughout the entire blanket of sediments that cover most of the deep ocean basins.

The drilling operations on board the *Glomar Challenger* are done in a manner very similar to the rotary drilling method used for oil and gas on the continents and continental margins. The drilling is done with a long steel pipe that extends to the bottom of the ocean. This pipe, which carries a drilling bit on its end, is turned to thereby cut the sediment and rock. The samples, in the form of cores, are recovered in another pipe on the inside of the drilling pipe. This sampling tube is dropped to the bottom, inside the drilling pipe. During drilling the sample, or core, comes up into this sampling pipe through a hole in the bit, and when this inner pipe is full it is pulled up to the ship inside the long drilling pipe, by means of a cable on a large winch. The actual sample is taken in a plastic tube or liner. This process can be repeated for almost continuous coring. It is also possible to drill without sampling. Recovery of core can be almost continuous—in some holes, more than 90 per cent of the sedimentary section has been recovered in the form of cores. In other holes, samples were taken only where desired in order to use the time to drill more deeply.

In order to operate in very deep water without anchors, the *Glomar Challenger* is designed so that she can hold position above a place, or site, chosen on the ocean. She does so by receiving signals from a sound source that is put on the bottom of the ocean at the desired place. These signals are received by listening devices called hydrophones fastened to the hull of the drilling ship. An electronic computer on the ship calculates from these signals the distance that the ship is away from where she ought to be above the sound source, and provides command signals to the ship's engines and propellers to give the necessary power to return the ship to the proper position and to hold her against winds and water currents. The ship has operated in winds as high as 40 knots with gusts up to 60 knots without having to abandon station, as well as also in surface water currents approaching 3 knots. The *Glomar Challenger* can move sideways because of special propellers that operate in tunnels, or tubes, that pass sideways through the hull of the ship. In this manner, the ship can remain continuously within about 25 meters of a point above a chosen location for drilling into the floor of the deep ocean basin.

The drilling program is carried out in a series of cruises, each of which lasts about two months. The number of sites that can be drilled on each cruise ranges from about six or seven to about twelve. The drilling program is presently planned to last for a period of forty-eight months and to include twenty-four cruises. During this forty-eight-month period, the *Glomar Challenger* will steam well over 200,000 kilometers and will drill at approximately 300 places in the deep oceans. Already the

Glomar Challenger has drilled more than 100 holes at approximately seventy locations. The ports of call in this far-flung project are widespread over the world. The ship has already called at New York; Dakar, Senegal; Rio de Janeiro, Brazil; the Panama Canal; San Diego; Honolulu; and Guam. In the near future, the ship is expected to visit Tahiti; two more ports in the United States; Portsmouth, England; Lisbon, Portugal; and some port in the Mediterranean Sea. Later the *Glomar Challenger* will operate in the Pacific Ocean and the Indian Ocean.

The scientific program is designed to create a body of knowledge that will lead to an understanding of the age of the ocean basins, their history, and the processes of formation and change.

These long core samples are studied by scientists from many countries. For example, the fossils in the cores show how old the sediments are; they also show how many and what kinds of animals and plants lived in the oceans at the time the sediment was laid down. Many other qualities of these sediments are studied, and the scientists use all these pieces of information to work out the history of the ocean basins. Indeed, this information helps us to understand the history of the entire earth.

We know that we are living on a dynamic earth, one in which changes are taking place continuously. Erosion is one of the most obvious of these dynamic processes that we see taking place on land. We can also see some of the sediments that form as the result of this erosion. Yet even in these obvious processes is evidence of other more deep-seated activity in the earth. If the observed rates of erosion were to continue for very long by geological standards, the continents would soon be reduced to featureless plains near sea level. Instead, we see high mountains actively being sculptured by ice and water and deep trenches near the borders of the continents that are not yet filled with sediment.

One of the most important ideas in modern geological thinking by scientists who study the history of the earth is that the floor of the ocean is spreading slowly from areas or zones in which it is being formed. As an example, there is a very large mountain range found along the central line of the Atlantic Ocean—called the Mid-Atlantic Ridge. It is one of the longest and largest mountain chains in the world rising from the floor of the Atlantic Ocean and reaching above sea level at only several islands in the middle of the Atlantic Ocean. Similar large rises from the floor of the ocean are also found in the Pacific and Indian oceans, which all form a long continuous mountain system.

Different ideas have been proposed for the age and history of the ocean basins—they have either existed largely as they are now for a very long time, or else they have changed and formed as the continents have moved across the surface of the earth. If the first idea were correct, then the sediments that accumulated on the floor of the oceans would provide a continuous record that could be recovered and understood, extending far back into the early geological history of the earth. We know that there are rocks on the continents that are as old as 3.5 billion years. If the ocean basins have existed and accumulated sediment through this long period of time, then the ocean basins would contain a record in these sediments of the history of the earth through this period. If, on the other hand, the second idea is true, and the ocean basins are relatively young features, having been formed as the continents migrated across the surface of the earth, then we should find that the newer portions of the ocean floor have only thin and young sediments, whereas the older portions of the ocean floor would have thick and old sediments laid down on them. Deep-sea drilling offered a chance to test which of these ideas was correct. Beneath the layer of sediments on the floor of the ocean, one would expect to find rock that is not formed from the sediments. This rock would be igneous rock and would have been formed from the crystallization of hot, melted rock. By discovering the age of the sediment first deposited on top of the original ocean floor at various places, we should be able to tell how old the ocean basins are or to tell which portions of the basins are younger and which are older.

Because of the strong possibility that the Mid-Atlantic Ridge or mountain chain was involved in the formation of the Atlantic

Ocean, two sets of drilling locations were chosen to cross this ridge. The first was in the North Atlantic and the second was in the South Atlantic. In addition, a set of drilling locations has been chosen for studying a similar feature in the eastern Pacific Ocean.

Prior to deep-sea drilling, it was known that in the Atlantic Ocean there was evidence suggesting that the sea floor was being formed at the central portion of the Mid-Atlantic Ridge and was slowly spreading apart. For example, the magnetic properties of the rock can be measured from the surface of the sea; and it was found over much of the world ocean, especially on either side of these midoceanic mountain range systems, that there was a pattern of magnetic banding that ran generally parallel to the crest of these midoceanic mountain systems. These magnetic patterns could be interpreted to have been formed as the result of changes in the earth's magnetic field during the slow formation of this igneous rock floor of the ocean throughout a long period of time. In this sense, then, one might interpret the floor of the ocean as behaving very much like a magnetic tape recorder faithfully recording, on a worldwide basis, the changes in the magnetic field of the earth. It was also discovered that the magnetic patterns on one side of the midoceanic mountain system were closely duplicated on the other side of the mountain system, providing additional important evidence of a spreading process taking place away from the central ridge system. In addition, it was known from surveys using sound pulses, which are bounced or echoed from sediment layers beneath the sea floor, that the sediments, for example, in the Atlantic Ocean are very thick near the edges of the oceans and near the continents, but that they become thin toward the central portion of the ocean and are very thin on the very top of this midoceanic ridge system. This, again, is consistent with the idea that the central portion of the Atlantic Ocean floor is young and that the floor of the ocean becomes progressively older further away from this central line that follows the Mid-Atlantic Ridge mountain system. The oldest portion of the ocean floor would be that part nearest the continents.

Drilling from the *Glomar Challenger* has penetrated in a number of places in the Atlantic Ocean all the way through the sedimentary material and has recovered samples of this old sediment at many places on either side of the midoceanic mountain range. In every case, the ocean floor was found to be continuously older and older in age as one moved away from the central ridge system.

It appears, then, that the continents on either side of the Atlantic Ocean have been separating slowly through time and that new ocean floor is being formed along the mountain ridge system in the central part of the ocean. Some process must exist that has slowly torn apart a large continental mass and has built a new ocean basin in the Atlantic Ocean over a long period of time. There may be examples of this kind of breaking of the continents where other midoceanic mountain range systems that are also spreading centers approach the continent. Examples of this might be the Red Sea or the Gulf of California —in which a midoceanic rise system passes beneath the continent and the continent is being torn apart. These may be modern examples of the beginning of a break in the continent that is similar to the very first stages of the formation of the Atlantic Ocean basin.

Based on the age of the sediments above the original floor of the ocean as recovered by deep-sea drilling, it is possible to measure the rate at which, for example, North America is separating from Europe and that at which South America is separating from Africa. This rate of several centimeters per year is a very rapid process by geological standards. For example, during a man's lifetime the sea floor will migrate a distance roughly equal to the length of his body. It is possible, also, to calculate back in time to when the Atlantic Ocean began to form. We believe now that the North Atlantic began to form as an ocean about 200 million years ago, and the South Atlantic began to form about 150 million years ago.

Prior to the beginning of the Atlantic Ocean there existed an ocean; however much of the evidence for this old ocean has been destroyed by the same processes that have formed the

Atlantic Ocean. The sea floor appears to be continuously renewed along these spreading centers and to be continuously destroyed in other places, such as the deep marginal trenches. A remnant of this old ocean floor may still exist in the Northwest Pacific Ocean, where the drilling recovered sediments 140 million years old, but the entire sedimentary layer was not penetrated, and sediments even older probably exist at greater depths.

The Deep-Sea Drilling Project has made highly important contributions to the study of geology. This field is changing very rapidly and now includes a great deal of information and understanding of the earth as a whole, largely as a result of studies of the oceans, which cover most of the earth's surface. This information will be important to all mankind, both in terms of our understanding of the development and formation of the earth on which we live as well as enabling us to make predictions and evaluations of the marine resource potential of the world's oceans. In addition to our better understanding of these broad problems, there are immediate practical aspects of the work being done that are significant to deep-sea engineering, mining, and construction. We have found evidence that in places—particularly in sediment-filled pockets on the ridge systems—the degree of compaction and consolidation of the sediment is very small. At depths in excess of 304 meters below the surface of the sediments, the sediment is still extremely soft. In such places, one would expect that heavy construction or machinery would sink very easily into the sediment.

The deep-sea drilling will also help us to understand where oil and gas in the deep sea may be found, and also give us an appreciation of how much there may be. Salt domes, similar in almost all respects except depth of water to the important petroleum-producing structures of the Gulf Coast of the United States, have been proven to exist in the central Gulf of Mexico. These are the Sigsbee Knolls, and the discovery of oil and gas on top of the knoll that was drilled by the *Glomar Challenger* is a distinct milestone in the understanding of the formation and accumulation of petroleum in deep oceanic areas. It is far more than just the discovery of a potential new oil province; it is a new direction in thought. It is now clear that hydrocarbons can form and accumulate in the deep sea if the proper conditions are available. We need to know more about these conditions.

The Deep-Sea Drilling Project has produced many other new and exciting collections and measurements in addition to the work on sea-floor spreading and continental drift. Some complete sections have been cored that will become standards for biostratigraphic correlation in the ocean basins and between continents. Some of these are where several groups of fossils exist together in the same sediments. The velocity of sound has been measured for the first time in sediments under their natural conditions at depth, and this knowledge will help us to interpret the geophysical surveys over much of the oceans. Many of the reflecting horizons have been identified, and these layers can now be traced in the surveys to places where drilling has not been done. We have evidence that many minerals form in sediments of the deep sea after deposition by chemical processes. Some of these may result from hot waters containing chemicals, which come from the igneous processes that form the original floor of the ocean. Samples from the drilling will be available to qualified scientists throughout the world for study in the years ahead.

The building of the drilling vessel *Glomar Challenger* with its deep water drilling ability and the decision to carry out the Deep-Sea Drilling Project are most timely. Study of the oceans has grown rapidly throughout the past twenty to thirty years to the point where we have some knowledge of much of the formerly unknown oceanic areas of our planet. About 1.5 million kilometers of travel have been made by ships studying the ocean floor. Their voyages have told us much about the global pattern of many properties of the ocean basins and about the thickness and layering of the sedimentary cover of the deep sea and continental margin floor. We can pick choice drilling sites and extend the knowledge from each of the holes that are drilled into the surrounding area. The Deep-Sea Drilling Project comes at a time when a study of the earth has matured from a science in which information was collected to one in which theories or ideas about major earth-forming processes exist. Thus, specific predictions can be tested by sampling the deep sea and continental margin sediments and underlying rocks. We are well on the way, even in the first year of drilling, to having made a historic contribution to our understanding of the world in which we all live.

10 MINERALS FROM THE SEA

H. R. Gould

Although man has long depended upon the ocean for food and transportation, we have only recently begun to appreciate its potential as a source of fuels and minerals. Through recent advances in science and technology, we have developed the ability to explore the oceans to ever-increasing depths. This ability, coupled with the world's rapidly expanding population and growing food and minerals requirements, has generated an interest in the oceans that has never been greater. In recognition of this interest and of the world's need for new resources, the United States in 1968 proposed to the United Nations the launching of "an historic and unprecedented adventure—An International Decade of Ocean Exploration for the 1970's." This proposal invited international collaboration to probe the mysteries of the sea, to increase our knowledge of food resources, and to develop new sources of minerals and fossil fuels. The United Nations has since endorsed this proposal as the initial part of an expanded program of ocean exploration, and efforts are currently under way by member nations in the planning of this unparalleled venture.

It is timely, therefore, to consider the potential mineral resources of the sea. The ocean doubtless contains all known minerals in some measure, but only those that can be extracted economically in competition with other sources will benefit mankind. Thus, we must examine three critical questions: (1) what minerals are now or potentially economically recoverable,

(2) where are they, and (3) what is their present and potential worth?

The minerals of the sea having present and possible future economic value consist of two types—petroleum, including both oil and gas, and nonhydrocarbon minerals and mineral substances in various forms. The latter minerals occur as surface deposits on the sea bottom, in bedrock beneath the ocean floor, and as dissolved solids in sea water. Petroleum, on the other hand, occurs exclusively in sediments beneath the sea floor, generally at subbottom depths of a few hundred to several thousand meters.

Although the list of minerals in the sea is a long one, relatively few of them have economic potential, and fewer still have actually been produced commercially. Other than oil and gas, only a dozen or so mineral substances are presently being recovered from worldwide ocean sources. These consist of sand, gravel, and shell, and minerals of titanium, zirconium, tin, uranium, and iron—all of which are recovered from surface deposits; coal and iron ore mined from beneath the sea floor as extensions of deposits on land; sulfur recovered in molten form from subbottom deposits; and salt, magnesium, and bromine extracted from sea water. The total annual value of these products, together with oil and gas produced from the oceans, is about $4.5 billion, which amounts to only 6 per cent of the estimated $73 billion annual value of all mineral products produced on land. Of the ocean minerals recovered, oil and gas account for four-fifths and the other minerals for only one-fifth of the total value.

To date, all of these mineral substances have come from the continental shelves, chiefly from their shallower inner part. But as exploration intensifies in these areas and extends to the lesser known, deeper-water regions of the outer continental margins and deep ocean basins, we can expect that other economic ocean minerals will be added to today's relatively short list. However, before examining these possibilities, let us first consider the subsea petroleum resources that are of far greater importance, both now and for the remainder of this century.

PETROLEUM

Petroleum, unlike most of the other minerals recovered from the sea, is of organic origin. Its formation involves a complicated process that begins with the accumulation of organic remains of plants and animals deposited along with other sediments, such as sand, silt, and clay eroded from the continents. With increasing depth of burial, a portion of the organic matter is transformed by chemical processes into hydrocarbons, including both oil and gas. The principal conditions required for commercial accumulation of these products include thick sections of sedimentary strata, hydrocarbon source beds (commonly organic-rich shales), porous reservoir beds such as sandstones, and impervious caps, commonly consisting of tight shales. Also required is some sort of trapping mechanism such as structural upwarping or updip termination of porous strata so as to localize the oil and gas within these reservoir beds.

Through use of geophysical and drilling techniques, which permit mapping and exploration of sedimentary strata to great depths below the continental shelves, we have found the conditions in many areas favorable for the accumulation of oil and gas. Not only are the shelves underlain generally by great thicknesses of sediments, but they satisfy locally, at least, the other conditions required for oil and gas entrapment.

Although the first marine discovery of petroleum was made about seventy-five years ago in very shallow water off the California coast, it was not until 1946 that intensive exploration of offshore areas began. Since that time, more than 16,000 wells have been drilled on the continental shelves in ever-increasing water depths and at progressively greater distances from shore. Today, oil is being produced in water depths as great as 100 meters and as far as 110 kilometers from the coast. Exploration is presently under way on continental shelves off seventy-five countries, twenty-eight of which are producing or are about to produce subsea oil and gas. Worldwide offshore production has now grown to 17 per cent of the total world daily output of 5.5 million tons of oil, and offshore reserves amount to 21 per cent of the total world reserve of 60 billion tons. Moreover, the world demand for petroleum is expected to double by 1980 and to triple by 1990. By 1980, the offshore region is expected to provide a third of the world's projected daily output of petroleum.

The principal reason for this widespread offshore exploration activity is the rapid growth in world energy demand and the proven capacity of the continental shelves to supply a substantial part of it. Even though the continental shelves are expected to meet a significant part of future petroleum requirements, industry is already looking to the deeper water areas of the continental slopes for future petroleum supplies and possibly, in years to come, to the even deeper continental rises and deep, semienclosed seas characterized by thick sedimentary sections.

Technology is already available to investigate not only the outer parts of the continental margins and semienclosed seas but the deep ocean basins as well. For example, hundreds of thousands of kilometers of geophysical traverses have already been run across the outer margins and deep ocean basins. In addition, more than one hundred 300-meter core holes have been drilled by deep-water drilling ships in water depths upward to 1,500 meters on the upper continental slope of the Gulf of Mexico and the western Atlantic ocean. Many similar core holes are currently being drilled in the semienclosed seas and deep ocean basins in water depths up to 6,000 meters by the drilling vessel *Glomar Challenger* as part of the United States' Deep-Sea Drilling Project as described in Chapter 9. These holes have not been drilled to search for oil but rather to obtain basic scientific information as it relates to the geologic framework of the sea floor and its resource potential. Although information from these deeper water areas is still scanty, sufficient data is available to outline at least their broad general features. These data suggest that sediment thicknesses of 3,000 to 6,000 meters or more, similar to those beneath the continental shelves in many areas, are not uncommon beneath the slopes, rises, and deep, semienclosed seas. These great thicknesses of sediments, together with the probability of hydrocarbon source rocks, reservoir beds, and structural and stratigraphic traps, argue favorably for the future oil potential of the outer continental margins and semienclosed seas, provided that the reservoirs are of sufficient size and richness to support the anticipated high cost of extraction. It is of interest to note that the *Glomar Challenger,* in drilling one of the many structural highs beneath the Gulf of Mexico abyssal plain in water depth of 3,580 meters, recovered both oil and sulfur in the cap rock of a salt dome 137 meters below bottom. Although by no means a commercial discovery, this is the best evidence to date that petroleum has been generated in such semienclosed seas.

In contrast with the continental margins and semienclosed seas, the deep ocean basins are characterized by a thin sedimentary section with an average thickness of probably no more than 500 meters, minimum reservoir beds, little folding, and less favorable hydrocarbon source rocks. These factors, together with others, tend to downgrade the petroleum potential of the deep open ocean basins.

Although we now have the tools to investigate the ocean's petroleum potential to great water depths, our ability to drill controlled exploratory wells aimed at discovery and to produce the oil, once found, is much more limited. In the development of offshore petroleum resources, floating platforms and ships are conventionally used to drill exploratory wells. Technology for drilling such wells is currently limited to maximum water depth of about 450 meters. Upon the discovery of commercial accumulations, the floating vessels are replaced by large fixed structures in order to drill the many production wells required and to house the elaborate production and storage facilities. To date, large platforms anchored to the bottom by piles and extending above the water surface have been used almost exclusively for this purpose. The maximum water depth in which such structures have now been installed is only 100 meters, but it is probable that they can continue to be used to at least twice that depth.

In deeper water areas other types of structures will be required. Among the possibilities now being considered are totally submerged structures raised above bottom to depths where divers can perform many of the tasks required in production operations. Through saturated diving techniques developed by industry and by the U.S. Sealab and French Conshelf programs, man can now work efficiently for prolonged periods in water depths as great as 225 meters. Furthermore, it appears that such free diving capability will soon be extended to at least 360 meters and perhaps eventually to as much as 600 meters. Another approach under consideration is the use of large underwater chambers maintained at normal atmospheric pressure in which wellheads and other production facilities can be enclosed and in which man himself can operate as required. Such structures, accessible to submersibles, may be either bottom mounted or raised above the seabed. Several facilities of this type have already progressed through the design and engineering stages, and one or more may be developed in the near future. Whatever type of structure is finally decided upon, industry expects to have the facilities available for producing oil and gas in water depths up to 450 meters in the very near future. In fact, the first such facilities could or may be used in the development of a large oil field recently discovered in 400 meters of water in the Santa Barbara Channel off the California coast. Eventually, production facilities will be developed for even greater depths if warranted by the petroleum potential of these deeper water areas and by economic factors.

NONHYDROCARBON MINERALS AND MINERAL SUBSTANCES

Let us now consider the nonhydrocarbon minerals and mineral substances. Projections of future requirements are similar to those for petroleum; world demand for most such minerals is expected to double by 1985 and to triple by the year 2000. However, with a few exceptions like gold, silver, and uranium, our best estimates indicate that conventional land sources will be adequate to meet most of the mineral needs until at least the end of this century. Because of the few subsea minerals with known economic potential, our lack of adequate exploration and recovery technology, and the higher cost of offshore mining, relatively little attention has heretofore been given to offshore potential mineral resources. For example, only about 2 per cent of the total annual world production of nonhydrocarbon minerals is currently recovered from the sea. Moreover, unless major technological breakthroughs are forthcoming to significantly lower finding and recovery costs, it seems unlikely that this small percentage will change much in the next several decades.

Even though there is no necessity now for a crash program to develop subsea mineral resources, it is appropriate to assess their present and future potential. Although data is far from adequate, available information on the occurrence of certain minerals and knowledge of the general geology of the ocean floor and the chemistry of the water mass permit at least a qualitative assessment of the potential of the three regimes—the surface deposits, the subbottom bedrock deposits, and the dissolved solids in the water mass—from which the nonhydrocarbon minerals of the sea can be extracted.

Surficial Deposits

The surface deposits of the ocean floor with present economic value consist of unconsolidated detrital sediments, including mineral grains and rock fragments eroded from the continents, and accumulations of shell debris and lime mud of biologic origin. The detrital sediments are of two types—sand and gravel, and concentrations of certain heavy minerals containing valuable metals such as tin and uranium. These latter concentrations are called placer deposits.

Sand and gravel as well as shell and lime mud, which are widespread on the continental shelves, are mined off several countries, principally to supply local coastal markets that are otherwise deficient in these materials. Shell and lime mud are recovered chiefly off Iceland and the United States, whereas sand and gravel are mined locally to supply markets in the United States and in the United Kingdom and other European countries. Because these materials are low-value products, they are recovered only in shallow water near the shore, where dredging and transportation costs are low. Even so, the cost of mining is about twice that involved in the recovery of sand, gravel, and lime from conventional land sources. The annual worldwide value ($130 million) of these resources is about three times the combined value of all other minerals now mined from the surface of the sea floor. Subsea sand, gravel, and shell deposits represent a practically inexhaustible resource, and their recovery has every prospect of increasing as demands of the world's heavily populated coastal cities grow.

Placer deposits are much more restricted in their occurrence. The heavy minerals of placers are derived solely from weathering and erosion primarily of igneous and metamorphic rocks on land. Because of their high specific gravity, they usually do not occur far from these primary sources. Moreover, as strong current and wave action is required to concentrate the heavy minerals in placers, they are restricted almost exclusively to stream channel and beach deposits. Thus, economic placers in the marine environment can be expected chiefly in modern beaches or in submerged beaches and buried stream deposits on the inner continental shelf in the vicinity of nearby primary igneous and metamorphic sources on land. For the very heavy minerals, such as those containing platinum, tin, and gold, commercial deposits on land are usually found within twenty kilometers of their primary sources. On the other hand, economic deposits of less dense heavy minerals, such as zircon and magnetite, may be located several tens of kilometers from their sources. Presently, tin, magnetite, zircon, monazite, ilmenite, and rutile are the chief minerals being economically recovered from marine placers. Tin is being mined off Thailand, Indonesia, and Malaysia from submerged stream deposits that are continuations of those on land. Tin is also dredged off England, and magnetite is being recovered from submerged beach placers off Japan.

These mineral deposits are all located in less than 35 meters of water and within 10 kilometers of shore. Diamonds are also being produced from submerged beach placers off southwest Africa in comparable water depths. The other minerals—zircon, ilmenite, rutile, and monazite—are presently being mined only from modern beaches; the first three are dredged principally from Australia and Florida beaches, whereas monazite is produced chiefly from the beaches of Australia and Brazil. Although other placer minerals are not mined commercially today from marine environments, those such as gold, platinum, and chromite show some promise for the future. The total worldwide annual value of all marine placer minerals currently produced is estimated at $46 million, of which tin accounts for more than half. Because of the very special geologic conditions required for the formation of economic placers in the marine environment and the high cost of subsea mining compared with that of onshore mining, only a very modest expansion in the recovery of subsea placer minerals is expected in the near future.

Other surface mineral substances of the seabed with possible resource potential are phosphorite and manganese nodules that are formed as chemical precipitates on the ocean floor. However, neither of these subsea materials has yet been mined commercially. Phosphorite is restricted to the continental margins chiefly along the outer continental shelves and upper continental slopes in water depths generally less than 300 meters. It occurs principally along the western margins of continents where upwelling brings phosphate-rich waters to the surface and where deposition of detrital sediments is slight, as off the desert regions of the world. The best known large deposits of phosphorite lie off southern California and the southeastern United States, western Mexico, Peru, Chile, and the Union of South Africa. Additional large deposits probably also occur off northwest Africa and western Australia. Although sea-floor phosphorite accumulations are large, they seldom contain sufficient phosphate to meet the cutoff grade for fertilizer production, which is the chief use of phosphorite. Moreover, present known land deposits of high quality phosphorite are adequate to supply the world's needs for several hundred years. This fact, together with the probable high cost of subsea mining, makes it unlikely that offshore phosphorite will soon be economic, except possibly in phosphate-deficient countries where the extra cost of mining offshore phosphorite may be less than the cost of transporting supplies from more distant sources.

Manganese nodules are restricted generally to the deep ocean floor in water depths greater than 4,000 meters. However, there are exceptions, such as on the Blake Plateau off the southeastern United States, where they occur at depths as shallow as 300 meters. Although manganese is precipitated chemically from sea water, the exact nature of the formation of the nodules is unknown. These nodules occur in the Pacific, Atlantic, and Indian oceans, where they apparently cover tens of millions of square kilometers. It has been estimated that the Pacific alone contains 1.5 trillion tons with concentrations as high as 40,000 tons per square kilometer. In addition to their manganese content, which averages about 18 per cent, these nodules contain small amounts of copper, cobalt, and nickel, generally in amounts of 0.2 to 1.0 per cent. If only a small portion of the total known deposits were producible, they would provide a virtually inexhaustible source not only of magnanese but of copper, cobalt, and nickel as well. But the metallurgical problems are severe, and although numerous attempts have been made to solve them, no process has yet been devised to recover these metals economically. This factor, and others, including the probable high cost of mining, the lack of necessary technology, and the availability of large, relatively low-cost sources on land, make it unlikely that these deposits will become economical in the near future.

The only other known near surface subsea minerals with possible future economic potential are those recently discovered in deep, hot, brine-filled depressions of the Red Sea. The fine-grained sediments filling these basins contain about 5 per cent zinc, copper, lead, silver, and gold, with an estimated total potential value of about $2 billion. Whether or not these minerals can be recovered economically is presently unknown. It has been suggested that they are of hydrothermal origin, produced by hot, metal-rich brines issuing from faults related to the Red Sea rift. If so, other deposits of this type may exist in similar rift valleys of the world's midocean ridge system.

Subbottom Bedrock Deposits

Of the mineral substances in bedrock beneath the sea floor, only three materials—coal, iron, and sulfur—are being recovered economically today. Coal and iron ore are obtained exclusively from land-based mines extending laterally only a few kilometers beneath the sea floor or from vertical shafts drilled through artificial islands constructed near shore. Coal is mined in this way off Canada, the United Kingdom, Chile, Japan, Taiwan, and Turkey, and iron ore is similarly produced off Finland and Canada. Sulfur, recovered in molten form through bore holes, is being mined at only two offshore sites, both in cap rock of salt domes located only a few kilometers offshore in the Gulf of Mexico. The total annual world production of these offshore minerals is valued at $370 million, with coal accounting for 90 per cent and iron ore and sulfur, 5 per cent each.

Although our knowledge of subbottom minerals elsewhere beneath the continental margins (the continental shelves and slopes) is meager, we expect that these minerals will consist of the same type found on land, but probably in different proportions. Minerals of sedimentary origin will no doubt dominate because of the generally thick sedimentary sections beneath the shelves and slopes. Coal and salt deposits with potash layers have already been encountered beneath the continental shelves at a considerable distance from shore in several areas in wells drilled for petroleum, and it is likely that other types will be found in the future. The prospects for discovering mineral deposits associated with basement igneous and metamorphic rocks are less promising because of the generally thick sedimentary overburden of the continental margins.

Except for materials such as potash and sulfur, which can be mined by solution or melting, or for exceedingly large and rich ore bodies of other types, the prospect for economic recovery of subbottom minerals beneath the continental margins would seem to lie far into the future.

As for the deep ocean floor, the only subbottom mineral prospects to be expected there are chromite and nickel, which are commonly associated with basic and ultrabasic rocks of the type that form the oceanic crust.

Dissolved Solids in Sea Water

If all the dissolved substances in sea water could be extracted economically, they would provide an inexhaustible resource for most of man's mineral needs. The oceans contain 1,370 million cubic kilometers of sea water, and each cubic kilometer holds about 40 million tons of dissolved solids. It has been estimated that the elements in a single cubic kilometer of sea water would be worth more than $1 billion if all of them could be extracted. Although about seventy-seven elements have been identified in sea water, most are so low in concentration that only a few are presently or prospectively recoverable.

Today, only three substances—salt, magnesium metal together with magnesium compounds, and bromine—are being recovered commercially from sea water. Their total annual value is $335 million, with salt accounting for about half of this amount. Of the total world production of these materials from all sources, the ocean provides one-third of the salt, two-thirds of the magnesium metal, and one-half of the bromine. For all practical purposes, the ocean is an inexhaustible source of these substances, and production is limited only by demand and competition from land-based sources. Although techniques are available for extracting some other inorganic substances from sea water, the economics are such that there is little prospect in the near future for commercial production.

In addition to the minerals mentioned, it should be noted that the ocean is increasingly becoming a source for the world's growing freshwater needs, particularly in desert regions and in highly populated coastal belts, which have inadequate freshwater supplies. Worldwide production of desalted water now amounts to slightly less than 1 million cubic meters per day, valued at $60 million annually. At the current increasing rate of consumption, production of fresh water from the ocean is expected to increase fourfold in 1978.

In conclusion, it is clear that the oceans have great potential as a source of minerals to meet man's growing needs for minerals, but the potential is not the same for all areas or for all minerals. The continental margins and the deep semienclosed seas have a more abundant, a more diversified, and a more readily recoverable assemblage of minerals than do the deep ocean basins. Furthermore, the potential for petroleum resources, at least in the near future, is more favorable than that for the nonhydrocarbon minerals.

But potential resources are of no value unless they can be recovered economically and in competition with other resources. We really know very little about the distribution of minerals in the sea and even less about how to recover many of them. To meet future foreseeable human needs, we must therefore accelerate our scientific investigations of the oceans and develop our technology to utilize their potential mineral resources more effectively. The International Decade of Ocean Exploration provides a magnificent opportunity for the nations of the world to cooperate and share in this great endeavor.

However, scientific and technological capability alone will not guarantee future success in harvesting the ocean's minerals. In order to attract the huge investments required to convert the potential resources into economic resources, security of operations and a favorable investment climate must be assured. While space does not permit elaboration of these matters, there are many uncertainties today regarding the ownership of the ocean's resources, particularly the mineral resources on and beneath the seabed. It is important, therefore, that we move ahead in an orderly and timely fashion to solve the many legal and jurisdictional problems that presently becloud the development of the ocean's resources. Then and then only will mankind be able to utilize the wealth of the oceans to the fullest extent.

References

Emery, K. O. 1966. Geological methods for locating mineral deposits on the ocean floor. Ann. Marine Tech. Soc. Conf., 2nd, Washington 1966. Trans., 24–43.

————. 1969. Continental rises and oil potential. *Oil and Gas Jour.* 67, No. 19: 231–243.

Emery, K. O., and Noakes, L. C. 1969. Economic placer deposits of the continental shelf. *Offshore,* 29, No. 3: 91–105.

Fye, P. M.; Maxwell, A. E.; Emery, K. O.; and Ketchum, B. H. 1968. Ocean science and marine resource, in *Uses of the Seas.* Englewood Cliffs, N.J., Prentice-Hall, Inc. Pp. 17–68.

Hedberg, H. D. 1967. Why explore the deep offshore?, in *Exploration and Economics of Petroleum Industry,* vol. 5. Houston Gulf Pub. Co. Pp. 61–84.

McKelvey, V. E. 1968. Mineral potential of the submerged parts of the United States. *Ocean Industry,* 3, No. 9: 37–43.

McKelvey, V. E., and Chase, L. 1966. Selecting areas favorable for subsea prospecting. Ann. Marine Tech. Soc. Conf., 2nd, Washington, 1966. Trans., 44–60.

Mero, J. L. 1965. *The Mineral Resources of the Sea.* New York: Elsevier Pub. Co.

————. 1966. Review of mineral values on and under the ocean floor. Ann. Marine Tech. Soc. Conf., 2nd, Washington, 1966. Trans., 61–78.

Ocean Industry. 1968a. Ocean-bottom minerals. *Ocean Industry* 3, No. 6: 61–73.

————. 1968b. Updating ocean bottom mineral activity. *Ocean Industry* 3, No. 11: 39–42.

Sverdrup, H. U.; Johnson, M. W.; and Fleming, R. H. 1942. *The Oceans.* Englewood Cliffs, N.J., Prentice-Hall, Inc.

U.S. Commission on Marine Science, Engineering, and Resources. 1969a. Our nation and the sea—a plan for national action—Report of the commission. Washington: U.S. Government Printing Office.

————. 1969b. Science and environment—Panel reports of the commission, vol. 1. Washington: U.S. Government Printing Office.

————. 1969c. Industry and technology—keys to oceanic development—Panel reports of the commission, vol. 2. Washington: U.S. Government Printing Office.

————. 1969d. Marine resources and legal-political arrangements for their development—Panel reports of the commission, vol. 3. Washington: U.S. Government Printing Office.

U.S. National Petroleum Council. 1969. Petroleum resources under the ocean floor. Washington: U.S. Government Printing Office.

Weeks, L. G. 1969. Offshore petroleum developments and resources. *Jour. Petroleum Technology* 21: 377–385.

11 UNREST IN THE DEEP SEA

D. James Baker, Jr.

On Tuesday, August 29th, 1893, the *Fram* got into the open water in the sound between the isle of Taimur and Almqvist Islands and steamed in calm weather through the sound to the north-east. At 6 in the afternoon I saw from the crow's nest thick ice ahead, which blocked further progress. . . . We approached the ice to make fast to it, but the *Fram* had got into dead-water, and made hardly any way, in spite of the engine going at full pressure. It was such slow work that I thought I would row ahead to shoot seal. . . . According to the unanimous calculations of myself, of Sverdrup in the log, and of Scott-Hansen, the speed must have been reduced to 1.5 or 1 knot in the dead-water. About 6 o'clock the dead-water was still not fully developed. . . . The ice that covered the sound north of Taimur Island was in a state of dissolution and apparently melting very rapidly, and this was probably the main cause of the sea in the sound being covered with a layer of fresh water. . . . The water at the surface was almost fresh (drinking-water), whereas through the bottom-cock of the engine room we got perfectly salt water. I suppose that the bottom-cock at that time was about 4 m. or more, below the surface of the water, and accordingly the *Fram* struck the salt water. *Aug. 30th,* in the morning, we went on to anchor in a bay at Cape Laptev. . . . The bay lay a few miles farther south, and I am sure that it might have been at most 3 nautical miles. But we took 4 hours and more, to steam that little distance. . . . The speed under ordinary circumstances (i.e., with no deadwater) would have been 4 knots. We could hardly get on at all for the dead-water, and we swept the whole sea along with us. It is a peculiar phenomenon this *dead-water.* We had at that time a better opportunity of studying it than we desired. It occurs where a surface layer of fresh water rests upon the salt water of the sea, and this fresh water is carried along with the ship, gliding on the heavier sea beneath as if on a fixed foundation. Dead-water manifests itself in the form of larger or smaller ripples or waves stretching across the wake, the one behind the other, arising sometimes as far forward as almost amidships. We made loops in our course, turned sometimes right round, tried all sorts of antics to get clear of it, but to very little purpose. The moment the engine stopped, it seemed as if the ship were sucked back. In spite of the *Fram's* weight, and the momentum she usually has, we could in the present instance go at full speed till within a fathom or two of the edge of the ice, and hardly feel a shock when she touched.

These are the words of Fridtjof Nansen, leader of the Norwegian North Polar expedition to the Arctic in 1893–1896 aboard the small research vessel *Fram*. He was tracking the ice drift across the Arctic in one of those pioneering oceanographic expeditions for which the Scandinavians are famous. In the course of trying to understand this curious "dead-water," Nansen wrote to his friend Wilhelm Bjerknes, who in turn asked his pupil at the Stockholm Hogskola, V. Walfrid Ekman, to study the problem.

Ekman, who was later to become famous for his wide-ranging contributions to oceanography, including theories of ocean currents, ingenious instruments, and measurements, sought to find other examples of "dead-water." He learned that as far back as Pliny, the naturalist, stories of sudden slow-downs by ships in certain areas were common:

> In his *Historia Naturalis*, Book IX, Chapter 41, Pliny narrates that a ship, carrying the boys of noble families who, by the order of Periander, the despot, should be castrated, was checked on her way, though she had all sails set. The cause was attributed to a species of Mollusc (Murex), which, by affixing itself to the vessel, stopped her speed and thus saved the boys.
>
> Commonly the checking power was attributed to a fish, *Echeneis Remora*. This fish has on its back a haustellum by means of which it can affix itself to the rocks or to floating bodies as, for instance, to vessels. Pliny says that but one of these fish kept back a vessel even

in the strongest wind; and to produce this effect it only needed to affix itself to the body of the vessel. Thus, in the naval battle of *Actium*, it held Antonius' own ship fast, so that he was obliged to board another vessel.

At the same place Pliny mentions another event which happened in his own time: Caligula, the emperor, on his way from *Astura* to *Antium*, was detained, because one single vessel of his whole fleet was stopped and could not move from the spot. The vessel—a quinquereme—was overhauled, and a *Remora* was found sticking to the rudder. When the fish was loosened and brought before the emperor, to the emperor's great astonishment, its power was gone, and the ship could be rowed again.

Intrigued by these stories, and by countless others from all parts of the world, Ekman set to work experimenting in his laboratory to see if he could discover the causes of this remarkable effect. It was through these studies that he was led to the explanation that the effect is caused by internal waves, which had first been studied by Stokes in 1847, and forms one part of this chapter.

We shall return to "dead water" in a moment. We will first deal with commotion in the ocean—that unrest in the deep sea consisting of waves, currents, and turbulent fluctuations far below the surface, some of which we have come to learn about only quite recently. Thus we shall consider coherent waves—not those on the surface with which everyone is familiar but *internal waves* that may be 20 or 30 meters high and yet that go unnoticed by the casual observer of the sea. And we shall delve into the random unrest of the deep sea, for example, the fluctuating motions and staircaselike density field, whose recent discovery upset the notions of earlier times that the waters of deep ocean were quiet, and that the density smoothly increased toward the bottom. Since our space is limited, we must exclude some equally fascinating aspects of the deep sea: for example, the abyssal currents that originate in Antarctica and flow north beyond the equator, or the deep-sea tides, and others, all of which are essential to an ultimate understanding of both deep ocean and coastal problems. These will fortunately be covered by other chapters in this volume. We must also confine our attention to phenomena in the deep sea.

Nansen did not know it at the time, but the *Fram* was being held back by waves, not waves generated at the surface of the ocean, whose pattern is familiar to everyone who has seen a duck swim across a pond, but waves generated at another surface. That surface is the one between the light fresh water from the melting ice and the salty, heavy water below. Here the layer was just thick enough so that the bottom of the *Fram* stuck into the salty water. Just as a ship makes waves at the surface between the water and the air, it also makes waves at the surface or interface between the light water and the heavy water. Such waves are called internal waves, and their existence was first proved by Nansen as well as Bjorn Helland-Hansen in later investigations. The term "puzzling waves" that they used to define this effect is still appropriate today. These "ship-waves" trail off behind, carrying away some of the ship's momentum; in other words, the ship is subject to wave drag. The *Fram,* as she came into the region of two layers of water, was suddenly subjected to double wave drag from two surfaces, and was therefore slowed considerably. Ekman did a careful series of experiments with a small model of the *Fram* to study the magnitude of this "double" wave drag to verify that that was indeed the case, and that ships as slow as the *Fram* would be subjected to wave drag. Most modern vessels travel fast enough to avoid this effect, so that today it remains a problem only for the slow-moving sailing vessel.

These experiments are easy to repeat at home; try it just to get a "feel" for internal waves, by floating some oil on top of ordinary vinegar to make a salad dressing "ocean." The resulting interface is easy to see and internal waves can be excited by moving a pencil at the interface. The waves "formed" at the interface will have a large amplitude while at the same time very little happens at the surface. Potential energy is the clue here. Although large amplitudes are involved, the amount of mass displaced (we could equally well say the potential energy) is small because the density difference between the two layers is small. At the surface, the density difference between air and water is large, so that it takes much more energy to produce a large amplitude wave there. The small density difference also leads to a low wave speed. Typical gravity waves travel 100 times slower at the internal interface than at the surface. This explains why faster ships are not subjected to dead-water—they outrun the internal waves. Some more interesting effects can be produced by placing the experimental "ocean" on an ordinary record player turntable and rotating it.

This so-called "two-layer" system is just a crude approximation to the real ocean. There the density continually increases as one goes deeper. Thus, instead of just one internal surface, as in the model, the ocean has many and, in fact, an infinite number of internal surfaces, and therefore internal waves can exist everywhere in the ocean.

The character of the waves is, however, subject to two limitations. The frequency, or number of beats per second, of a free-traveling internal wave cannot be lower than the inertial frequency, related to the rotation frequency of the earth of one rotation per day, and it cannot be higher than a characteristic frequency called the Brunt-Väisälä frequency. The upper limit is easy to understand. Imagine a particle floating in water that is continuously stratified and heavier at the bottom. Our imaginary particle floats halfway between the surface and the bottom, having the density of the water surrounding it. If the particle is moved up a bit, it will be surrounded by fluid that is lighter and the particle will therefore tend to sink down to its previous position. If, on the other hand, the particle is pushed down a bit, it will be surrounded by fluid that is heavier and thus will tend to rise back to its previous position. The particle is in stable equilibrium. Therefore, if it is disturbed, it will tend to oscillate about its equilibrium position. The stronger the stratification, that is, the greater the density difference between the top and the bottom, the stronger is the restoring force on the little particle. So, when the particle is disturbed, its oscillation frequency will depend upon the stratification, the stronger the stratification, the faster is the oscillation. This frequency of oscillation is the Brunt-Väisälä frequency and is a natural frequency of oscillation for a stratified fluid.

The Brunt-Väisälä frequency is thus an upper limit to the internal wave frequency, or in other words, internal waves with frequencies greater than the Brunt-Väisälä frequency are not allowed because the fluid cannot respond with a freely traveling internal wave that oscillates any faster than its natural frequency. It can only "wave" at a frequency equal to or less than the Brunt-Väisälä frequency. The Brunt-Väisälä frequency varies in the ocean, of course, since the stratification is strongest nearest the surface. Typical periods may vary from minutes to hours. The other limit on the wave period takes us too far afield at this point, but we note that it restricts internal waves to periods of less than two days. Thus, besides being almost invisible at the surface, internal waves also differ from ordinary surface waves by having very long periods of oscillation.

Nansen first observed internal waves in one way—loss of steerage way on the *Fram*. There are, of course, many other ways to observe internal waves, and a variety of sophisticated electronic instruments are used today, together with simple indirect ways, to detect this internal motion. We have noted that although the internal wave may have a relatively large amplitude under water, its amplitude at the surface is relatively small. However, there are still ways in which one can observe internal waves by looking at the surface. These are areas commonly called "slicks" located quite near the coast, which look oily or very smooth, compared to the rest of the surface. Eugene Lafond (1962) of the U. S. Navy Electronics Laboratory has shown that one possible explanation of slicks—at least of long, narrow slicks —is that they are formed by the converging motions near the troughs of internal waves. This can be simulated by putting some powder on the surface of the model "ocean" and exciting some internal waves. Of course, there are other plausible explanations of slicks that involve other physical phenomena in the sea, but internal waves are certainly one possible explanation.

What are some other techniques?

In order to explain the first method, let us consider again the little two-layer model of the ocean as consisting of two layers of water, one hot, and therefore light, the other cold, and therefore heavy. The interface is then marked by a jump in the temperature. Regions in the ocean where such a sharp temperature difference occurs are called "thermoclines." When the internal waves travel by, the interface moves up and down. A thermometer placed near the thermocline records the ups and downs of the internal wave, which is one way that internal waves are measured in the ocean. One of the longest records taken in this way was made by Bernhard Haurwitz, Henry Stommel, and Walter Munk (1959), who placed thermometers (actually thermistors—small resistors whose resistance is proportional to temperature) off-shore from Castle Harbor on the island of Bermuda and recorded the temperature for almost a year at depths of 50 and 500 meters, 1.5 kilometers apart. They found much evidence for both internal waves in the ocean and other kinds of internal turbulence. Lafond, who was mentioned earlier, has used a different kind of device: the isotherm follower, which can be used from a ship or a tower in the ocean by being suspended into the water from a servo-controlled winch and set for a given temperature. When the temperature changes (as it would if an internal wave went by) a signal is sent to the winch that raises or lowers the device in order to maintain it at the same temperature. The resulting record of height for the present temperature is then analyzed for evidence of internal oscillations.

A second way to measure internal waves is to use a particle that floats with the water—much like the imaginary particle used to discuss the Brunt-Väisälä frequency earlier. The easiest way to do this is to mark some of the water with dye and then watch the subsequent movements. Indeed, this has been done in the Mediterranean Sea by J. D. Woods of the Meteorological Office of Britain (1968), who studied the motion of streaks of fluorescein dye at various levels near the thermocline in order to learn more about heat transfer in the upper ocean. With the dye technique Woods could watch the internal waves grow, become unstable, and even form breakers. However, this technique is obviously limited to the depth that a skin diver can safely go or to the small area visible from a submarine. In order to penetrate the depths, we must have a float that can be placed at a given level and tracked by a ship. This type of float must have some buoyancy to offset the weight of the tracking equipment that produces a sound pulse. The first successful float of this type was built by John Swallow of the National Institute of Oceanography in England (1955) who used a long, thin aluminum tube to provide buoyancy and to carry the batteries and sound-making equipment.

The tube is weighted so that its density matches the density of the water at the desired depth. Since the tube is less compressible than water, it oscillates about the proper level: if it overshoots that depth, it is too light and rises again; if it rises too far, it will sink back. More modern versions of the "Swallow float" are made of glass spheres having similar properties. Swallow floats can be used to measure deep currents, and indeed have yielded many unexpected results there, but they can also be used to measure vertical motion or internal waves. A Swallow float modified by the Woods Hole Oceanographic Institution in Massachusetts has been designed for this purpose (Webb and Worthington, 1968). This device has fins mounted all around the outside, not vertical fins, which would cause the float to spin if placed in a vortex, but fins arranged at an angle so that if water moves vertically past the float, the float will spin. The effect is the same as that of a propeller spinning when air moves past it. Pairs of sound pulses, whose time separation is proportional to the speed of rotation, are transmitted through the water to the mother ship. This device has shown vertical motion of large extent in several areas, including the Cayman Trench and the Mediterranean Sea.

But how do we know that we are observing coherent *waves* and not just random turbulent motion? This question cannot be answered with observations from a single probe. An array of many probes must be used to measure both phase and amplitude of the waves. The coherent picture thus built up yields information about any possible wavelike structure. The first person to do this was C. W. Ufford in 1947, who hung probes from both ends of a ship and from several ships simultaneously and saw a two-dimensional wavelike structure in the water (1947). Another way to determine the coherent structure is available for those waves that move much slower than a ship. In one experiment, a single ship with a probe was guided in a star-shaped pattern over an area in order to determine the two-dimensional wave structure. One of the most ambitious projects of this nature has been established by the Massachusetts Institute of Technology at Bermuda. Here a whole string of the electronic thermometers or thermistors on a line has been horizontally strung from the island pointing out toward the South Atlantic, at a depth of about 600 meters. The many wave probes here allow the directions and magnitudes of the internal motions to be determined. The line of thermistor probes is thus the equivalent of a telescope—an oceanic internal wave telescope.

Although we know that internal waves exist in the ocean, we do not have a good explanation of their source of energy. Tides, winds, and surface waves have all been suggested, but each fails at one or another crucial point. This lack of knowledge of the source of energy is not unique for internal waves, and we shall see that it arises again for other internal motions. But it would be misleading to continue any further into internal waves—this is only one class of internal motion. Not only does the water move up and down in the sea, but it also moves from side to side, in the horizontal direction.

The old-fashioned idea that motions in the deep sea were weak and steady was disproved by Swallow, who, although not the first to make deep current measurements that showed unsteady motion, provided a convincing set of measurements that established the present belief in considerable unsteady motion in the deep sea. In 1959 Swallow (1961) brought some of his floats to Bermuda to measure the deep currents. At that time, oceanographers did not expect the currents at depth to be large, and the floats that were brought had a long lifetime: six months. Swallow quickly discovered, however, that some of the currents at depth had velocities up to six miles per day, which took the floats out of reasonable range of his ship, the *Aries* of the Woods Hole Oceanographic Institution. In order to make efficient measurements, he had to convert each of the long life floats to two short life floats. Swallow's final results were striking: the deep water tended to move in circles at times; two floats placed together would eventually move apart, that is, their motion was incoherent; and the magnitude of the speed was much larger than expected. This unsteady motion in the sea has still not been properly accounted for by the modern theories of ocean circulation.

Some of the longest and most reliable series of deep ocean current measurements have been made by the Woods Hole Oceanographic Institution from moored buoys. The concept of a moored buoy is simple—an anchor at the bottom, a line to which current meters are attached that runs to the surface, and a float or buoy at the top. The idea is simple, but the execution is difficult. For example, strong currents such as the Gulf Stream will wash the whole buoy string away, and no reliable long life surface mooring has yet been developed to withstand the 1 million flexing cycles that occur every two months because of waves. The combination of these is a formidable opponent. The new large buoys will probably do better. The original Woods Hole Plan, initiated in 1961, was to put in a line of moored buoys from Woods Hole, near Boston, to Bermuda, crossing the Gulf Stream. There were to be thirteen stations lettered "A" through "M." But the loss of equipment because of the Gulf Stream and general exposure curtailed this ambitious program. In fact, one could always tell where the Gulf Stream was because the buoys would be missing there. In fact, a series of experiments designed to study currents and to learn the technology necessary to produce a reliable buoy has been carried out at Station "D," in 2,600 meters of water off the continental shelf.

In the course of these measurements, a great deal has been learned about the "spectrum" of currents in the deep sea, and the remarkable motions observed by Swallow have been confirmed by many months of data. "Spectrum" is a central concept in a discussion of unsteady motions. If we have a wave motion of just one frequency, then all the energy of motion, or kinetic energy, is associated with that one frequency. However, in nature, when we look at surface waves or internal waves or underwater currents, we see that there are motions at all frequencies, and that the energy is unevenly distributed among these. The spectrum represents the distribution of energy among the various frequencies. The spectra of ocean currents as measured by current meters at station "D" are complicated, but invariably show a peak at the "inertial" frequency. That is, a maximum of energy is observed at the inertial frequency, which was mentioned earlier in connection with internal waves. In fact, current measurements in all parts of the world, not only at site "D," have shown evidence of inertial currents even at the deepest stations, and it has been said that inertial currents are the single phenomenon in the ocean that oceanographers agree upon (Webster, 1968)! As observed, the motion shows greater coherence over several miles in the horizontal, than it does over only 100 meters apart in the vertical. This independent motion of layers of water is difficult to explain.

But what is an inertial current? It can be thought of as a horizontal circular motion of the water where the necessary inward centripetal acceleration is provided by the deflecting force caused by the earth's rotation, the Coriolis force, which is known to students of mechanics as that effect that makes a Foucault pendulum rotate its swinging plane. Thus the inertial frequency is related to the earth's rotational frequency and is twice the earth's angular frequency times the sine of the latitude. Near the north pole the inertial current has a period of one-half day, at 30 degrees N a period of one day (the same as the earth), and at the equator an infinite period. The inertial frequency is another "natural" frequency of water movement, like the Brunt-Väisälä frequency, on the rotating earth. Once started in motion, the water will oscillate at this frequency until the motion is dissipated. But unlike the Brunt-Väisälä period, the inertial period is very long, as we have seen, with a longer period than one day in most of the ocean. Therefore, whatever it is that forces the motion must also oscillate with a period longer than one day, and measurements must be made at least over a period of several days in order to properly describe the motion. An anchored buoy is necessary for accurate measurements over such a long time.

What causes this inertial motion, which has been seen everywhere in the ocean, in fact even in the Arctic, where an ice island was observed to oscillate with an inertial period? The complete answer is not known today, but there is some good evidence to show that the inertial oscillations near the surface are caused by the wind stress on the ocean surface. In fact, the wind stress appears to be able both to start the oscillations and to stop them by blowing in a different direction. The cause of deep inertial oscillations is still a mystery, and until we have more observational evidence and theory we must remain in the dark. Like the generation of internal waves, the cause of inertial currents remains a major problem in oceanography. What we have learned so far from these experiments is that there is a rich variety of current motions at all frequencies, and that it is necessary to make observations over a long time in order to properly describe all the motions that exist at a given location. Scientists from a number of different countries are presently experimenting in order to further explore the nature of inertial motions and other currents. Plans are being made to set up arrays of buoys to take data simultaneously in order to reveal the horizontal and vertical scales of the motion, whether great sheets of water move in circles, whether the inertial motion is broken up into smaller eddies, and what the size of these eddies is.

But internal currents are only one aspect of what we call geophysical turbulence. Another aspect of turbulence has recently come to the attention of oceanographers as the result of some very accurate and detailed measurements of the temperature and salinity of the ocean. These new measurements will have far-reaching consequences on our knowledge of diffusion in the ocean, and their explanation requires the drawing of an important distinction: the difference between molecular diffusion and turbulent diffusion.

Molecular diffusion, which is well understood theoretically, is that effect that causes, for example, dissolved sugar in a cup of coffee to eventually spread evenly throughout the cup if left by itself. Unfortunately, molecular diffusion must be dismissed in ocean studies because the kind of diffusion that really occurs in the ocean is more like the mixing that occurs when a spoon is used to mix the sugar. This kind of motion is not well understood, and is extremely difficult to describe theoretically. The cause of this vigorous mixing and the exact way in which substances diffuse in the ocean are subjects of great interest and activity in oceanography today. A knowledge of diffusion and mixing is certainly important near the coast in estuaries and bays where rivers mix with the ocean. Likewise, the dumping of waste far out at sea requires knowledge of how the waste will diffuse and possibly contaminate an area.

But how do we know that diffusion is turbulent in the sea? Because measurements of temperature and salinity (that is, salt content), two completely different quantities, over great depths show that in the deep ocean each is diffused in exactly the same way. Since the molecular diffusion of salt is 115 times smaller than the molecular diffusion of heat, it is clear that some other mechanism, which tends to treat all substances in the same manner, is at work. This behavior is typical of turbulent processes. The turbulent eddies of the water carry the physical quantities about. Since the agitated motion of the fluid is the determining factor in how the substances are mixed, the kind of substance is not important; all substances tend to be mixed the same.

In order to look into this question further, oceanographers have developed a number of ingenious and precise instruments for studying the temperature and salinity characteristics of the sea. One of these that is used in various forms and given various names and that is of particular importance is a device that can be lowered from a ship continually to sense and send the temperature, the salinity, and the depth data back to the ship.

The resulting data is far more detailed than data gleaned from bottles spaced many meters apart on a hydrographic wire.

The picture that is emerging from these and other similar measurements is that the ocean temperature and salinity are highly structured—in some areas there appear to be broad sheets of constant density water separated above and below by regions where the density of water changes rapidly; that is, instead of being a smoothly increasing function of depth, the density of the water increases like a staircase. This kind of "layering" has also been observed visually in the Mediterranean Sea by J. D. Woods, who put dye into the water and saw it spread out into sheets. These sheets did not remain quiet, however: after the dye had spread, it occasionally erupted at points in spurts of water or turbulent eddies; this intermittent turbulence is an important factor in transferring heat near the surface. Such turbulence is probably also present in the deep sea—but proof of its existence there awaits further measurements. The intermittent "erupting" may be an important part of mixing in the deep ocean as well as in the surface layers.

Such "layering" has been observed in model experiments that use salt and sugar instead of heat and salt as the substances to be diffused. The application of the ideas learned from the experiments will be used to further guide our understanding of turbulence in the ocean. Plans are also being made to use small research submarines to carry salinity probes and temperature probes in order to carefully explore in detail the regions above and below the thermocline. These measurements should lead to a much greater understanding of this "small-scale oceanic turbulence."

This chapter has covered a wide variety of subjects, and yet one feature of the present state of matters stands out clearly: as our knowledge of phenomena in the deep sea increases, so does our awareness of our own ignorance—the discovery of internal waves and deep inertial currents leads us to the question of their source of energy, and more detailed measurements of the temperature and salinity in the ocean open up whole new areas of studies in turbulence. The deep sea is restless—

substances are transferred by turbulent eddies, and deep currents oscillate to and fro with a slow, steady beat linked to the turning of the earth. The many efforts put forth by scientists of all countries will help lead to the explanation of this unrest in the deep sea.

References

Ekman, V. W. On dead water. *Norwegian North Polar Expedition 1893–1896, Scientific Results* 5, No. 15: 1–152. See also *Farthest North,* by Fridtjof Nansen. 1898. London: George Newness, Ltd.

Haurwitz, B.; Stommel, H.; and Munk, W. H. 1959. On thermal unrest in the ocean. *Rossby Memorial Volume.* New York: Rockefeller Institute Press, 74–94.

Lafond, E. C. and Cox, C. S. 1962. Internal waves, in *The Sea:* I, ed. by M. N. Hill. New York: Wiley, Interscience, 731, 753.

Stokes, G. G. 1847. On the theory of oscillatory waves. Trans. Cambridge Phil. Soc. 8:441.

Swallow, J. C. 1955. A neutral-buoyancy float for measuring deep currents. *Deep-Sea Research* 3: 74–81.

Swallow, Mary. 1961. Deep currents in the open ocean. *Oceanus* 7, No. 3. Woods Hole, Mass. Woods Hole Oceanographic Institution.

Ufford, C. W. 1947. Internal waves measured at three stations. Trans. Amer. Geophysics Union 28: 87–95.

Webb, D. C. and Worthington, L. V. 1968. Measurements of vertical water movement in the Cayman Basin. *Deep-Sea Research* 15: 609–612. See also Measurements of vertical motion and the partition of energy in the New England slope water by A. D. Voorhis in the same issue.

Webster, F. 1968. Observations of inertial-period motions in the deep sea. *Review of Geophysics* 6: 473–490. See also Coherence and band structure of inertial motion in the sea by Walter Munk and Norman Phillips in the same issue.

Woods, J. D. 1968. An investigation of some physical processes associated with the vertical flow of heat through the upper ocean. *Meteorological Magazine,* 97: 65–72. See also Wave-induced shear instability in the summer thermocline by the same author, 1968, in *Journal of Fluid Mechanics* 32: 791–800.

12 WAVES

Willard J. Pierson

Waves occur in all sizes as moving bumps and hollows on a water surface. Tides are very long waves caused by the effects of the sun and the moon. The distance from a place on the ocean at which the tide is highest to the place where it is lowest can extend from one continent to another, and thus the length of a wave caused by the tide may be measured in thousands of kilometers. Tsunamis, another form of wave, caused by submarine earthquakes have lengths that vary from tens to hundreds of kilometers. The waves to be described here are those generated by the winds that blow over the ocean. These waves vary in length from 1,500 meters to fractions of a centimeter, the capillary waves.

Wind-generated waves have been studied for more than a century, and before then their behavior was a part of the lore of every seafaring man. During the past twenty years tremendous progress has been made in the forecasting of sea and swell and in the scientific understanding of these waves.

The scientific study of waves requires both the development of theories and the ability to measure waves of all sizes in nature. The development of numerous ways to record the waves and to analyze the records by appropriate statistical and analytic methods by means of electronic computers has paralleled the theoretical advances and has provided us with the basic data with which to verify these theories.

Theoretical advances began when the irregular, random nature of wind waves was understood and when this understanding was combined with what had been previously known about regular periodic waves. This led to the idea of a wave spectrum, analogous in many ways to the spectrum of sunlight. It then became possible to develop ways to record and measure waves, to analyze these records, and to describe the spectrum of the waves as it changes from place to place over the ocean as a result of the changes in the wind velocity and the dimensions of the areas over which the wind blows. Methods based upon the wave spectrum also make it possible to describe how swell is formed and how it travels across the ocean.

At first the behavior of the wave spectrum was studied in terms of the analysis of direct observations of the waves on the ocean surface. A number of significant developments occurred in the middle 1950s when the first really adequate mathematical and physical theories were developed for describing the manner in which the wind blowing over the oceans causes the waves to grow with time and to change from place to place. These theories were tested in wave tanks by blowing wind over the water and by means of new kinds of observation methods for naturally generated waves such as towed arrays of wave recorders and the cloverleaf buoy of the National Institute of Oceanography in Great Britain.

A new subject is concerned with the interaction of one wave with another and with changes in the nature of waves that are only recently understood in terms of further study of the properties of the mathematical equations that describe wave motions in general. Studies of these interactions, for the little waves called capillary waves—or ripples—and for the bigger waves called gravity waves, predicted very interesting effects (that are presently being reproduced in wave tanks) such as the creation of many smaller waves by one single wave.

Also under active development at the present time are ways to compute what the waves are like over the oceans, given the winds over the ocean, and ways to describe what the waves will be like in the future given forecasts of what the winds will be. The problem is a complex one, and large-capacity, high-speed electronic computers are neeeded to carry out the required extensive computations at a speed that will make the results useful.

Another new idea is that the waves on the surface of the ocean can be used to determine the speed of the winds over the ocean. When electromagnetic waves, approximately three centimeters long, are beamed onto the sea surface, they are scattered back toward their source. The strength of the return radiation depends upon the angle that the electromagnetic waves make with the wavy sea surface and on the smaller waves on the sea surface, which, in turn, have properties determined almost solely by the strength of the wind blowing over the water. It has been proposed that a combination passive microwave-active radar on a spacecraft could measure the wind speed over the oceans of the world at 40,000 data points per day. If this can be done, a very important part of the data needed for worldwide weather forecasting will become available.

One of the most practical immediate applications of wave knowledge is that it permits the design of better ships. The naval architects of the world are using theories that describe the motions of ships in waves and our knowledge of waves to design better ships.

Ways to measure waves can be divided into two categories, depending upon whether the waves are measured on the deep ocean or at a point where a fixed platform has been built in relatively shallow water. There are five ways to measure waves in the deep ocean, and there are two ways to measure waves in relatively shallow water.

The greatest amount of data on waves has been obtained by the routine use of shipborne wave recorders carried on relatively small weather ships. This wave-recording instrument, which was developed at the National Institute of Oceanography of Great Britain and has been in use since about 1952, records the vertical acceleration of the ship at a point near its bow and the height of the water on the side of the ship. The vertical acceleration can be used to determine the vertical motion of the ship as a function of time. This motion is added to the elevation of the water on the side of the ship, and the result is a record of the rise and fall of the surface of the ocean as a function of time at the place on the ocean surface where the ship is hove to.

Shipborne wave recorders have recorded several extremely rough storms at sea. The highest wave recording to date was one in which the average distance from the crests to the troughs of the third-highest waves to pass the ship was about eighteen meters. Those who study waves call this the significant wave height, as it represents the higher and better-formed waves to pass an observer. Under such circumstances, since waves in nature are irregular in height from wave to wave, about one wave in every hundred will be about twenty-seven meters from top to bottom.

Many thousands of wave records have been obtained with this type of recorder and the data gathered in this way provide a valuable source of wave information for the eastern North Atlantic Ocean.

The waves on the ocean travel in many different directions at the same time. A record of the rise and fall of the sea surface at a fixed point cannot tell which way the waves are going. The different directions in which the waves are traveling can be sorted out either by taking stereo photographs of the waves or by using a special, freely floating instrument package that measures its own vertical motions and the tilts and curvatures of the water surface. Stereo photographs and a specially designed instrument are two other ways to measure waves in the deep ocean.

In the United States, a special platform has been built called FLIP, an acronym for Floating Instrument Platform. That platform bobs slightly up and down on waves and consequently it is a stable platform in the deep ocean on which shallow water wave measuring devices can be installed.

For the deep ocean, or even for shallow water, ways to use a simple wave photograph to measure certain properties of waves have only been recently described. For the scattered light that comes from the blue sky, the wavy surface of the ocean has regions of light and dark that are proportional to the slope of the water surface. A transparency from such a photograph can be analyzed by means of laser light to obtain a hologram, which turns out to be directly related to the spectrum of the waves, as will be described later. Laser light is light that is perfectly coherent or collimated and of the same wavelength. This new technique is very promising.

Briefly, then, waves on the deep ocean can be measured by a shipborne wave recorder, by stereo photographs, by special buoys, from FLIP, and by means of ordinary photographs.

At any place where a platform, such as a tower or mast, can be installed on the sea floor in shallow water, the platform can be used to support wave-measuring devices. These devices usually consist of vertically stretched wires, or poles, and sense the rise and fall of the water elevation on the wire or pole. Arrays of such wires can be employed to obtain information on the direction of wave travel. The final method of measuring waves, if the water is shallow enough, senses and records pressure variations of passing waves on the sea floor.

An essential feature of ocean wind-waves is that they are random. The laws of chance govern the behavior of the individual waves on the sea surface. In a storm at sea, high waves and low waves follow each other in a completely random manner. Just as one can never predict the exact sequences of heads and tails when a coin is tossed, so also one can never predict, more than a few seconds ahead, the sequences of high waves and low waves. Popular beliefs that high waves come in groups of three, or four, or seven, as the case may be, are all equally unfounded.

These statements are somewhat exaggerated in that successive waves are not completely unaffected by the waves that have just passed. The next toss of a coin has no memory, in a sense, of the results of the past tosses, but the next wave has some memory of the height of the last few waves.

Although it is difficult to tell exactly when a high wave will occur, it is not difficult to describe the number of waves above a given height that will occur during the passage of a hundred, or a thousand, waves by means of probability theory. Extreme waves occur by chance in storm seas, and reports of individual waves 25 meters or 30 meters from their crest to trough are to be expected every once in a while. Waves of this magnitude have disastrous effects on even the largest ocean-going ships as reports in newspapers frequently document.

Another essential feature of waves is that, although they are random, they must satisfy certain physical laws concerning the motions of water bounded at a surface that can move. Since the middle 1800s, these physical laws have been well understood for a train of waves all of the same shape, which are characterized by the direction toward which they are traveling, by their height, and by the distance between successive waves. The distance between successive waves, in turn, determines their speed and the time interval between them.

The basic discovery that permitted the rapid new developments in the study of real waves on the real ocean was a way to combine the randomness of waves with previously obtained knowledge about regular trains of waves. The idea was to combine by addition a very large number of low regular waves with different directions of travel and different distances between crests.

We have all seen a sheet of corrugated metal of the type that can be used for a roof on a shed or other small building. The corrugations consist of a series of regularly spaced ridges and hollows extending uniformly from one side of the sheet to the other. Now imagine many hundreds of such sheets each having a different distance between the ridges and each having its ridges lined up in a different direction and through an angle of about 50 degrees. Then imagine that these sheets are all stacked up one on top of the other. Each sheet has an average position. If a point somewhere on the stack is chosen, the departure of each sheet in the stack from its own average can be found and the sum of these departures represents the combined effect of all the different sheets.

The sum of all these departures at a given point can be either above the mean level or below it. It can be large or it can be small. Thus the surface is highly irregular. If the right kinds of mathematical rules are set forth for deciding on the properties of the individual sheets in such a stack, the resulting sum can be made to look very much like a photograph taken from an aircraft of the waves on the surface of the ocean. One can imagine doing the same thing for a great many different trains of waves, similar to these different sheets, but, of course, the individual trains of waves are moving at different speeds in various directions. The rules for combining the regular waves so as to get irregular waves are determined by the spectrum of the waves. It then becomes a problem to observe the waves adequately so as to determine this spectrum. A spectrum, in general terms, divides the total variance of a quantity into frequency bands. Sunlight, for example, is described by certain levels of intensity in all of the colors of the rainbow for a wide range of wavelengths in the electromagnetic spectrum. An ocean wave spectrum describes how much of the total variance of the sea surface is assigned to different ranges of wavelength, or, equivalently, frequency, and traveling in different directions.

When waves are recorded by means of the various methods just described, the problem of how to sort out the different waves so as to determine how much of the total wave disturbance should be assigned to different frequency and direction intervals arises. The ideas on how to carry out such an analysis were set forth in 1949 by an American scientist who was interested in totally different physical events that happen to be described by the same mathematical and probabilistic concepts as waves. The methods that he developed, which are made possible only by the use of electronic computers, apply very nicely to the analysis of wave data and yield a statistical estimate of the spectrum. To analyze wave data in this way, it is common practice to perform on a computer several hundred thousand arithmetical operations on the numerical values for the points representing the wave records to obtain a final result consisting of about 100 numbers that yields a graph of the wave spectrum. Roughly the numerical analysis corresponds to the physical analogue of passing colored light through a prism and measuring the intensity of the different spectral colors that result.

The spectrum of the waves covers a wide range of wavelengths for those more than a kilometer long to those less than a centimeter long. Ways to describe this spectrum were first developed for the condition that the wind had blown at a constant velocity for a long enough time over a large enough area of the ocean so that the spectrum would not change even if the wind blew longer over a larger area. An equation resulted that described the wave spectrum as a function of frequency with wind speed as the defining parameter just as temperature defines the Planck black body radiation spectrum.

One of the basic problems in the understanding of waves is the development of an adequate explanation for how wind blowing over the ocean causes the waves, an explanation that has only been known for about ten years. There are three parts to the explanation of how winds cause waves.

The first part of the problem is to explain how waves get started in a flat, calm ocean. A basic observed feature of winds is that there are variations in the wind over both space and time that move along at some average speed over the water. Those variations that move at the right velocity and that have the right magnitude affect the water surface in just the right way to start the waves growing. The actual rate of growth is different for different wavelengths and different directions of wave travel.

Once the waves get started, other properties of the wind cause the spectral wave components to grow at a rate proportional to how high they already are. The average wind velocity over the ocean increases with height above the sea surface and the waves extract momentum from this wind speed variation with height. Certain highly interesting properties of the air motion over a wavy surface have been deduced that have actually been measured under laboratory conditions. These laws apply to the shorter waves in the spectrum but do not seem to be able to explain completely what happens to the longer waves.

The third part of the explanation of how the wind causes waves, which appeared in 1966, uses the variations of wind fluctuations with height above the sea surface to explain how the longer waves are caused to grow at a rate proportional to how high they are already. In all of the situations in which the waves grow, their growth is ultimately stopped when they break. This limit in growth appears to be described by this previously mentioned spectrum.

Waves with different lengths travel with different speeds, and thus those on the surface of the sea are dispersive. This dispersive property yields the result that the disturbance caused by the waves travels at half the speed of the waves. The swell that arrives at a given point is caused by higher winds hundreds or thousands of kilometers away from the places at which the swell is observed.

In a way analogous to the way in which sunlight is spread out into colors by a prism, the waves in a storm sea spread out as they travel across an ocean. The long waves travel faster and arrive sooner followed by waves of intermediate length, and finally, much later if at all, because of effects that may destroy them en route, the short waves arrive. The swell thus has waves in it at a particular time that are all nearly the same length. Swell for this reason is much more regular than storm waves.

The mathematical laws that describe the motions of waves on the surface of a liquid are complicated. To study these motions requires various kinds of simplifications, which have been only recently questioned, and, when they are not made, a whole range of different kinds of wave motions are possible. The technical term for these effects is "nonlinear interaction." There are still a great many aspects of this work that have to be studied in greater detail, but there appears to be observed phenomena that cannot be explained without the use of these concepts.

For example, a Japanese scientist has measured irregular waves, acted upon by the wind, in a large tank of water. After the waves travel out of that portion of the tank where the wind is blowing, the changes that occur, namely, new lower frequencies in the spectrum, cannot be explained without considering nonlinear interactions.

To sum up briefly, the irregular waves on the surface of the ocean can be represented by a spectrum that changes its properties from place to place and as time changes, because of the changing winds over the ocean and because the waves travel from the areas where the winds build them up to other areas as swell. The physical laws that describe all of these effects can be written down in terms of mathematical formulas. One of the conclusions that these results cause one to reach is that the waves at any point on the ocean can depend upon what has happened everywhere else on the ocean so that it is necessary to know what is happening everywhere to know what will happen anywhere.

Waves are caused by winds, and so by starting with knowledge of winds over the oceans, it is possible to compute what the waves are like. If the winds can be forecasted, it is then possible to compute, and thus predict, what the waves will be like several days into the future.

The first part of the problem of forecasting waves is to analyze the available data from ships as to the weather over the oceans. The way that the waves will build up depends on how the winds vary with height from quite close to the surface to about 100 meters above the surface. The way that the wind varies with height depends on the temperature structure of the air over the water. If the air is colder than the water, the air is heated from below. The winds are gusty and capable of raising waves rapidly. If the air is warmer than the water, the winds are much less gusty and the waves grow more slowly. By the analysis of meteorological conditions, it is possible to characterize the winds in such a way that the changes in the waves from hour to hour can be computed.

It is thus possible to compute what the waves are like at a set of points over the ocean as of the latest available weather information. To forecast waves, it is necessary to forecast what the winds will be like at about six-hour intervals into the future for a day or so. The waves can then be computed. A computer-based procedure that a group of scientists working with me has developed describes what the wave spectra are like at certain times beginning with the latest available meteorological charts and at six-hour intervals for about three days in the future. The changes in the wave spectra are computed every three hours and are computed for over 500 points on the North Atlantic by means of about 8 million arithmetic operations. This operation takes twelve seconds on the computer. We are presently developing ways to describe and forecast the waves for all the oceans of the world.

Good wave forecasts require good weather forecasts over the oceans. For the Northern Hemisphere, very recent computer-based forecasts of the weather are proving to be quite good for three days ahead.

There are parts of the world where wave forecasts are needed and yet where the available weather information is inadequate for both the proper description of the waves present at a given time and for forecasts of future wave activity. There are not enough weather observations at the surface and at higher elevations in the atmosphere over vast expanses of the ocean. The lack of weather data degrades the accuracy of weather forecasts.

The latest United States NIMBUS spacecraft provides a new and valuable source of data about temperature versus pressure for the higher elevations of the atmosphere, but there still remains the problem of describing weather conditions at the surface of the oceans, which cover 70 per cent of the earth.

The shorter wind-wavelengths on the sea surface are excited almost in direct response to the wind velocity over the ocean. The sea surface reflects electromagnetic waves beamed toward it in a way that is strongly dependent on these shorter ocean waves. The stronger the wind, the rougher are the waves, when atmospheric stability is properly accounted for, and the stronger is the returned electromagnetic signal. It seems to be possible to put a combination active radar-passive microwave instrument on a NIMBUS * spacecraft that should provide, along with other kinds of useful data, information on the speed of the winds near the ocean surface at about 40,000 points each day. These data should make it possible to improve weather forecasts and to provide better wave forecasts in a few years if these concepts are verified by observations made from aircraft.

The people who design and build ships have known for many

* Skylab, to be launched May 1973, will test this concept.

years how to describe the manner in which a ship will move in perfectly regular waves. For waves of certain lengths and for a ship moving through the waves in a certain direction at a certain speed, a ship will respond in a resonant manner just as a pendulum can be made to swing violently if pushed at just the right times. If the spectrum of the waves contains these lengths, then the motions of the ship will be large. To obtain the motion of a ship, it is simply necessary to multiply the spectrum of the waves by a function determined from the design of the ship and the result is the spectrum of the motion of the ship. By using such ideas, it is possible to compute how often a ship will slam and how often the bow will go under water.

As can be concluded from this examination, we have made great progress in the study of ocean waves over the past twenty years. This progress has been achieved by scientists from many parts of the world. When studying something as complex as ocean waves, there are still other things that have to be studied by a combination of mathematical analysis, theory, and observation. The achievements up to the present time, however, provide useful forecasts of waves and results of practical importance to those who study the sea.

13 TIDES

Walter Munk

Tides are caused by the sun and the moon. The moon is more important, exerting a gravitational force equal to almost 2.2 times that of the sun; the moon's gravitation (neglecting the sun for the moment) pulls the part of the earth nearest to it away from the center of the earth, and so produces a high tide directly beneath the moon. At the same time, the moon pulls the earth, as a whole, away from the part of the earth furthest away, thus giving a high tide beneath the so-called "anti-moon." There are, then, two high tides on opposite sides of the earth, and with the earth turning through one revolution in a day, a given place will experience two high tides and two low tides each day.

This is, of course, a highly simplified picture; in fact, so simplified that it is quite misleading as far as the ocean tides are concerned. It would be approximately the correct picture if (1) the entire earth were covered by water, (2) if there were either a moon or a sun, but not both, and (3) if the attracting body (moon or sun) were moving in a circular orbit over the equator. Now, let us drop each of these idealizations, one by one, and see how much more complicated the real tides are. The fact that there are both a moon and a sun implies that they sometimes reinforce one another and some-times interfere with one another, and this leads to spring tides and neap tides, respectively. Furthermore since the orbits are not quite circular, we experience somewhat stronger tides when the moon or sun is closest to the earth; finally, since the orbits of the moon and sun are inclined relative to the Equator, this leads to further complexities.

In spite of all of this, tide predictions are really very good. Errors of 30 centimeters in height or 50 minutes in time are rare, which confirms the popular opinion that there is nothing more to be learned about tides. But this is far from true, as I hope to show.

Let us first consider two extreme cases in which tide predictions are not very useful. One is the case of an extreme storm tide. Extreme meteorological disturbances may change the mean sea level by many meters relative to the predicted astronomic tide. In the North Sea such storm tides have been known to lead to devastating floods. Can these be predicted? A possible scheme for such a prediction has been worked out by Cartwright of the National Institute of Oceanography in the United Kingdom. Essentially, the scheme consists of recording some of the significant meteorological variables—for example, atmospheric pressure at a dozen key stations. From studying past storm tides, it is possible to correlate the storm tide at any given point in the North Sea with the observed pressures at these twelve stations. The technique is then to make the pressure observations instantly available to a computer that produces a combined astronomical-meteorological prediction of tides. I would guess that within a few years, this method should yield quite satisfactory predictions of storm tides about six to twelve hours in advance, or even better.

A second circumstance is the occurrence of tidal waves, or tsunamis, which are waves caused by geological disturbances—the displacement of the sea bottom during an earthquake, an undersea landslide, or an undersea volcanic eruption. Tidal waves are now predictable to some extent by a method that depends upon the fact that seismic waves caused by such events travel very much faster than the tsunamis, 10,000 kilometers per hour for seismic waves as compared to 1,000 kilometers per hour for tsunamis. As a result, a seismograph will receive a warning of a seismic event within a fraction of an hour;

whereas, typically, a tsunami will not arrive for approximately six hours. All seismograms of major earthquakes are immediately analyzed as to whether they occurred on land or under the sea. If they are at sea, they are a potential tsunami source. Not enough is known as yet to evaluate the expected size of the tsunami from the seismogram, so one depends upon tide gauges near the earthquake source for evaluation. If, in fact, a high tidal wave has been generated, the warning is sent at once to many coastal cities. Some places, for example, Hilo, in Hawaii, and Redwood City, in California, seem to be particularly vulnerable to tidal waves, presumably because the offshore underwater topography somehow enhances the incoming tsunamis.

Substantial progress in the prediction of tsunamis will come some day when we are able to predict the earthquakes themselves; a few years ago this would have seemed absurd. Now, one finds oneself in the position of cautious optimism. At least at land locations, one has observed that earthquakes are often preceded by swarms of micro earthquakes, and sometimes by unusual straining. Moves are underway to instrument the major fault systems for the purpose of tying down these indicated precursors. Once such a development has been successfully undertaken on land, I see no fundamental difficulty in adapting this procedure to the sea bottom.

Ocean tides are well known; what is much less known is that the "solid" earth itself undergoes a tidal distortion as well. The amplitudes of these so-called "body tides" is typically one-half meter, and what is observed as an ocean tide is actually ocean tide minus earth tide. If the earth were absolutely rigid, then the ocean tides would be even higher on the average. Until about ten years ago, it was a matter of great difficulty to record earth tides. Now, scientists have succeeded in building a number of highly sensitive instruments that show earth tides very clearly. Among these are sensitive gravimeters, strain meters, and tilt meters. Earth tides are much simpler than ocean tides, varying smoothly from one place to the next and exhibiting the typical two high tides and two low tides per day that were mentioned at the beginning of this chapter. On the other hand, a plot of ocean tides shows that the tidal characteristics vary in a most complex manner across the ocean basins and from one basin to another. The ocean tides are much more complicated than the earth tides for the reason that by some kind of freak accident, the natural resonance periods of ocean basins, the periods at which the water in them would slush back and forth, are typically of the same order as the tidal periods. So, in some places, there are local enhancements of tides, and in other places, the tides are unusually low. The resonance period of the solid earth, on the other hand, is so short, as compared to the tidal period, that no such resonances can occur.

There have been attempts at making so-called cotidal maps that contour tidal amplitudes and phases of all oceans; but these maps are largely guesswork, dependent upon measurements at coastlines and islands, and extrapolated with some general knowledge of how tides behave in mathematically described basins. In fact, the cotidal charts drawn by Dietrick (in Germany) and Bogdanov (in the Soviet Union) and others show very substantial differences.

Nevertheless, some system of tidal waves, not wholly different from the published cotidal charts, must be set in the large oceans by the action of the moon's (and the sun's) gravity. Where these waves impinge on the shallow seas surrounding the continents, two things occur. The associated tidal currents are funneled up from some 5,000 meters depth to some 100 meters and hence reinforce by a factor of about 50. For similar reasons these waves have to travel more slowly, so that their amplitude increases to preserve the power transmission, in this case by the square root of 50, or about 7. Both of these effects tend to make the tidal waves in coastal waters larger and more complicated than in the open ocean and more sensitive to small coastal irregularities. Notable features of tidal waves are the enormous local magnification produced by France's Cotentin peninsula south of Cherbourg, where the range is more than fourteen meters, and by Canada's Bay of Fundy, where the range is sometimes as much as eighteen meters. The complexity of the tidal pattern in a small area such as the North Sea can be computed with some precision. However, such computations are not based upon the moon's gravitational field at all, but upon the known characteristics of the waves entering the area from the open sea. Thus, only a subsidiary technical problem is solved.

In broad outline, then, there are two connected but distinct zones of tidal activity—the wide deep ocean basins that respond directly to the external, gravitational disturbances; and the shallow seas surrounding the continents, in which the tides are driven by the system generated in the deep ocean basins but that tend to have much larger amplitudes, especially in their associated tidal currents. Unfortunately, the vast majority of tidal measurements are crowded into certain parts of the shallow seas surrounding the continents. Practical requirements also tend to direct research activity into this zone. The problems of principal interest to tidal science, however, are mostly concerned with the deep oceans.

How are we going to arrive at an accurate picture of the global tides? One method is by solving the "theoretical tide problem," which can be defined as follows: given the motion of the moon, sun, and earth and given the boundaries (bottom and sides) of the world's oceans, what are the global tides? This is essentially a giant boundary value problem that we can now hope to solve as a result of the development of modern electronic computers. Pekeris in Israel first tackled this problem five years ago, and he is now being joined by Bogdanov in the USSR and Hendershott at the Scripps Institution. There are some difficulties, particularly with regard to the boundary conditions, and the problem has not yet been solved.

Thus far all of the authors working on this problem have assumed the boundaries to be perfect reflectors, but we know from studies of motions of the moon that a good deal of tidal energy is dissipated, and some of the boundaries at least must be highly absorbent. The physics of the tidal dissipation in shallow water is not yet clear, and herein lies the principal difficulty of this problem.

Another method being developed depends upon actual measurements of tides in the deep sea itself. Eyries at the Service Hydrographique, in Paris, has successfully tested a differential gauge that is connected by wire to a surface buoy that transmits an analog signal to a nearby vessel. Snodgrass at the Scripps Institution of Oceanography, La Jolla, California, has built a self-contained capsule that is dropped to the sea floor, records absolute pressure in situ, and is subsequently recalled to the surface by acoustic signals from a surface vessel. Both gauges record temperature as well, because it is required for a correction of pressure readings (but, of course, the temperature records are of great interest in themselves). Other tidal authorities have exhibited a marked interest in the program and stand ready to cooperate in an international program when the required instruments become routinely available.

At a tide symposium in Paris in 1965, an international working group on deep-sea tides was formed to organize systematic measurements and analyses of deep-sea tides. When the group met again in Moscow in 1966 to review the program, representatives of eleven nations attended and expressed some interest in the program; an associated committee was formed to deal with the theoretical problems related to deep-sea measurements of tides. The working group met again in January, 1967, to participate in sea trials of the Snodgrass gauge. Eyries organized the symposium on deep-sea tides held in conjunction with the meetings of the International Union of Geodesy and Geophysics in Switzerland during the fall of 1967. In short, the growing interest in the program is international and promises much for the future.

From a knowledge of the global tides (beyond the continental shelf) it may be possible to infer tide predictions on the shelf for which land-based tide records are not available. But the use of such measurements will have many other applications. Although at the moment one cannot envisage all related geophysical objects of the program, the following appear to be possible:

1. For geophysical measurements on land, the tidal frequencies

cannot be interpreted without allowance being made for the effect of oceanic tides on a global basis; this point applies to measurements of gravity, magnetic field, and so on.

2. Observations of the motions of the sun and moon indicate that energy (presumably tidal energy) is dissipated at the rate 3×10^{19} ergs per second and this is equivalent to 3,000 kilomegawatt (a very large power plant generates 1 kilomegawatt). The deep-sea program will eventually yield accurate figures concerning how much of this is dissipated in the oceans. The residual dissipation, that is 3×10^{19} ergs per second minus ocean dissipation, would provide important information concerning the plastic properties of the solid earth.

3. The fluctuating tidal currents flowing in the earth's magnetic fields generate electric potentials that can be measured with suitable electrodes on the sea bottom. The generated potential depends also on the conductivity within the earth; and with the tides known, the effective conductivity can be estimated for various frequencies (and hence various depths). These estimates in turn provide us with information about the distribution of temperature in the earth's upper mantle. Horizontal temperature gradients within the earth, particularly beneath the ocean boundaries, are associated with a stress field that may be responsible for the principal belts of volcanic and seismic activity.

4. Pressure signatures of passing storms, which will be superimposed on tidal fluctuations as measured with a bottom-pressure recorder, represent an interesting problem of air-sea dynamics. It would be especially interesting to have a long series of simultaneous observations of horizontal currents at great depth (away from surface noise). Weather phenomena are closely associated with "planetary" waves of global dimensions. The propagation of planetary waves is intimately connected to the rotation and sphericity of the earth. Planetary waves have not been convincingly demonstrated in the oceans, perhaps because they are poorly generated and poorly transmitted, or perhaps because the observations have not yet measured the proper variables. Such measurements are simply not available

185

at this time. Well-documented current flow near the bottom would provide a far better reference for geostrophic computations than do theoretical levels of no motion; estimates of mass transport could thus be significantly improved.

5. We have already noted the existence of a sharp increase in temperature in the bottom few meters of the oceans. The existence of a warm bottom layer had been reported earlier by Van Herzen and coworkers from measurements made with a geothermal probe. Is this warm layer maintained at a greater density because of its higher content of salt or of sedimentary particles? In fact, in the measurements of temperature gradients in sediments, what is the role of tidal "pumping" of interstitial water within the sediments? For these studies as well as those of intermittent turbulence, long, reliable records of temperature are necessary; we hope they will be supplemented by measurements of heat flow.

6. The observations may be helpful in explaining the origin of internal waves of tidal frequencies, and, if tsunamis are generated during periods of tide observations, they may be well documented if the time period of the observations is short enough. In any case, the instrumental development can be used in a tsunami-measurement program.

Thus the proposed program has applications in much of the earth's environment, air-sea dynamics, various ocean-wave phenomena, and the inelasticity and stress fields of the solid earth. The bottom of the sea is perhaps the least explored of the "accessible boundary layers" on this planet, and we may be in for some surprises.

I wish to devote the remainder of this chapter to the history of the earth-moon system. I have already mentioned that large amounts of energy are dissipated by tides. This energy derives from the energy of the sun-earth-moon system and leads to a slow decrease in the spin of the earth and in the orbital motion of the moon around the earth. As a result, the day was shorter in the past, and if one extrapolates backwards, one estimates the length of day at about five hours about one billion years ago. The month was also much shorter, more of the order of a present earth day. Most importantly, the moon is now separating itself from the earth at the rate of a few centimeters per year; and was presumably very close to the earth about one billion years ago.

There is no question that the length of day now increases, and the moon is moving away. On the other hand, the extrapolation backward through geologic history is most uncertain. There is one curious bit of experimental evidence that supports this extrapolation. Corals show tiny striations that are associated with a differential uptake of carbonates between night and day. These corals also show "lunations" and "annulations." The former are some effect of the monthly tides on the coral growth, and the latter are presumably the result of seasonal variations (like tree rings). By counting the number of daily striations in the month or year, we can ask what were the number of days per month and the number of days per year in the ancient past. We do find that, whereas modern corals show 365 days per year, Devonian coral, alive 400 million years ago, indicate something like 405 days per year. This is consistent with the implied effects of tidal friction from modern astronomic observations.

But now, we run into difficulties. Most of the theories of the origin of the moon presume that the moon was captured at an early stage in the formation of the solar system, that is, about four-and-one-half billion years ago. A calculation of capture probabilities makes it very unlikely that the moon could have existed in a near-earth orbit for many tens of millions of years without being in fact captured. On the other hand, the backward extrapolation of the present tidal friction would indicate that the moon was very near the earth only one billion years ago. There are numerous speculations and theories on this subject, which I shall not go into here. I hold the conviction that we may learn as much about the origin of the moon and the earth by studying tidal friction on the earth as we may by the forthcoming direct sampling from the lunar surface. It will be interesting to see if this is the case.

14 THE GREAT ALASKAN TSUNAMI

William G. Van Dorn

Throughout the history of civilization occasional large earth-quakes beneath the sea floor have produced unusual wave-like disturbances that have spread havoc among shoreline habitations around the entire affected perimeter of the ocean. These oceanic catastrophes were first observed in the eastern Mediterranean Sea by the Egyptians, and were reported in both the Atlantic and Pacific oceans by the twelfth century A.D. They have been given many names in many languages, but are commonly known in English as "tidal waves," or by the Japanese word "tsunamis." Despite their long history, relative infrequency, mysterious origins, and very complex local behavior widespread misconceptions have resulted as to their real nature. Only very recently has a reasonable explanation of tidal waves—or "tsunamis"—become available.

Tsunamis usually occur following undersea earthquakes that have focal depths less than 50 kilometers beneath the sea floor and magnitudes greater than 6.5 on the Gutenberg-Richter scale. Such earthquakes must be regarded as being very shallow, since in many areas of the world focal depths as great as 600 kilometers have been recorded. In rare cases, landslides, bottom slumping, and volcanic eruptions produce tsunamis, but of these, only the great explosion of the Krakatoa volcano in the Sunda Strait in 1883 resulted in widespread effects. In that tremendous, earth-shaking event, in which over 25,000 lives were lost, it is not clear whether that tsunami was caused primarily by the subsidence of the land, or by the great explosion itself, during which the entire volcanic island disappeared.

Not all large, shallow earthquakes under the sea produce tsunamis. In general, tsunamis occur only when large areas of the sea floor are vertically dislocated, in which cases, the sea surface is immediately altered to conform in shape to the sea floor change, following which, waves spread out in all directions like the familiar ring pattern produced by tossing a pebble into a large, shallow pond. This symmetrical pattern continues to spread outward, increasing in local wavelength and reducing in amplitude until it strikes the continental shorelines, where about two-thirds of the wave energy is absorbed along the shoreline and about one-third is reflected seawards. After about twenty-four hours, because of repeated reflections and distortions by the shoreline, the initial symmetry of the disturbance is entirely lost and the entire ocean is set into random oscillations that slowly die away over a period of several days.

Almost all the damage from tsunamis is caused by the first two or three waves—usually within a period of several hours following the first wave arrival, which has moved across the ocean at a velocity of several hundred kilometers per hour from the point of origin. In the shallow-water environment the complicated nature of the coastline completely alters the pattern of the incoming tsunami waves so that they appear locally as a periodic succession of tides of extraordinary amplitude, rising and falling within an hour or so, instead of twelve hours, as do the ordinary tides. These local waves can be as much as twenty times higher than the tsunami offshore in deep water. As a result, they often rush far inland beyond the range of normal tide and wave action, and then withdraw so far that large areas of the sea floor normally covered by water are temporarily bared. The rapid movement of water in and out generates swift currents, and the combined action of these currents and any prevailing surf can cause great destruction to low-lying waterfront structures. In extreme cases, water marks as high as 30 meters above normal sea level have been recorded in the wake of great tsunamis.

Whereas the devastation is usually greatest along the shoreline nearest the point of tsunami origin, it is a characteristic of tsunami waves that their great wavelength tends to maintain their amplitude with distance, and thus tsunamis are capable of producing destruction at great distances. Because the earth is round, there is a tendency for the tsunami wave energy to be refocused at a point on the earth opposite to that where the tsunami originated. The Pacific Ocean is large enough so that this refocusing tendency can result in large tsunami effects in Japan from tsunamis originating off the coast of Chile, and vice versa—these two countries being nearly 12,000 miles apart.

Because of special topographic differences, certain coastal regions have an unusual susceptibility to severe tsunami effects, while other regions characteristically appear to be immune. Severe effects are more likely to occur along continental shore-lines or large islands that have rather steep offshore slopes, whereas wide, shallow, coastal shelves afford substantial protection against tsunami. In highly restricted regions, such as the eastern Mediterranean Sea (a source of frequent seismic activity), these distinctions disappear and any stretch of coastline is likely to be devastated in the case of a large tsunami.

Within recorded history, most tsunamis have originated in the Pacific Ocean, although any region of the sea floor showing evidence of past seismic or volcanic activity is a potential tsunami source. The deep trenches circumscribing the Pacific Ocean are currently the dominant sites of strong earthquake activity, and the most recent tsunamis have originated therein, particularly off Japan, the Aleutian Islands, and the west coast of South America.

Within the past century, large tsunamis have been occurring in the Pacific Ocean about every five to ten years. Their relative infrequency and wide distribution make them difficult phenomena to study. Because their epicenters usually lie beneath the sea floor, there is no easy way to determine the precise nature of the sea-floor motion that produces a given tsunami, nor can we yet predict in advance the probable occurrence of a large earthquake—even on land, where it is easier to make measurements. For these reasons, our limited knowledge of tsunami behavior comes principally from theory and from observations of the waves themselves. There are two kinds of useful direct wave observations: observations of water level as a function of time registered on tide gauges, or special tsunami recorders, and observations of the greatest extent of water inundation. Examination of such data from past tsunamis shows that records made along continental shorelines cannot be used to infer the character of the tsunami waves in the open sea, because of the alterations caused by shoreline irregularities. Only records made at very small islands in midocean resemble the type of wave motion predicted by theory for abrupt dislocations of the sea floor. Even so, it was not until the great Alaskan earthquake of March 28, 1964, that a really clearcut example of cause-and-effect for tsunami generation could be established. Fortunately (for science only) this great earthquake occurred at the ocean margin in a region where previous accurate surveys provided enough evidence on the pre-earthquake state of topographic elevations so that the accurate comparisons could be made with new elevations established following the earthquake. This evidence, coupled with the wave observations in many places along the coastline, have permitted scientists for the first time to make a fairly convincing reconstruction of the generation process.

The Alaskan earthquake was the second most intense earthquake ever recorded, being exceeded in magnitude only by the great earthquake of May 22, 1960, in southern Chile. This latter earthquake produced the largest tsunami on record from the standpoint of circum-Pacific damage, particularly in Japan and Hawaii. Because it occurred at low tide in an area of very large tidal range, and also in very shallow water, the tsunami from the Alaskan earthquake was of only moderate size. Both of these great earthquakes occurred in regions of high mountainous shorelines bordered by deep oceanic trenches, within which hundreds of smaller earthquakes occur each year. Similarly, both regions can be described as actively tectonic in the sense that very large changes in land level with respect to sea level have occurred within recent geologic time. The Alaskan earthquake was outstanding in the great area over which substantial changes in ground elevation occurred within a few minutes following the initial major shock. A block about 500 kilometers long by 200 kilometers wide was deformed into an "S"-shaped profile about an axis passing roughly through the center of its longer dimension, such that half of the block subsided by as much as 2 meters while the other half was uplifted by a similar amount. These extremes were substantially exceeded in certain local regions, the greatest uplift being about 10 meters. The area affected (Figure 14–1) comprised the entire Cook Inlet, Prince William Sound, a large glacially excavated inland sea in southeastern Alaska, the Kenai Peninsula to the west of the Sound, extending all the way down to and including Kodiak Island, and the entire shelf of the Gulf of Alaska to the Southeast of this Peninsula. The axis of the tilting movement passed through the center of Prince William Sound, curved to the southwest, passing slightly southward of Seward, then continued across the Gulf of Alaska, passing east of Kodiak Island, and terminated near the Trinity Islands slightly further south. All of the region northwest of this axis subsided during the earthquake, and all that to the southeast was uplifted. The largest uplift was in the vicinity of Montague Island, which partially blocks the mouth of Prince William Sound from the Gulf of Alaska.

The initial earthquake shock occurred at 5:36 P.M., Alaskan time, at a point about 50 kilometers north of Prince William Sound and under the Great Columbia Glacier. Violent ground motion was experienced over the entire region, terminating in Kodiak Island about six minutes later.

The catastrophic results of the ground motion were easily visible the next morning to persons flying over the area, even at great altitude. Mountains and glaciers were split open, revealing great crevasses; innumerable avalanches occurred among the high mountains within a radius of 200 kilometers of Prince William Sound. The Alaskan railroad between Anchorage and Whittier, and the highway beside it were literally flipped upside down for several hundred meters. Along several hundred

FIGURE 14-1.

Area affected by the Alaskan earthquake.

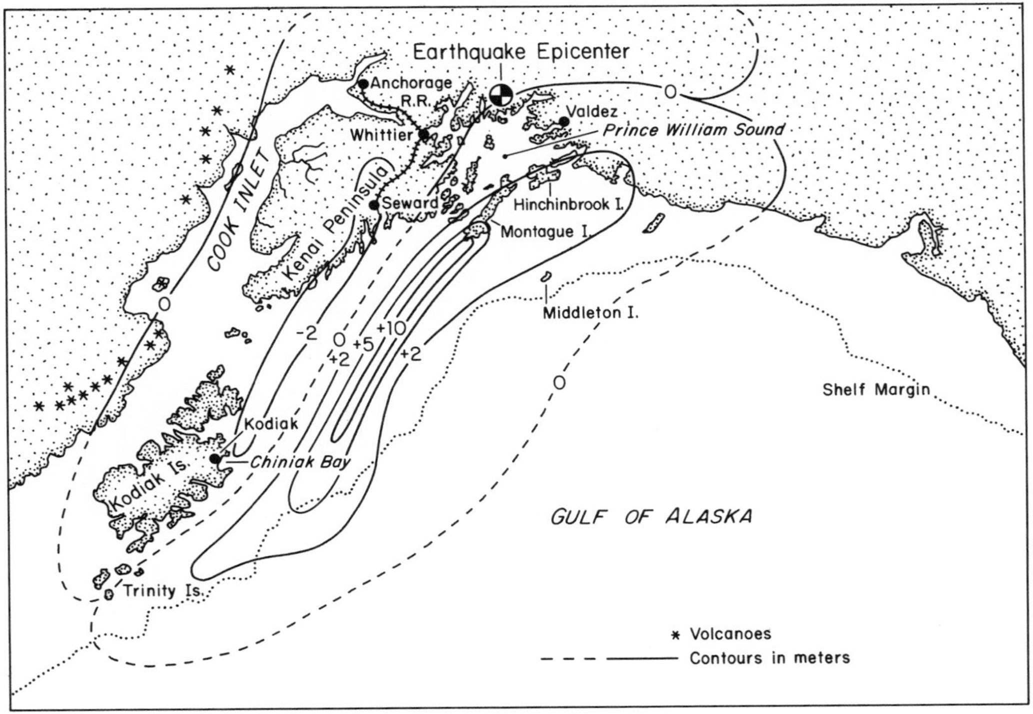

kilometers of seacoast, which is bordered by high cliffs in that part of Alaska, enormous landslides occurred, carrying with them thousands of tall trees. This accumulated debris at the base of the cliffs resembled mud thoroughly mixed with small toothpicks when observed from the air. The ice was shattered around the edge of every frozen lake and in many cases transverse cracks across a lake attested to violent oscillations of the lake level as it splashed back and forth like water in a bathtub. All of the ice about 1 or 2 meters thick filling the northern half of the Cook Inlet about 200 kilometers in length and 50 kilometers wide, as well as in innumerable small bays and inlets along the seacoast, was shattered and carried to sea by the ensuing tides almost a month prematurely.

Strangely, in this sparsely populated country, the principal direct earthquake damage to human habitation was restricted almost entirely to the city of Anchorage, which was well outside the zone of strong ground motion. At Anchorage, which was constructed on an alluvial plain consisting principally of interbedded sand, gravel, and clay, the extensive damage to large buildings was attributed to temporary liquefaction of a subsurface layer of clay, which resulted in local subsidence of an old stream bed running through the center of the city.

The remainder of the damage in southeastern Alaska, principally in the cities of Valdez, Seward, Whittier, and Kodiak, occurred as the result of ground shaking combined with subsequent water motion. These effects can be reasonably divided between those occurring within Prince William Sound and those outside of it, along the sea coast bordering the Gulf of Alaska.

Prince William Sound is a roughly circular basin, about 200 kilometers in diameter and 500 meters deep, and is almost entirely cut off from the sea by Montague and Hinchinbrook islands. The Sound is also the terminus for some 20 to 30 glacial fjords, several of which exceed 100 kilometers in length. Since the principal tilt axis of the gross block motion during the earthquake passed southwesterly through the center of Prince William Sound, the immediate effect of this tilting was to produce a strong northwesterly flow of water in all regions of the

Sound. Thus, massive flood waves were instantaneously created in all of the fjords tending northeasterly, which continued until enough water had piled up in these channels to arrest the flow, following which the flow was reversed and the entire process repeated in the opposite direction. The oscillations of the water within these many channels continued for over thirty-six hours.

However, direct effects of the earthquake were felt much earlier at the communities of Valdez and Whittier within Prince William Sound, as well as at Seward, at the head of nearby Resurrection Bay. In all of these localities, initial damage was caused by slumping of the edges of the river deltas upon which these communities were situated. These deltas comprise the only level and reasonably flat areas in an otherwise mountainous coastline, and originated from the slow accumulation of debris from the streams flowing from beneath retreating glaciers. Normally these deltas terminate seaward under water in very steep slopes. During the short period of intense ground motion, substantial sections of the terminal margins of these deltas simply slumped into the deep fjords, carrying with them the remains of all shoreline construction, including piers, wharves, warehouses, oil tanks, and even railroad switchyards.

The local waves generated by the slumping of material into the fjords were almost immediately augmented by the principally northeasterly flow already described, such that violent oscillations of water ensued in these fjords, playing havoc with ships and greatly increasing the damage caused by slumping.

Because the earthquake occurred at the time of low tide, and because the tide range in Prince William Sound exceeds 10 meters in some places, much of the damage caused by water motion occurred many hours later at the ensuing high tide, when the continuing large-scale oscillations engendered by the tilting of Prince William Sound began to overflow the existing high tide levels and to inundate whole sections of those communities that still remained intact.

Only in a secondary sense can all of these effects be called results of tsunami action. They are, however, entirely accurate descriptions of the kinds of water motion and resulting damage that has occurred quite frequently in the eastern Mediterranean Sea, a region that is topographically and tectonically quite similar to the Prince William Sound, and which has been the scene of many large earthquakes.

The tsunami proper originated on the broad, shallow shelf bordering the Gulf of Alaska, and extending from Prince William Sound, southwesterly to the Trinity Islands. This enormous area, as large as the Republic of Hungary, and averaging less than 200 meters in depth, was bodily uplifted, while the northern half of the tilt block, comprising most of the Kenai-Kodiak ridge was similarly depressed. The bulk of the uplifted region was under water, whereas a substantial fraction of the depressed region was on land. Thus, the net effect was the equivalent of the temporary addition of about 10,000 cubic kilometers of water to the shallow shelf, from which it poured into adjacent deep waters of the Gulf of Alaska. The northeasterly flow from the uplifted region was soon intercepted by the coastline and reflected back as a second wave that followed the first out into the Gulf after a time interval of nearly two hours. By this time the first wave had already radiated from the Gulf of Alaska and was already a third of the way toward Hawaii, where local run-up heights as high as 3 meters were observed on the north coast of the island of Oahu.

The situation along the entire coast of southeastern Alaska for the next twenty-four hours can only be described as chaotic. Because of the great waves impinging on the coastline, and the swift currents generated by the water encroachment and withdrawal, all seaports became unnavigable, channels were filled with debris, and navigation markers were swept away.

The city of Kodiak, which faces northeasterly and that had long enjoyed a high degree of immunity from the Pacific tsunamis as a result of its protected location, now bore the brunt of a vicious onslaught of waves and tides alike, both augmented by the fact that the entire island of Kodiak had been suddenly and permanently depressed with respect to sea level by two meters. With very little advance warning, owing to local power failure, the Kodiak fishing fleet put to sea out of Chiniak Bay in an attempt to escape from impending doom. But the boats had barely left the harbor when the first wave arrived, described by some as nearly 15 meters high, which swept them back across the harbor breakwater, continuing on into the center of the very city itself, where the boats careened around in the ensuing eddy motion, knocking down buildings and eventually being left high and dry by the retreating waters. Large waves continued to assault Kodiak at hourly intervals throughout the night as the tide rose and fell again, until most of the waterfront business district had been demolished. The fishing boats, which were of substantially stronger construction than the buildings with which they collided, survived serious damage, and were later returned to service by being slid back into the sea on special skids erected for the purpose.

Meanwhile, the major tsunami propagating seaward exhibited highly directional effects. Although the wave front was nearly circular by the time it left the Gulf of Alaska and emerged into the open sea, the wave height was much higher in a southeasterly direction parallel to the coast of North America than it was southwesterly along the chain of islands forming the Aleutian Arc. This effect was predictable for precisely the same reason that a rapidly closing door causes a greater pulse of air to be discharged in a direction perpendicular to the axis of the hinges than parallel to it.

Northwestern America from Alaska to California is one of the stormiest regions in the world, and the few communities that lie along that sparsely populated coastline are for the most part located in places well sheltered from direct exposure to prevailing storm waves. Thus, comparatively little damage was wrought outside the Gulf of Alaska, despite the fact that wave heights of 3 to 10 meters were observed in many locations. An outstanding exception was Crescent City, California, whose exposure to the direct path of the waves resulted in extensive inundation damage to waterfront facilities. South of San Francisco abnormal oscillations of sea level exceeding one meter prevailed down the entire coastline of western North America, increasing slightly in South America to a maximum of over 2 meters on the Palmer Peninsula of Antarctica, owing to energy convergence toward the opposite side of the spherical ocean.

Thus the great Alaskan earthquake and tsunami has served as a classic example for further study. It will probably go down in history as the most thoroughly investigated and documented natural catastrophe. These studies suggest that the Alaskan tsunami had much in common with other great tsunamis that had previously occurred in similar coastal environments, such as off Japan, along the Aleutian Island Arc, and off the coast of South America. These studies indicate that large tsunamis can only be produced by vertical sea-floor dislocations of the order of several meters in height and extending over tens of thousands of square kilometers. The parent earthquakes associated with these tsunamis also exhibit many similarities. In most cases the largest initiating earthquake shock occurred at one end of a zone of weakness in the earth's crust, usually parallel to an axis of a neighboring oceanic trench, and a zonal rupture propagated in the shallow crust of the earth with the velocity of several kilometers per second along the fault for a distance of several hundred kilometers. Detailed studies of the bottom topographic profiles across the great trench systems that border the Pacific Ocean show that in many areas there are series of steps, suggesting that such ruptures have occurred repeatedly in the geologic past. These multiple fault systems, in fact, appear to be an inherent part of the process of trench formation, which is currently thought to be caused by the attempts of the slowly moving sea floor to force itself beneath the continental margins. Such trenches always appear to be characterized by abundant volcanic activity, and largescale crumpling of the continental margins that results in multiple bands of highly folded mountains parallel to the sea coast, such as the Chugak Mountains in Alaska, and the Andes mountains of Peru and Chile.

As in the study of all natural disasters, our primary motivation is the development of a plan for minimizing hazard and damage from future events that must inevitably occur. In this connection much progress has been made in recent years toward the development of an effective international tsunami warning system.

Immediately following the tsunami of April 1, 1946, in the Hawaiian Islands, the United States Coast and Geodetic Survey conceived and implemented a tsunami warning service, officially known as the Seismic Seawave Warning System (SSWS), having headquarters in Honolulu. Its function was to detect any occurrence of a tsunami and to provide real-time advisory information on its subsequent development, in much the same manner as the U.S. Weather Bureau provides information on the history of hurricanes that develop in the equatorial Atlantic. The heart of the warning system, which has since been extended to all countries bordering on the Pacific Ocean, consists of an extensive communications network linking Honolulu with key tide and seismic stations extending from Chile counterclockwise around the entire Pacific to Japan, and also including numerous island stations throughout the central and southwestern Pacific.

The Honolulu Observatory is itself a seismic station, equipped with an alarm that rings upon receipt of seismic signals from any large Pacific earthquake. Following the alarm, messages are immediately sent to seismic stations in Tokyo, Sitka, Alaska, and Berkeley and Pasadena, California, requesting advisement of earthquake magnitude and epicenter distances. With this information it is usually possible for the Honolulu Observatory to determine the intensity and position of an earthquake epicenter within thirty to forty minutes. If the epicenter of the earthquake is on land and remote from the seacoast, no further action is taken; but if it has occurred under the sea, key tide stations are interrogated and requested to report any unusual wave activity. At the same time alert messages are sent to the international agencies concerned with tsunami warnings as well as to certain military facilities.

If no waves are reported, the alert is cancelled. When wave activity is observed that appears to be of marginally low amplitude, a second advisory message is sent out to all concerned, but a general warning is not yet issued. If, on the other hand, wave reports portend a dangerous tsunami, a general warning is issued, giving the predicted arrival times of first motion in all affected areas. Message traffic and additional wave reports continue until the danger has past at which time the alert is terminated.

The responsibility of the warning system is advisory only, and it is left to civil and military agencies to take whatever action they deem necessary in order to minimize hazard and damage. Because the interpretation of the advance wave reports is somewhat subjective, it is inevitable that warnings are sometimes issued when the actual hazard is minimal or negligible, but the number of such instances is being reduced as prediction capabilities improve.

The key to the effectiveness of any warning system, however, depends upon the thoroughness and dispatch with which precautionary measures are undertaken. Tsunami warnings have probably reached their peak of effectiveness in Japan, which has suffered more than any other Pacific country from tsunami damage, and where many thousands of lives have been lost. Low-lying areas of coastal Japan have possible areas of inundation marked out in advance on local area disaster maps, and regular drills are held in susceptible communities to ensure that a constant state of readiness is maintained. But there are many other areas of the Pacific coastline where sparse population and limited communications make it almost impossible to maintain the desired degree of readiness, and thus tsunamis will continue to exact their toll until sufficient levels of readiness can be achieved.

Because tsunamis arise from random seismic or volcanic events that are unpredictable, and because only a certain class of such events produces dangerous tsunamis, it is currently impossible to provide advanced information on the probability of a dangerous tsunami in any particular area, except on the basis of past statistics. As a result, tsunami warnings can only be made on a post-facto basis, and such warnings are of little value in the immediate vicinity of the epicenter, as was clearly demonstrated in the case of the Alaskan earthquake, where most of the areas severely affected were, in fact, within the perimeter of strong ground motion.

Turning now to the subject of tsunami prevention or protection, the only effective way of preventing damage from a remote tsunami is to provide sensitive areas with seawalls or breakwaters of sufficient size so that the largest anticipated tsunami will not overtop them. Such structures are necessarily extremely expensive, particularly because of the margin of uncertainty as to maximal, probable effects. The city of Hilo, Hawaii, for example, has a harbor protected by a breakwater over 2 kilometers long. Despite this protection, Hilo has been repeatedly devastated by tsunamis, owing to an unfavorable offshore topography that tends to concentrate and direct wave energy through the existing harbor entrance. Extensive model studies have indicated that although an effective system of additional breakwaters and seawalls could be provided to prevent future recurrences of damaging wave action, the cost of these structures cannot be justified in terms of commercial benefit to the city. If Hilo were to grow to the size of Honolulu, then such preventive measures might be warranted.

Where brute force methods cannot be economically justified, a number of ingenious schemes have been devised, particularly in Japan, to afford some protection for susceptible areas. These include careful selection of building sites in the light of previous experience with wave motion and theoretical studies of wave hydrodynamics. In some cases, merely changing the site of a building by several hundred meters can make the difference between survival and destruction. Given any choice of location for such structures, broad, low-lying areas are usually to be preferred to sites where high cliffs border the sea, since the latter are usually associated with extreme run-up heights. In low-lying areas, waves may advance over a coastal plain as a series of breaking waves or bores, which rarely exceed a few meters in height. In such cases, it may be possible to elevate large buildings on columns along the waterfront, thus permitting tsunami waves to pass beneath without impacting the structure itself. The space beneath such buildings can be used for automobile parking or for the storage of noncritical warehouse items.

Additional countertsunami measures adopted in Japan include the removal of houses to adjacent high lands and the construction of emergency escape roads; the building of low seawalls to impede the flow of water and the planting of dense rows of trees to reduce the velocity of water circulation over the land; and the design of frontage sheds and other important facilities as solid, permanent structures along the waterfront in order to shelter more fragile structures behind them. As is often the case with infrequent natural disasters, ever-increasing future use of the seacoast will require increasing ingenuity to outwit nature where it is not possible to directly withstand her vicissitudes.

15 DEEP OCEAN CIRCULATION

Joseph L. Reid

Everyone knows something about the currents at the surface of the ocean. Most of us know that there is a Gulf Stream that carries water from the warm, tropical areas of the North Atlantic Ocean northward along the coast of North America and then northeastward across the ocean past Great Britain and further northward toward the Norwegian Sea. There is such a flow in the Pacific Ocean as well: the Kuroshio Current carries warm water northward from Japan into high latitudes and eastward toward Alaska. These currents are parts of the wind-driven circulation of the upper segment of the ocean. In addition to the Gulf Stream and the Kuroshio, the trade winds move water westward across the oceans between the tropics, and the west winds blow water from the west to the east across the ocean in the higher latitudes far north and south of the equator. In the south, the Antarctic Circumpolar Current carries water from west to east all around Antarctica, connecting all the major oceans.

These are the currents that are important to seamen. They are systematic and fairly similar, but the forces that drive the waters at great depths are different in different oceans. How far down does the wind-driven circulation extend? We really don't know; it certainly extends well below a few hundred meters, and extends to some thousands of meters in various places such as the zone around Antarctica, but for the moment let us say that it extends to about a thousand meters' depth.

The next question, of course, is that if the wind does not move the deep waters, what does? The average depth of all oceans is about 4,000 meters, and, although the average depth of the Pacific Ocean is greater than that of the Atlantic or Indian Ocean, it is not very much greater. The Pacific Ocean is the largest of the various oceans, the Atlantic and the Indian Ocean together being about the size of the Pacific Ocean. The Antarctic Ocean is not really a separate ocean, but it is open all the way around the earth. The West Wind Drift of southern latitudes goes all around the earth from the south Atlantic Ocean into the south Indian Ocean, into the south Pacific Ocean, and back into the Atlantic Ocean. The Antarctic Ocean consists of the southern parts of all these oceans, yet it is referred to as a continuous ocean in itself.

One part of the Antarctic Ocean that will be mentioned is called the Weddell Sea, which lies against the coast of Antarctica just south of the Atlantic Ocean. The Norwegian Sea is that area lying between Norway and Greenland and north of Iceland. It is called a sea rather than an ocean because it is separated from the North Atlantic by a submarine ridge that runs from Greenland to Europe. Iceland lies on this ridge. The deeper parts of the Norwegian Sea are thus not directly connected to the Atlantic Ocean. The connection between the Atlantic Ocean and the Norwegian Sea is less than 1,000 meters deep; one connection is 800 meters deep and is very narrow, and the other passage, between Iceland and Greenland, is only about 400 meters deep. For this reason the Norwegian Sea is called a sea; it is a distinct area, and we will see that it has different water properties.

In addition to the ridge already mentioned, the one separating the Norwegian Sea from the open Atlantic Ocean, there are many such ridges in the ocean (see Fig. 15–1), although few are so shallow. A ridge runs down the middle of the Atlantic Ocean separating the deep waters on the west side of the Atlantic Ocean from the deep waters on the east side. In the Pacific Ocean another ridge runs from south of New Zealand northeastward across the ocean to the northern part of South

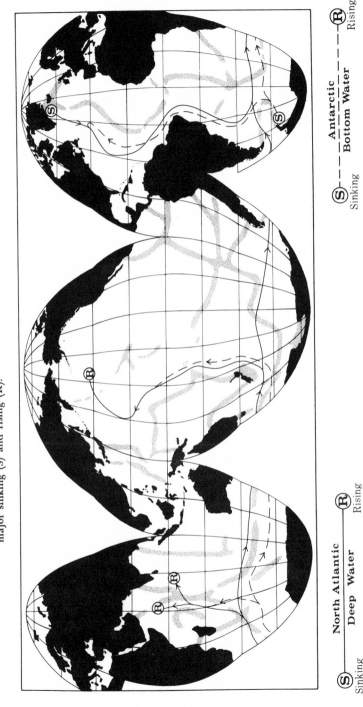

FIGURE 15-1.

The major ocean ridges (shaded areas) and the locations of the areas of major sinking (S) and rising (R).

Ⓢ——— Ⓡ
Sinking **North Atlantic** Rising
Deep Water

Ⓢ— — — Ⓡ
Sinking **Antarctic** Rising
Bottom Water

America. The importance of these ridges is that they channel the flow of the bottom waters of the ocean and make it possible for different kinds of bottom water to lie on the ocean floor in different places, without mixing. Extremely dense water may get into a deep basin and go all the way to the bottom. If the ridge surrounding this basin is very high above the bottom, however, this water may not be able to flow over the sides and fill the adjacent basins or get into the other oceans.

Our primary concern here is how water can be made dense enough to sink all the way to the bottom and secondly, once it is there, how it can flow from one ocean to another between the various ridges. The first ideas about the circulation of the deeper parts of the ocean, as opposed to the surface currents that people had studied and knew something about, began to be discussed about 200 years ago.

One of the earliest investigators of deep-ocean circulation was Count Rumford who thought about what might cause the deeper waters to move and considered the effect of the cooling of water in the high latitudes in winter. As water becomes colder it becomes denser, and the cooling of water at the surface in the Arctic and Antarctic oceans in winter might be expected to cause the water at the surface to become dense and sink toward the bottom and spread out there, filling the deep oceans with a supply of cold water that will be replenished each winter both from the Arctic and the Antarctic oceans. At the same time the surface waters in the tropics and near the equator would be receiving heat from the sun and would be made very warm. As the waters far from the equator become dense and sink, the less dense warm waters at the equator, would flow toward high latitudes to replace the water that is sinking. When the warmer waters reach high latitudes, they would be cooled and would sink. In this system water would sink to the bottom in high latitudes, flow toward the equator, rise from the bottom toward the surface at the equator, be warmed there, and then move toward high latitudes again to be cooled and sink.

This idea had been opposed by some people on the basis of their knowledge of fresh water. Warm water is less dense than cold water, and as it cools it becomes denser, but it is densest at a temperature of about 4 degrees C. As it cools below 4 degrees, water becomes less dense again and continues to decrease in density all the way to the freezing point. For this reason a lake in a cold country, if it is deep enough, has temperatures at the bottom near 4 degrees C. Cooling in the wintertime causes the surface temperatures to decrease, and, as the surface waters become colder than the waters beneath them, they sink through them, overturn, and cause mixing. This continues to happen until the entire lake is cooled to about 4 degrees. When all of the water in the lake is about 4 degrees and further cooling takes place, the surface waters, as they become colder to 3 degrees, to 2 degrees and 1 degree, become less dense and no longer overturn to mix. They may continue to cool to the freezing point, and an ice layer may form at the surface without any further cooling of the deeper waters.

Rumford noted that if enough salt were added to water, this characteristic would be changed. As sea water is cooled, its density increases all the way to the freezing point so that water at freezing temperature in the ocean, he supposed, might be dense enough to overturn all the way to the bottom. Thus he conceived this system of water flowing from the equator and rising at the equator.

Rumford cited some observations taken by a merchant vessel in the tropics in about 1751. The crew had lowered some thermometers a few hundred meters into the ocean and found that the deeper water was colder.

This is a very simple sort of explanation of what might happen. There is truth in it, of course, but the real ocean is much more complex. A few years after Rumford had proposed this hypothesis, Alexander von Humboldt examined the matter again. He noted that the amount of salt in the ocean varies from place to place and that the salt also affects the density of the water. Von Humboldt supposed that if evaporation from the sea surface were more important in changing the density of sea water (by increasing its salt concentration), then the sort of circulation that Rumford proposed might be reversed. If evap-

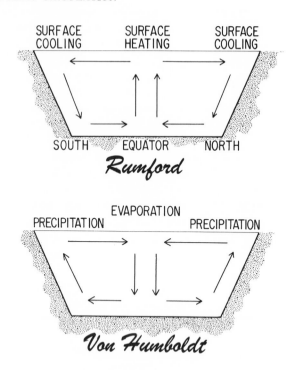

FIGURE 15–2.
Rumford's and von Humboldt's models of density-driven circulation.

oration were to take place in the warm areas near the equator, then the surface water would be densest there, and might sink to the bottom near the equator and flow toward the poles at the bottom, and then rise again in the Arctic and Antarctic oceans where evaporation would be very small and precipitation (snow and rain) might cause the surface waters to be very low in salt, and thus in density. In support of this idea, von Humboldt pointed out that some observations of temperature beneath the surface in high latitudes had shown that some water at depths of several hundred meters was warmer than the surface waters above. He added further that this seemed a sound idea, but there was not enough data about the ocean for it to be examined properly, and he thought that a real solution would have to wait upon more measurements of the salt content of the sea.

Many of the great exploring expeditions of the nineteenth century began to take measurements of temperature below the surface and (although their instruments were not very good at that time) a substantial fund of information began to come forth. In about 1875 an Englishman, Sir Joseph Prestwich, noted that the Pacific Ocean had a peculiar temperature distribution. It appeared to him to be well connected with the Antarctic Ocean but not to be very well connected with the Arctic Ocean; the connection from the Pacific Ocean to the Arctic Ocean through the Bering Strait is a very small one and not very much water can pass through it. On the other hand, Prestwich did find that at the bottom of the North Pacific Ocean the water is quite cold (Figure 15-3). He reasoned that this water could not have come from the Arctic Ocean through the Bering Strait, but must have come from the Antarctic Ocean through the South Pacific Ocean into the North Pacific. In other words, Rumford's notion of symmetrical circulation with sinking both in the north and the south and rising at the equator did not seem to be exactly fulfilled. There was sinking at one end of the Pacific Ocean in the Antarctic Ocean and flow toward the equator, but this flow did not cease at the equator. Instead, it continued into the North Pacific and presumably rose somewhere in the northern parts of the North Pacific to the sea surface, where it could be warmed and returned toward the equator and eventually to the Antarctic Ocean.

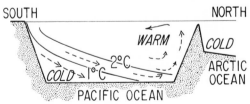

FIGURE 15-3.

Prestwich's model of circulation in the deep Pacific Ocean.

From this point of view, one might think that Rumford was partly right and von Humboldt entirely wrong, but this is not quite so. Both temperature and salinity are important in affecting the density of the world ocean and in creating in certain areas dense water that must then sink to the bottom and spread out. If we recall what we know of the rainfall and the evaporation over the world ocean, we find that rainfall is highest in high latitudes and near the equator, and is lowest in the middle latitudes. As a result, the waters over most of the high latitudes of the ocean, and certainly including the Arctic and Antarctic oceans, are quite low in salinity compared to the tropical zones where evaporation takes place and water of quite high salinity is formed.

The problem in forming water that will sink and spread out at great depths is to find some way of making it as dense as or denser than the deepest water that is already there. We know that this water is being replaced and not just remaining there over very long periods of time, because it is not depleted in oxygen: the deeper parts of the ocean are not stagnant but are still quite rich in oxygen. But if we look at the water in the deeper parts of the world ocean, we find that the salinity at the bottom of the great oceans is quite high compared to the salinity of the surface water around Antarctica and that the temperature is quite low compared to the salty surface waters of the tropics. Therefore we have a problem in forming water that is both salty and cold enough to be very dense.

If we take ordinary surface waters from the Arctic Ocean or from the Antarctic Ocean, we find that the salt content is extremely low. If we cool these to the freezing point, they become more dense but the salt content is so low that they will freeze without forming water that is dense enough to overturn and replace the deep water. Something other than cooling must be called upon if water is to be formed that is dense enough to sink to great depth and displace the water there. We must look for particular areas where special processes can form this kind of water.

Only in limited areas does this water form. The principal of these areas is the Weddell Sea, which lies south of the Atlantic Ocean. Here, for reasons we shall discuss later, some fairly saline water is brought to the surface from below. Near the coast of Antarctica this water can be cooled and made dense enough to sink along the slope to the bottom. This water is called Antarctic Bottom Water. Since it is not separated from the great ocean by any shallow sills, it is free to move northward into the Atlantic Ocean all the way to Greenland, and it is free to move eastward from the Weddell Sea all around Antarctica and to fill the deeper parts of the Indian Ocean and the deeper parts of the Pacific Ocean with water whose original characteristics came from the Weddell Sea. The only parts of the deep ocean that do not contain Antarctic Bottom Water are those basins that have shallow ridges surrounding them that this dense water cannot cross.

The other part of the ocean that contributes dense water is in the far North Atlantic in the Norwegian Sea. In the North Atlantic the Gulf Stream moves from middle latitudes up into high latitudes and carries warm, highly saline water from the evaporation zones. Some part of this water moves in between Norway and Greenland into the Norwegian Sea. It moves so fast and in such a quantity that it arrives in the Norwegian Sea still having a high salt content: it has a much higher salt content than any other waters at this latitude, either north or south. The surface water is so saline that when cooled, it becomes dense enough to overturn to great depths within the Norwegian Sea, and fills the deeper parts of the Norwegian Sea with cold salty water. This water is very dense; in fact it is about the densest water for its depth of any part of the world ocean.

We would expect this water, having sunk to the bottom, to spread out and fill the deeper basins of the rest of the ocean, but we must remember that there are various ridges separating the deep basins from each other. The deep oceans are separated not only by the continents but by various submarine ridges that run across some of the major oceans. The Norwegian Sea is cut off from the great part of the Atlantic Ocean not only by Iceland, which lies at the southern end of the Norwegian Sea, but also by a submarine ridge that runs from Greenland through Iceland to Europe. The deepest exit from the Norwegian Sea is only about 800 meters deep. This means that the Norwegian Sea water that flows into the North Atlantic does not enter at great depths, but must enter over the shallow sills between Greenland and Europe. Because it is so dense, it passes over these sills like water over a waterfall. The speed and violence of this passage over the sill and down the slope from depths of a few hundred meters to more than 3,000 meters causes the waters to mix rather violently and effectively with the less dense shallow waters. As the Norwegian Sea water pours down the slope into the North Atlantic Ocean, it loses some of its original high-density characteristics by this mixing and is no longer dense enough to go all the way to the bottom in the open Atlantic Ocean. This is because it is now not quite as dense as the Antarctic Bottom Water, which fills the deepest parts. This water which has overflowed from the Norwegian Sea should not be called Norwegian Sea water any more, since it has mixed so much with the water that it encountered as it crossed the sill. The shallow water with which it mixed was warmer and of about the same salinity, so that the mixture is still quite saline. This water sinks (but not quite to the bottom, since the mixture is not quite as dense as the Antarctic Bottom Water) to a great depth, perhaps 3,500 meters, over most of its area. Since it is denser than the water above it and less dense than the Antarctic Bottom Water beneath, it can neither rise nor sink, but flows southward through the North Atlantic Ocean as a great tongue of highly saline water.

This tongue can be traced even further. It can be seen to extend into the South Atlantic and then to turn eastward with the West Wind Drift and flow around Antarctica in a continuous stream, south of Africa, through the Indian Ocean, south of Australia, through the Pacific Ocean and south of South America, and into the Atlantic Ocean again. Since it always passes beneath less saline water and above less saline water, its own salinity decreases as it moves away from its source in the North

Atlantic Ocean. It is some of this saline water that reaches all the way into the Weddell Sea and rises near the surface there, is cooled and made more dense and finally forms the Antarctic Bottom Water.

Thus far this chapter has discussed tracing these waters and following their flows on the basis of their temperature and their salinity in general terms as they flow from one ocean to another. How fast do these waters move at great depths? When they are pouring over the sill from the Norwegian Sea down into the Atlantic Ocean, the density differences are great and they can move fairly fast, perhaps as much as a meter per second as they pour over the Iceland-Greenland ridge. However, in this case they are really flowing downhill: they are being pulled downward by gravity. Once they have reached depths of 3,500 or 4,000 meters, they cannot fall any further. When this happens, they can move only horizontally and they thus tend to flow more slowly. The waters are moved now by the push of the still newer waters falling behind them and, instead of a narrow channel to go through, they have the whole width of an ocean to move in. Naturally, they need not move so fast; their speeds are much less, so slow that it is extremely difficult to measure the speed with any of the ordinary meters we would use for measuring rivers or winds.

We know that there are also tidal currents that extend from the top to the bottom of the ocean, and these can confuse our work: if we were to make a measurement lasting five minutes at the bottom of the ocean, it would probably include primarily the tidal part; the tidal flow may be stronger at ebb and flow than the mean flow of the water itself.

As it moves down the broad, deep western side of the Atlantic Ocean, the water formed in the North Atlantic moves quite slowly. As it approaches and joins with the Antarctic Circumpolar Current, it speeds up again. Since that current is wind-driven, it is very strong all the way to the bottom, and where the flow is faster it is easier to measure it. A simpler device will provide a good reading.

Current measurements have been made at the bottom of the

Antarctic Circumpolar Current. Where the current is narrowest between South America and the Antarctic continent, measurements have been made for several days with meters placed near the bottom. Velocities from 2 to 12 centimeters per second are found in this passage, much higher than one finds in the broad, deep areas of the ocean.

But this passage between South America and Antarctica is not the only passage that is restricted. Remember that the early temperature measurements in the Pacific Ocean showed that the bottom water of the North Pacific flows in from the South Pacific. Also, if we were to look at a map of the bottom depths of the Pacific Ocean, we would see that ridges separate the deep South Pacific from the deep North Pacific everywhere except at one place—between the ridges where water can pass through from the South Pacific to the North Pacific at depths greater than 5,000 meters. Everywhere else the ridge extends higher above the bottom so that the densest bottom water cannot cross. If a large volume of water is moving northward from the South Pacific to the North Pacific, and if this is forced to go through a passage that is only about 50 kilometers wide, we might expect it to speed up so much that we could measure it with a simple current meter. When current measurements were made for several days in this area, they showed velocities as high as fifteen centimeters per second in the central, deeper parts of the passage. This velocity is higher than the bottom water velocity in the Antarctic Circumpolar Current, but only because of the funneling effect of the ridge across the South Pacific Ocean. A few hundred kilometers northward or southward of this passage, current meters indicate that the velocities are very low indeed and that this fifteen centimeters per second speed is something that can be found only where the water is tightly funneled. They show average velocities of less than 2 centimeters per second over most of the areas of the North Pacific where measurements have been taken.

Deep current measurements have also been made in the Atlantic Ocean, primarily under the Gulf Stream, which extends to the bottom along some parts of its path. Some of the measurements made there at depths below 3,000 meters show current velocities of between 10 and 20 centimeters per second. Other measurements made in the Atlantic Ocean show much lower speeds at such great depths, so we conclude that strong currents are rare at great depths. We can find them at the bottom of the Antarctic Circumpolar Current and beneath the Gulf Stream, both of which are notoriously fast, strong currents at the surface. We can also find strong currents where massive funneling of the deep flow occurs, such as in the central Pacific Ocean. Other strong currents doubtlessly exist, but they have not yet been examined.

We can think back now to what Count Rumford originally said about how the deep waters of the ocean might be formed and how they circulated. We can also think back to Alexander von Humboldt's countersuggestions, and we can see that the ideas of both men were basically correct. Their incomplete information led them to various bad guesses, which in turn kept them from describing the ocean as well as they might have, but their principles are correct.

The densest water is formed in very high latitudes as Rumford suggested. Of course not all high latitudes form dense water that sinks all the way to the bottom and spreads out at very great depths. If we look very carefully, we find that the places where the greatest sinking and formation of very dense bottom water occurs are at the Weddell Sea near Antarctica and in the Norwegian Sea, where the waters spill over into the North Atlantic Ocean. Rumford would have these two water masses flow along the bottom toward each other and, being of equal density when they met at the equator, they would simply stay there until they were warmed by the downward mixing of heat and made less dense and allowed to rise to the surface. They would then return poleward as warm surface water to be cooled at high latitudes and sink again.

We can see that this does not really happen quite the way that Rumford supposed it might, and the reasons that it does not behave just that way are partly provided by von Humboldt, who suggested that temperature alone might not account for all of the deep circulation, and that we might also have to consider the salt content of the ocean. Because these two water masses are not of the same density when they meet at the equator, they simply flow past each other at different depths (Figure 15–4). The water from the Weddell Sea continues to flow northward along the bottom and eventually mixes into the waters just above it. That water from the North Atlantic moves southward at a shallower depth and extends into the South Atlantic, into the Antarctic Circumpolar Current, and around into the Indian and Pacific oceans. And, of course, not all of the Antarctic Bottom Water moves into the Atlantic Ocean; some parts of it move westward with the Antarctic Circumpolar Current into the Indian Ocean and into the Pacific Ocean.

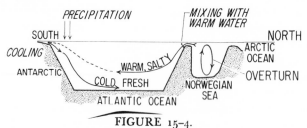

FIGURE 15–4.

Spreading of the cold, low-salinity Antarctic Bottom Water and the warm, salty deep water in the Atlantic Ocean.

These two layers of Antarctic Bottom Water and North Atlantic Deep Water together make up all of the deepest water in the world ocean. If we look at their behavior, we do not find them ever meeting at the equator and rising to the surface through local warming. Instead, we find them distributed throughout the entire world ocean at a depth that is proper to their density, and as they move away from their sources they mix with the waters above them, continuously losing a little of their high-density characteristic, but they are still recognizable over very long distances. We know, of course, that bottom water cannot continue to be formed in the Weddell Sea or in the Norwegian Sea without some kind of replacement of the surface waters.

How does this water once formed as deeper bottom water, very dense, eventually become less dense and get back into the open surface circulation of the world ocean? Vertical mixing takes place slowly in the ocean; the water is everywhere stable, with the densest water at the bottom. To mix a water column requires the use of a great deal of energy. As a result, the vertical mixing takes place very slowly. On the other hand, there is a great deal of time spent in the voyage from the Weddell Sea to the North Pacific. Geochemists have given us some estimate of the relative age of the waters in various parts of the ocean. For this reason we think there is perhaps 1,000 to 2,000 years of time required for water to move from the Norwegian Sea to the North Pacific Ocean and perhaps a little less time than that for water to move from the Antarctic Circumpolar Current into the depths of the North Pacific. So that, given 1,000 to 2,000 years of remaining in the deep water, we can see that, little by little, the upper parts of this water are eaten away and mixed into the wind-driven parts of the world ocean, the shallower parts. Once into the shallower, wind-driven parts again, they can move and mix more rapidly; they can be moved into the lower latitudes where they can be warmed and made much less dense. Eventually they can be carried back to the surface in the high latitudes of the Norwegian Sea and the Weddell Sea. And then, after some uncertain period, they can pass through the same paths to deep and bottom water to start the long cycle again.

16 ATMOSPHERE AND OCEANS

George S. Benton

During the last thirty years rapid advances have been made in man's understanding of the atmosphere and the oceans. In the field of meteorology this has been primarily the result of three new developments: first, the advent of high-speed computers which make it possible to forecast by the use of mathematical equations instead of intuition; second, the development of many new observational tools such as the weather satellite, which have completely revolutionized the opportunities for watching our atmosphere and knowing what is currently happening; and third, a new experimental capability to simulate the atmosphere, using rotating and stratified fluids and reproducing the physics of cloud phenomena in the laboratory.

The field of oceanography has gone through a similar rapid expansion. Again, the use of computers and the capability of using laboratory tools has made a substantial difference. In addition, new observational platforms, including many oceanographic research vessels, are now available. The resulting explosion in geophysical knowledge has occurred in a remarkably short time.

It is interesting to note that while this has been happening, the two disciplines of meteorology and oceanography have tended to remain distinct. Although the two sciences are very similar in that they each deal with a fluid that is rotating with the earth, and which is stratified, the oceanographers and meteorologists nevertheless tend to remain separate and each tends to look at his own particular discipline in a distinctive way.

Despite this we have come to realize in recent years that the atmosphere and the oceans are not independent of each other. They are closely related; that is, the behavior of one of these systems influences the behavior of the other. When we examine the atmosphere above the oceans, we see that there is a tremendous flow of mass, of energy, and of momentum across the sea-air interface from one fluid system into the other. The surface of the ocean is actually an uneasy moving surface, of fantastic complexity.

The zone of air-sea interaction immediately above and below the ocean surface at once repels and attracts competent meteorologists and oceanographers. It repels them because this is a most difficult zone to understand. It attracts them because the sea-air interaction zone is most important if we are to fully understand how either the atmosphere or the ocean truly behaves. In recent years, there has thus been a major effort to explore the sea-air interaction zone in an attempt to understand the various phenomena that take place in this region.

The ultimate objective of these studies is to be able to treat the atmosphere and the oceans as a single entity. Some day in the future, for example, we will simultaneously be able to forecast the hurricane and the storm surge that it produces on the ocean surface. Similarly, we will predict the severe cyclonic storm in middle latitudes with its high winds and we will also predict at the same time the waves it generates on the surface of the ocean that provide such a hazard to shipping.

The exchange of mass is particularly important in the consideration of sea-air interaction. If we consider all of the various substances that flow across the ocean's surface, the most important is water vapor. On the average about 100 centimeters per year of water are converted to vapor over the entire ocean surface. In the subtropics the amount of evaporation may be as high as 140 to 200 centimeters per year. In the equatorial regions, evaporation is slightly less, but in higher latitudes the amount is a great deal less, decreasing to a very small rate of evaporation in the cold water near the poles. There are also strong variations of evaporation from east to west across the ocean; for example, the evaporation over the warm Gulf Stream off the east coast of the United States is about twice as large as the evaporation over the eastern part of the Atlantic Ocean at the same latitude.

The importance of the evaporation is obvious. First, it forms the source of most of the earth's fresh water, since it falls back to earth as precipitation over the land surfaces and over the oceans. Second, the evaporation process uses great amounts of energy. This energy is lost as far as heating the oceans is concerned, and therefore evaporation is very important in understanding the temperature balance of the oceans. Finally, oceanographers know that evaporation has an important effect on the salinity of the oceans. Evaporation tends to concentrate the salts that occur naturally in the oceans; therefore it tends to increase the salinity. On the other hand precipitation tends to dilute the water near the surface of the oceans and thus tends to decrease the salinity. As a result of this balance, the salinity is highest in the subtropical regions at about 20 degrees north or south latitude where the evaporation is substantially greater than the precipitation. There are, however, substantial inaccuracies in our estimates of the rates of evaporation. It is extremely difficult to measure evaporation over the oceans, and the best information we have is indirect data that has been carefully obtained from research vessels and from island stations.

In addition to the exchange of mass represented by the flow of water vapor, other substances move across the sea-air surface. Of these several gases are extremely important—for example, oxygen and carbon dioxide, both of which are vital to the biological systems in the ocean. Oceanographers are greatly concerned with the problem of oxygen at great depths. This is, of course, necessary for oceanic life, and the process by which oxygen is absorbed by the oceans and transported downward by turbulent mixing is only imperfectly understood.

Perhaps the whole problem of the gas balance of the oceans can best be illustrated by the complex characteristic of the carbon dioxide cycle. For the last hundred years there has been very heavy use of fossil fuels—that is, of oil, coal, and natural gas. Approximately 2 billion tons of carbon dioxide were added to the atmosphere each year. If all of the carbon dioxide were retained in the atmosphere, the carbon dioxide content would increase about 1.6 parts per million per year. This would be a rate of about ½ of 1 per cent per year. The increase in carbon dioxide is important in the energy balance of the atmosphere since carbon dioxide tends to act as a blanket to trap energy near the surface of the earth by absorbing the outgoing radiation from the earth and sending the energy back down toward the surface of the earth. For this reason, and also because of the importance of carbon dioxide for biological systems, the carbon dioxide cycle is extremely interesting to many fields of science.

If we study the observed rate of increase of carbon dioxide in the atmosphere, we find that it is not 1.6 parts per million per year, which it would be if all the burned carbon dioxide remained in the atmosphere. Instead it is only about 0.7 parts per million per year, a little less than half as much as might be expected. The decrease is primarily caused by the flow of carbon dioxide across the sea-air interface and into the oceans. In other words, the oceans act as a buffer to withdraw carbon dioxide from the atmosphere.

There are many unanswered questions about the carbon dioxide cycle. For example, the mechanics and chemistry of the carbon dioxide exchanges at the sea surface are only poorly known. In addition, we do not have a very adequate idea about what effect oceanic warming has on the carbon dioxide content of the oceans and thus of the atmosphere over a long period of time.

There are many other exchanges that take place at the air-sea interface. In the atmosphere, condensation nuclei play a very important role. These are tiny particles, often as many as 1,000 per cubic centimeter, each of which is less than one thousandth of a centimeter in diameter. The most common condensation nucleus in the atmosphere is sea salt, which moves into the atmosphere from the ocean surface when spray is blown into the air in regions where waves are breaking. The salt particles remain after the water droplets are completely evaporated. The largest particles of salt are heavy and settle back to the surface of the earth but the very tiny ones remain aloft and are carried around the world in the atmosphere where they play a very important role in the formation of precipitation. It would be fair to say that if it were not for the exchange of sea salt at the earth's surface, the nature of our precipitation process in the atmosphere and, in fact, our entire supply of fresh water over the continents would be very different from what is actually observed.

It is thus clear that the atmosphere and the oceans cannot be considered as being two physically distinct and separate entities. There is a continuous flow of mass in many forms across the surface—water, gases such as oxygen and carbon dioxide, and salt nuclei. In addition, dust is precipitated from the atmosphere on to the ocean surfaces where it settles to the bottom of the sea; and even ions, the small, charged particles that carry electricity, move from the ocean surface into the atmosphere and affect the difference in electrical potential between the atmosphere and the ocean below.

But in addition to the exchange of mass, there is an important exchange of energy. The atmosphere and the oceans are a coupled heat engine; that is, both the atmosphere and the oceans are in circulation as a result of the differential heating of the earth between the poles and the equator. In low latitudes, the input of energy from the sun is greater than the loss of energy to space by radiation. At high latitudes the input of energy from the sun is less than the loss to space in the form of radiation. Therefore, if we were only to consider the effect of radiation, there would be a steady change in the temperature of the earth. The tropics would tend to grow warmer, and the polar regions would steadily grow colder. Fortunately for us, this is not what actually happens. There is a flow of energy from the heated tropics to the poles that occurs in the fluid portions of the earth; that is, in the atmosphere as well as in the oceans. The primary carrier in this exchange is the atmosphere, and therefore one might be tempted to think that the oceans play a secondary role in the exchange of energy between latitudes. But this is not so. The oceans are heavily involved in the entire process. The reason for this can be seen by considering the tropical oceans where the balance is particularly clear. A great deal of solar radiation enters the atmosphere. Most of it moves directly through the atmosphere, without being absorbed, to the surface of the earth where it is absorbed either by the continents or by the oceans themselves. And since the oceans cover about 70% of the globe, it is fair to say that most of the incoming solar radiation moves through the atmosphere and is absorbed by the oceans. It is this oceanic surface that warms the atmosphere. In other words, our atmosphere is heated from below and once having been heated the warm air in the tropics is then free to be carried to higher latitudes where it radiates its energy to space. Therefore, the entire heat balance of the earth involves the sea-air interaction zone—the incoming energy from space moving through the atmosphere and being absorbed by the oceans, the oceans heating the atmosphere above them, and then the atmosphere acting to transport energy to the polar regions where it can be emitted in the form of radiation to space. This exchange of energy by radiation between the oceans and the overlying atmosphere is the most important way in which energy moves from the oceans to the atmosphere.

But there are several other ways in which energy exchange also can occur, such as a result of the evaporation of water from the oceans. We have seen that very large amounts of evaporation occur over the oceans, especially in the subtropics and other lower latitudes. This evaporation uses up energy, about 600 calories of energy for every gram of water vapor that is evaporated. The water vapor, once it leaves the ocean surface, moves up into the free air, and ultimately the water vapor condenses to form precipitation. When this occurs, the energy that was used in evaporating the water is released. Therefore, the entire process of evaporation and later of precipitation results in an exchange of energy from the oceans to the atmosphere. This is the second-most-important way in which energy flows across the sea-air interface.

A third way, which is not as important as the other two, is by direct heating. When cold air flows from the continents over the oceans an exchange of energy takes place, with heat being transferred from the warm water to the colder air above. Similarly, when warm air moves from continents over cold water, there is an energy flow from the atmosphere down to the oceans. On a global scale this direct exchange of energy is fairly unimportant; it is much smaller than the first two mentioned. However, locally, it can be of very great importance. For example, when cold air from Siberia sweeps out over the warm ocean currents to the east of the Asian continent there is a very rapid heating of the air that results in substantial convection and the development of thunderstorms.

Similarly, this heating phenomenon plays a very important role in the formation of hurricanes. The air that is flowing into the hurricane immediately above the ocean surface tends to be cooled by evaporation of spray as the air moves in toward the lower pressure at the center of the storm. This effect would tend to quench the hurricane except for the fact that the cooling air is warmed by the warm sea underneath, which therefore tends to replenish the energy of the storm. Hurricanes, however, only form and remain vital for long periods of time over the ocean where such a heat and moisture supply is available.

One other means of energy exchange is the exchange of mechanical energy. Waves are formed as a result of pressures and winds acting upon the surface of the water. The resulting exchange of energy, which may whip up tremendous waves on the surface of the ocean in a very short time, is caused by the exchange of mechanical energy from the winds above to the oceans below. In a global sense, there is only a trivial amount of energy transferred by this method, but this is a small consolation to someone caught in an ocean liner in a raging storm.

To summarize, then, the ways in which energy can be transferred between the oceans and the atmosphere are, in order of importance: first, radiation; second, evaporation and subsequent condensation; third, the direct exchange of thermal energy resulting from the heating or cooling of the overlying air; and fourth, the exchange of mechanical energy caused by pressures and winds occurring in the atmosphere.

In conclusion, the effect of the exchange of momentum between the atmosphere and the oceans should be mentioned. The huge ocean circulations cause important changes in climate. For example, the entire climate of Northern Europe is changed and made milder as a result of the warm current that carries ocean water far to the north along the East Coast of North America, across the North Atlantic and into the vicinity of Northern Europe. These ocean circulations have a certain amount of momentum; that is, they possess both mass and velocity, and we learn in physics that momentum cannot be destroyed except by friction. Actually these oceanic circulations are also driven by the atmosphere. There is a steady exchange of momentum between the atmosphere and the oceans, an exchange that makes it possible for the oceans to continue their circulations long after the currents would normally have lost their speed because of dissipation of momentum against the margins of the ocean.

We have seen that there is a substantial flow of mass, energy, and momentum across the sea-air interface, and that these processes control the atmospheric and oceanic circulations to a very high degree. We must learn more about the way in which these processes occur at the ocean surface. We have a need for quantitative information, for actual measurements of the rates of flow of mass, energy, and momentum. These are necessary if we are to understand the circulations of the atmosphere and the ocean. Such information is also of great significance in forecasting the motions of both the atmosphere and the oceans because only if we understand how mass, energy, and momentum are added at the boundary of a fluid can we then be able to forecast what will happen many days in advance.

Meteorologists and oceanographers during the last ten years have become increasingly aware of the need for new information in this challenging field. As a result, a series of special studies are being planned by the international scientific community. Some of these programs are being carried out under the Global Atmospheric Research Program with the full cooperation of oceanographers. A good example of such a special study is the Barbados Oceanographic and Meteorological Experiment that was concluded during the summer of 1969 in the area to the east of the West Indies. This large experiment, which was participated in by many universities and many government agencies in the United States, sought to gain further information on the nature of the sea-air interaction process in tropical regions.

As our knowledge of the sea-air interaction processes improves, and as we obtain more quantitative information about the rates of exchange, we can expect this information to be used increasingly in making forecasts of the motion of the atmosphere and of the ocean. This is done by putting this information into the computers that are used today in forecasting such systems, especially within the atmosphere. Unfortunately, we do not have at present a large enough computer to enable us to completely forecast the atmosphere and the oceans as a coupled system. That is, we forecast the atmosphere using computers. As a separate process, in some special cases such as in the study of storm surges, it is also possible to study what will happen in the oceans using high-speed computers.

But if we look ahead into the future, it is fair to say that we can expect that there will be much larger computers, and that as our knowledge of the exchange rates at the sea-air interaction zone improves, we will begin to develop a unified forecasting system for the combined atmosphere and ocean system.

Only when that day arrives can we expect the accuracy of our forecasts to reach the levels we anticipate today. For example, weather forecasts are accurate only for periods of up to twenty-four or thirty-six hours. Beyond this point, the accuracy of the forecasts decreases steadily, and after three to four days, there is virtually no skill left in the sense that the forecasts are not much better than can be obtained simply by referring to normal climatic conditions. With adequate sea-air information and with other information as well, such as the radiation received from the sun that we are beginning to know better as a result of satellite and other studies, meteorologists believe that the period of accurate forecasts can be extended as far as possibly two weeks in advance. This could be of extreme economic importance to many people in all walks of life.

As part of the Global Atmospheric Research Program, the efforts to understand sea-air interaction can be expected to proceed at an accelerating rate. Plans include additional studies in the tropics and a number of studies near the continents where the problems of sea-air interaction are especially difficult to understand. Meteorologists and oceanographers are beginning to work together to a substantial degree in understanding and exploring these fields, and certainly we in meteorology and in oceanography anticipate that this will increasingly be the case in the future. As the years go on, the joint interests of these two sciences will become ever closer. In many ways this union will be brought about by their common area of interest at the surface of the oceans.

Improved knowledge of sea-air interaction will open yet another very interesting field of science, the problem of understanding how and why the climates of the globe have varied through the ages. In this problem the nature of the oceans is of key interest because the oceans change only slowly with time. For example, the waters in the deep oceans are at near-freezing temperatures, and it would only be possible to change the temperature of this water substantially over a time interval of many centuries. In this sense the ocean is quite different from the atmosphere, which has a much shorter reaction time. The atmosphere can change quite markedly from one week to the next but the ocean, except in its special details, is constant in the sense that its major circulation and temperature structure do not change substantially except on much longer time intervals, such as seasons and even centuries.

As our knowledge of sea-air interaction increases, we should develop increased insight into how major changes in the ocean-atmosphere structure might come about, and surely these kinds of changes can in part explain the extremely variable climate that man has encountered on this earth over the last hundreds of thousands of years. It was only 11,500 years ago that the Pleistocene epoch, the Ice Age, came to its end. Our oceans are now very cold, much different certainly than they were during the Mesozoic era, let us say, when there were huge reptiles living in a very tropical climate on the surface of the earth. How does the ocean today differ from the ocean in those days? We really do not know the answers to these questions, but we do know that major differences exist and that increased insight into the linking of the atmosphere and the oceans can help us understand how these changes came about.

17 UPWELLING AND THE MONSOONS

Colin S. Ramage

As we have seen, the surface layers of the atmosphere are inextricably meshed with the surface layers of the oceans. In fact, meteorologists and oceanographers now treat these gaseous and liquid realms as parts of a single engine, fueled by the sun. Winds make waves and cause horizontal and vertical currents; heat used for evaporation, and later released to the atmosphere when water drops form and fall as rain, provides most of the energy for driving the winds.

Before we consider the problems of upwelling and the monsoons, we must examine the ways in which the sea, land, and air interact and how this interaction changes conditions in each of the three realms.

Upwelling in the ocean is the upward movement of the subsurface water to the surface. Various processes can produce upwelling, but by far the most important of these is the action of the wind on the surface of the ocean. The wind acts everywhere on the ocean surface through a frictional linkage. Waves are the visible evidences of this linkage—known as wind stress. The stronger the winds, and the longer they blow, the higher are the waves and the greater is the stress. Wind stress tends to move the surface water on a course directed at 90 degrees to the direction of the stress itself. This turning of the effect of the wind stems from the interaction of the wind and the apparent force exerted on moving water by the earth's rotation, the so-called Coriolis force.

To an observer facing downwind, the Coriolis force acts to the right of the wind direction north of the equator and to the left of the wind direction south of the equator. The effect is strongest at the North and South poles and diminishes with latitude, becoming zero along the equator. In what follows conditions in the Northern Hemisphere will be referred to. Interchanging the adjectives "right" and "left" would make the statements apply to the Southern Hemisphere.

Let us consider a steady wind blowing across the open ocean. Wind stress and Coriolis force generate an ocean current, appearing to an observer looking downwind to be directed 90 degrees to the right of the wind direction. Water that is moved in this direction is replaced by other surface water lying to the left. Now imagine this same steady wind blowing along and parallel to a simple, straight coastline lying to your left as you face downwind. The water is once again moved 90 degrees to the right of the wind direction but now, since there is no *surface* water available to the left, replacement water must come from below. Thus the coastline forms an essential part of one upwelling mechanism, forcing replacement of the surface water by subsurface water. Of course, unless the water brought up from beneath has different characteristics from the water it replaces, upwelling would produce no noticeable effect. Generally speaking, however, in the upper 60 to 100 meters of the sea the surface water is considerably warmer than the layers beneath and is less rich in chemical nutrients. Thus upwelling usually brings colder and biologically richer water to the surface.

The stronger the wind the greater is the stress that it exerts on the ocean surface and the deeper is the layer through which the water rises. Farther seaward, surface water must undergo a compensating sinking and in time a vertical circulation develops. After a few weeks of upwelling, the previously stratified upper layers have been so thoroughly mixed that temperatures now diminish only slightly with depth and the sea surface, although remaining cold, does not become colder.

Upwelling is most likely to develop where the wind blows strong and steady parallel to a coastline to the left of the wind. (See Figure 17–1.)

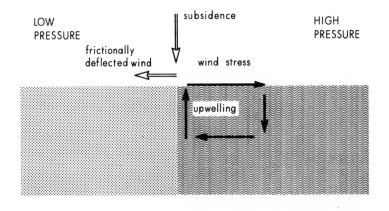

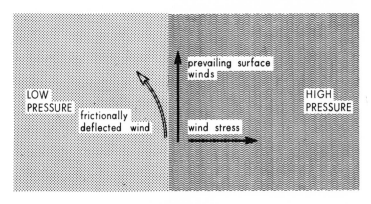

FIGURE 17–1.

Schematic diagram with land to the left and ocean to the right showing the effects of wind blowing parallel to the coastline of a Northern Hemisphere continent during summer. *(Top)* Cross-section with the surface wind blowing into the paper. *(Bottom)* Plan view.

Wind direction and speed are determined by the interaction of three forces: first, the pressure force of the air (proportional to the horizontal pressure gradient); second, the Coriolis force resulting from the earth's rotation; and third, friction. Under the influence of the pressure force and the Coriolis force, which almost balance, lower pressure lies to the left of the wind direction. The frictional force deflects the wind toward lower

231

pressure; the greater the frictional force, the greater is the deflection.

Let us return to the same wind still blowing along our straight coastline lying to the left of the wind. Over land, inland from the coastline, and to the left of the wind there is lower pressure. The air moving over the sea is deflected by friction with the sea surface, but the air moving over the coast and inland is deflected even more by the rougher land surface. The rougher the surface, for example, if mountains rim the coast, the greater is the difference between ocean friction and land friction and the greater is the deflection difference. Since along this model coastline the air flowing over the rugged coastal land turns inland toward low pressure at a greater angle than the air flowing over the smoother coastal waters, the coastline marks a line of air-flow divergence. Along this line of divergence, air from higher levels sinks to make up the deficit. When air sinks, it is compressed and made warm, and when it warms, any clouds that may be present are thinned or evaporated.

To sum up, along our hypothetical straight coastline, cold water upwells and weather, particularly inland, is fine. Since the sun can effectively heat the land, air temperatures are higher inland and lower offshore—that is, the interaction of coastline, sea, and wind increases the temperature gradient between land and sea.

Before considering the interactions between these processes and the monsoons, we need to review the characteristics of monsoons. Monsoons, which are great seasonal reversals in the surface wind circulations, extend from western Africa across the deserts of north Africa and Arabia to eastern Asia and Australia—a region in which large continents border large oceans. During the summer the continents heat very rapidly, particularly over the deserts. The air in contact with the land is also heated, and it becomes less dense and its surface pressure falls. The sea, on the other hand, since it has much greater heat capacity than the land, remains relatively cool during the summer, and the air in contact with it also remains relatively cool and dense. The continental interiors, therefore, become centers of low pressure, lying to the left of the wind.

As summer gives way to winter, the interiors of the large continents cool very rapidly. The overlying air also cools and so its density and consequently its surface pressure increase. On the other hand the ocean's greater heat capacity keeps it from cooling as rapidly as the land. Thus in winter, high pressure areas prevail over continental interiors and now the oceans lie to the left of the wind.

The summer monsoon is strongest over India, the Arabian Sea, and the Bay of Bengal because a chain of great mountains extending from Turkey to west China bars the movement of cold air from the north. Consequently heating to the south of the mountains becomes so intense that a vigorous depression forms with strong winds circulating around it. These winds are generally directed from the west or southwest across the Arabian Sea and the Bay of Bengal. That the strongest winter monsoon develops off the coast of East Asia is also related to the South Asian mountain chain. The Himalayas do not extend east of Burma and so in winter the extremely cold air mass, which develops over central and eastern Siberia and produces the highest air pressure anywhere, can act untrammeled throughout the length and breadth of China. The winds around this dome of high pressure blow from the northeast predominantly, across the China Seas through the Formosa Channel and south as far as Indonesia.

Monsoons develop only where large continents border oceans, whereas upwelling develops along coastlines. The two coexist; how do they interact? Because air circulates in an anticlockwise direction around a low-pressure center, and the continents are seats of summer depressions, some parts of the continental coastline would certainly be both parallel to and to the left of the wind. There upwelling should develop, and in fact the strongest upwelling occurs along the coast of Somalia and the southeastern coast of Arabia during the summer or southwest monsoon where ocean surface temperatures of greater than 10 degrees C below the latitudinal and seasonal normals have been measured. As pressure falls inland over Arabia and eastern Africa, the southwest winds set in and upwelling begins. The surface water is then replaced by cooler subsurface water that in turn cools the air. At the same time the relatively rough land and the relatively smooth sea cause the surface winds to diverge. Air from aloft sinks along this line of divergence, skies clear, and the brilliantly shining sun heats the land and the air in contact with it. Upwelling and divergence of the surface wind jointly increase the temperature gradient between hot land and cool sea. This increase in the temperature gradient causes a corresponding increase in the gradient of surface pressure. Since wind strength is proportional to the pressure gradient, this, in turn, intensifies the wind, an example of the phenomenon of feedback. The monsoon initiates upwelling. Upwelling and frictional discontinuity at the coastline intensify the monsoon, which then intensifies the upwelling, and so on. Under these circumstances surface winds blow stronger and steadier along the coast of Somalia and Arabia than they do anywhere else in the world, sustaining gale force and constant direction for three months every summer.

During the winter monsoon, the continents are colder than the oceans and are seats of high pressure about which the air circulates clockwise. And in some places coastlines parallel the wind but lie to the *right* of the wind. Frictional stress on the sea then forces water toward the coast where it sinks, to be replaced by warmer surface water from farther offshore. Thus the winter monsoon tends to increase the amount of warm surface water along the coast rather than to diminish it, so that no upwelling is observed.

Now, the relatively rough land and the relatively smooth sea cause the surface winds to converge and the air to rise. Rising air expands and cools, and if it cools enough, moisture will condense and clouds form. These clouds keep the land cooler than it would otherwise be.

Surface transport of water in the winter monsoon and the frictional effect of the coastline on the wind tend to intensify or at least maintain the strength of the winter monsoon circulation by increasing the sea to land temperature gradient.

Thus far we have considered only cases in which upwelling or downwelling intensifies the monsoon and is in turn intensified by the monsoon. However, along some continental coastlines vertical motion in the ocean retards rather than enhances the monsoon. This effect limits the extent of the monsoons off western Africa and prevents the monsoons from developing off western South America.

The huge equator-spanning continent of Africa possesses a peculiar monsoon regime. While one-half of the continent is being cooled in winter the other half is being heated in summer. Thus a considerable pressure gradient is established between the two halves of the continent causing winds to blow in response. During the Northern Hemisphere winter, air pressure is high over the Sahara Desert and low over the Kalahari Desert in southern Africa. Air would normally flow out of the high pressure area over the Sahara into the depression over the Kalahari and across the equator in the process. In other words, a winter monsoon in the Northern Hemisphere would be meshed with a summer monsoon in the Southern Hemisphere. Over western Africa it doesn't quite work out in this way. In the southeastern Atlantic, strong steady southeast trade winds, blowing along the west coast of southern Africa, cause considerable upwelling. Currents generated by the trade winds carry the cold upwelled water to the equator where it significantly reduces the temperature gradient between the Sahara and the South Atlantic. This reduced temperature gradient, by reducing the pressure gradient, significantly weakens the monsoon current, so much so that winds seldom blow across the equator during January. Along the east coast of southern Africa where upwelling is absent, sea temperatures are 3 degrees to 7 degrees C higher than they are off the west coast. Consequently, the winter monsoon of the Northern Hemisphere extends into and becomes the summer monsoon of the Southern Hemisphere as far south as Madagascar.

Upwelling exerts an even more dramatic effect off the West Coast of South America. Strong, persistent southeast trade winds circulating around a large high pressure area in the South Pacific blow parallel to a long coastline rimmed with very high mountains—a perfect upwelling situation. During the Southern-

Hemisphere summer a steep pressure gradient prevails between the hot interior of South America and the very cold waters along the west coast. For a monsoon regime to be established, the wind circulation must reverse between summer and winter. However, off South America the trade winds intensify rather than weaken from summer to winter. Upwelling also intensifies to such a degree that even in winter the coastal water remains colder than the land. Since the temperature gradient is only weakened but not reversed between summer and winter, the pressure gradient is not reversed. South America therefore lacks a monsoon regime because of the overwhelmingly powerful role that upwelling plays in controlling the direction of the temperature gradient.

Extensive upwelling occurs off the west coasts of North and South America and Africa, where winds and wind-driven currents are directed toward the equator. A continuous, although often narrow ribbon of cold surface water extends from higher latitudes to the area of maximum upwelling. Fish can move along this ribbon, benefiting from increased food but not being exposed to severe temperature changes. Vast fish populations, most notably off Peru, inhabit these upwelling regions.

Off Somalia, on the other hand, winds and wind-driven currents directed away from the equator suddenly set in at the beginning of summer. Very cold water appears at the surface, unconnected in space or time with surface cold water elsewhere. Fish (and presumably plankton) in the area are subject to sudden cold stress. Oceanographers have reported seeing large numbers of dead fish and remarkably few sea birds. Considering the wealth of nutrients, the sea off Somalia is poor in plankton.

Perhaps, then, the only upwelling that is entirely monsoon generated may prove to be less of a food resource than many have hoped.

The general principles that apply to monsoons and upwelling and the major "classical" examples that illustrate these principles have been described. However, of all ocean phenomena, none is so liable to local changes as upwelling. Upwelling may be extremely strong on the leeside of a small headland and nonexistent on the windward side. A slight change of wind direction or wind speed or both can shift the region of upwelling or cause it to disappear. In detail it is very much a will-o'-the-wisp phenomenon. However, this does not alter the fact that upwelling occurs on a massive scale in certain large regions off the coasts of continents.

During the summer, pressure is low over inland Australia and high over the South Indian Ocean. Fresh, steady southerly winds blow parallel to the coast of western Australia, but no upwelling had been detected. Why? (Wyrtki suggests that upwelling does in fact occur but that the upwelled water is replaced by warmer subsurface water drifting southward around Northwest Cape. This water upwells but its effect is to raise the sea surface temperature slightly along the coast. The upwelling warm water should therefore reduce the land-sea temperature gradient in summer and so weaken the Australian summer monsoon. Conversely, in winter the sea-land temperature gradient and consequently the Australian winter monsoon would be increased. In contrast to the western Australian situation, cold upwelling occurs only where a source of relatively warm subsurface water cannot readily be tapped.

Does this difference explain the anomaly? Men making measurements from ships and making mathematical models in computer centers will one day solve this and many other riddles of the sea.

18 PROCESSES OF AIR–SEA INTERACTION

Robert G. Fleagle

Anyone who has experienced a storm at sea knows a great deal about some of the consequences of air-sea interaction. He knows that even a huge ship may roll and pitch so that the crew and passengers are thrown violently about, small boats may be smashed in a second, and even steel plates may buckle under the force of the sea. All of this violent energy, which is imparted to the sea by air blowing along the surface, also erodes the shore lines and fills harbors and bays with silt. It drives the great ocean currents: for example, the Gulf Stream, which flows northeastward along the east coast of North America, the Kuroshio, which flows northeastward off the coast of China and Japan, and the Peru current, which sustains the rich harvests of sea life in that region off the South American coast.

Another consequence of air-sea interaction is even more important than the destructive effects of waves and the influence of ocean currents, although we may not be so aware of it. The water that is necessary to support life constantly circulates: evaporating from earth's surface, condensing in clouds, falling from the atmosphere as rain or snow, being utilized by the earth and its inhabitants, and then running off into the sea. The whole process is referred to as the hydrologic cycle. At any given time the atmosphere holds about 10 trillion tons of water; 1 trillion tons falls to earth each day and 1 trillion tons is evaporated into the atmosphere from the oceans. The atmosphere is thus a great reservoir for water vapor, a reservoir with a residence time of about ten days. The process of evaporation is one of the crucial links in the hydrologic cycle. Not only are the other phases of the cycle dependent on evaporation but evaporation and subsequent condensation also provide most of the energy to the atmosphere that is responsible for the generation of storms. One way to illustrate the importance of condensation within the atmosphere is to point out that the energy released by the condensation of water vapor equals the electrical energy utilized by ten cities the size of New York City.

When we realize that evaporation from the ocean surface increases rapidly with wind velocity, we begin to understand the subtlety of air-sea interaction. Evaporation provides the fuel that generates storms, as storms develop evaporation increases, providing much more energy for further storm development. This process of feedback is one of the important factors in the development of the destructive tropical storms called hurricanes or typhoons, which sometimes continue to increase in severity as long as they are over the warm ocean, and only begin to weaken after they move over land or over colder ocean areas where evaporation is reduced by the lower surface temperature.

Most evaporation occurs from the tropical oceans, but storms are generated at all latitudes and over land as well as over the sea. We may refer to three stages in the large-scale transfer of energy. First, water vapor is transported upward from the ocean surface to a height of 10 to 100 meters by random or turbulent motions. This occurs so rapidly that if one measures the water vapor transported upward through a surface 20 meters or so above the sea, it is often an accurate measure of the rate of evaporation occurring at the same time at the sea surface. Next, water vapor within the layer near the ocean surface may be carried upward to heights of several miles by convection cells that can be seen as bulging towers of cumulus clouds. Condensation occurring in these clouds releases latent heat and warms the air at cloud level. Thus, these two processes together transport thermal energy upward from the warm ocean to the atmosphere. The final step in the transfer is provided by the large-scale wind systems, which may carry water vapor and warm air

239

thousands of kilometers from the region of evaporation, and in these remote regions the energy may be utilized in storm generation. The details of this process are very complex; they are studied by weather forecasters who use mathematical models of the atmosphere and the largest available electronic computers to predict atmospheric behavior. Atmospheric scientists are now engaged in an international program aimed at securing the worldwide observations that will be needed to extend useful weather predictions to a week or more. At the same time research is underway that is directed at developing mathematical models that can utilize the global data.

At the present time mathematical models of the atmosphere, which are used for forecasting, ignore the process of evaporation and transport of water or, at best, represent these processes only in the crudest way. If we think of water in the atmosphere as the fuel for winds and storms, and if we recall that all the fuel in the atmosphere at any time is utilized in a period of ten days, we can then understand the importance of evaporation to making forecasts for periods as long as ten days. Overlooking these processes would be analogous to predicting how an automobile would operate without considering the ignition and fuel system.

At the boundary between the sea and the air, water molecules are constantly passing upward from sea to air and downward from air to sea. The number of molecules impelled upward from the sea depends upon the temperature and salinity of the surface water. Each water molecule is attracted downward by the mass of the earth below it, but those molecules that by chance gain sufficient energy by collision with other molecules may escape from the surface. Their energy is added to the atmosphere and is subtracted from the sea. At the same time water molecules in the air near the surface are in constant agitation. Some of them by chance fly downward, enter the water, and give up some of their energy. The difference per unit surface area between the number passing upward and downward through the surface is called the evaporation rate. Clearly, this rate depends upon the temperature of the water surface and the

density of water molecules in the air just above the surface—
that is, the humidity of the air.

What determines the humidity of the air just above the surface? We can recognize that some water molecules will move
upward away from the surface. If they are then carried away by
air currents, the humidity near the surface will be lowered.
Thus, vigorous air motions or turbulence in the air above the
sea carries water vapor away from the surface and increases
the rate of evaporation. Of course, downward air motions carry
water vapor downward, but if there is drier air at some distance
above the surface, as is usually the case, the net effect of upward
and downward currents is to transport water vapor upward. The
intensity of turbulence increases with the rate of increase of the
average wind velocity with height, the vertical shear of the wind.
Turbulent intensity also increases as temperature increases
downward toward the surface. This relationship is demonstrated
by the fact that with strong heating of the ground by the sun's
rays on a warm summer afternoon, airplane landings are likely
to be rough. If we put together these dependencies on wind and
temperature, we can express the rate of evaporation for periods
of an hour or so as a mathematical function of the vertical
gradients of wind velocity, humidity, and temperature. Similar
functions can be developed for heat conduction and wind stress
within the lowest 10 meters or so of the atmosphere. These
relations have been refined and tested in recent years; they are
accurate to within 10 per cent to 20 per cent under suitably
favorable conditions, and this limit is determined mainly by the
statistical uncertainty associated with scales of turbulence that
are comparable to the averaging period.

Our next concern is with the processes that generate waves
on the ocean surface. Although waves are easily observed and
exist on all water surfaces wherever there is appreciable wind,
the basic mechanism of wave generation and development is
complex and far from clear. As Owen Phillips of Johns Hopkins University has pointed out, two processes added together
account for at least the major effects. Waves are generated
when atmospheric pressure differences act on adjacent portions

of the surface. We may visualize turbulent elements imbedded in an air stream flowing over a smooth water surface. Localized regions of relatively high and low pressure are associated with the turbulent elements. Where air pressure is high, the air will press the water surface down and where air pressure is low, the surface will bulge upward and a wave will be formed. As we well know from observation, this wave will travel along the surface with a characteristic speed; and if this speed happens to coincide with the speed of the turbulence imbedded in the flowing air, the amplitude of the wave will grow larger with time. Many different wavelengths are present on a natural water surface, each having a different characteristic speed. We can visualize a kind of resonance between the moving pressure disturbance and a particular wavelength with the result that selective growth occurs. This process is believed to be particularly effective in the initial generation and the very early stages of wave development.

After finite amplitude waves have developed, a second effect becomes important, which is a consequence of the asymmetry of pressure over the wave surface induced by air flowing over the wave surface itself. The water surface and the flowing air are coupled in such a way that for suitably short waves, the pressure is higher on the rear slope of the wave than on the front slope so that the net force adds energy to the wave. A detailed account of this process is complex and depends heavily upon mathematical development. Under a steady wind the waves grow for several hours, but beyond this time energy is dissipated as rapidly as it is added to the surface, and we can refer to the sea state as being saturated. Some quantitative estimates are interesting for the saturated sea state. For a moderate wind velocity of about 20 knots, the wave energy of the sea surface is roughly 1 per cent of the total energy of the mean flow of the whole atmosphere, or about the energy of the lowest 50 meters. Turbulent energy of the atmosphere is only about 1 per cent of the mean energy, so that we see that surface wave energy is comparable to the turbulent energy of the entire atmosphere. These numbers suggest that wave energy in large part comes from the energy of the mean-air flow above the surface rather than from the turbulence. Important aspects of these processes are still not adequately understood.

We next turn to the problems of air-sea interaction on a somewhat deeper scale, processes that transport water vapor and heat from near the surface to heights of one or two kilometers. This layer, which is referred to as the planetary boundary layer, serves to link the "free" or frictionless atmosphere to the surface where the frictional force is significant. To understand the dominant processes occurring here, we must recognize that air near the surface flows with a component toward low pressure, but that in the free atmosphere the flow is in equilibrium; that is, the effect of the pressure force is only to turn the wind as seen from a point outside the earth and not to increase its speed. The rate of turning is approximately equal to the rate of rotation of the earth about a vertical axis, so that as seen from a point on the earth the air flows approximately at a constant speed in a fixed compass direction. Thus, air flow in the free atmosphere tends to follow lines of constant pressure and is referred to as geostrophic.

Unfortunately, these concepts are not simple or obvious, but they are necessary to understanding the processes of the planetary boundary layer. Within this layer the wind turns gradually with height toward the geostrophic or constant pressure direction. This turning with height may be visualized as forming a spiral (referred to as the Ekman spiral), and the planetary boundary layer is often referred to as the Ekman layer. At the sea surface the wind typically makes an angle of 10 degrees to 30 degrees with the geostrophic direction.

Before discussing some of the transport mechanisms operating in the atmospheric Ekman layer, a corresponding ocean Ekman layer will be mentioned that links the ocean surface that is acted upon by the wind and the ocean layers below depths of perhaps 2 to 20 meters. In this layer, current is driven by the force of the wind at the upper surface, but because of the rotation of the earth, the water is impelled to flow at right angles to the wind direction, to the right in the Northern Hemisphere, to the left in the Southern Hemisphere. The most important consequence of this is that air flowing parallel to a nearby coastline may drive the surface water away from the coast and cause upwelling of water from depth.

We have seen that within the atmospheric Ekman layer there is a component of flow toward low pressure. In consequence, a circular low-pressure area is an area of inflow toward the center. One result is that the air is forced to rise in areas of low pressure, and the rising air produces clouds and rain or snow. The planetary boundary layer thus provides a mechanism for extracting the water and the latent heat that is supplied at the sea surface through evaporation.

A second systematic effect arises from the fact that the Ekman spiral is characteristically unstable to small disturbances, which means that although the Ekman distribution describes a balance of pressure force, frictional force, and the geostrophic force, this balance is disturbed by any slight change, perhaps associated with ever-present turbulence. Small disturbances may then grow in a characteristic manner to form a regular pattern of helical circulations. Evidences of these helical circulations are seen in the regularly spaced "cloud streets" that are frequently present over extensive regions at heights of one or two kilometers.

The cloud streets lie approximately along the direction of the wind, and their centers are typically a few kilometers apart. The strips of cloud reveal regions of upward flow whereas the clear strips reveal downward flow, so we may visualize that as we look along the axis of the wind, alternate right-hand and left-hand roll vortices lie side by side filling the entire planetary boundary layer and extending up into the free atmosphere. Glider pilots may take advantage of the ascending regions of the roll vortices to gain or maintain altitude.

Helical roll vortices occur in well-defined air currents, and their energy increases with wind speed. In the case of weak, variable winds, another form of organized flow may occur. Especially over heated land or distinctly warm water convection cells may develop that can carry water vapor and heat from near the surface high into the atmosphere. These cells may be visualized as columns or chimneys of rising, warm air imbedded in the more or less static and cooler environment. If the rising air is moist, as it would necessarily be over the ocean, clouds form; and the released latent heat may then add greatly to the energy of the cell. Convection cells may be identified visually by the bulging, cumulus-type clouds that they produce. Often they appear to develop more or less randomly over warm surfaces, but photographs taken from earth satellites sometimes reveal a variety of astonishingly regular patterns. For example, we sometimes observe ring-shaped arrangements of convection cells with horizontal dimensions of 100 kilometers or more. What determines these patterns is not known.

Evaporation from the tropical ocean areas of the earth provides most of the energy that drives the atmosphere. Two mechanisms, found only in the tropical atmosphere, are especially important in transporting water vapor upward. They are the tropical storms called the *hurricane,* in the Atlantic Ocean, and the *typhoon,* in the Pacific Ocean, and the *intertropical convergence zone,* a belt of closely spaced convection cells found over the Atlantic, Pacific, and Indian Oceans.

Hurricanes or typhoons develop over tropical oceans between about 5 degrees and 20 degrees latitude usually in the late summer or early fall. They occur in the North Atlantic Ocean, the North and South Pacific, and the Indian Ocean, but hurricane development has never been observed in the south Atlantic or southeast Pacific, and they never develop within 2 degrees or 3 degrees of the equator. In their beginning stages hurricanes may appear as areas of convective clouds indistinguishable from many other similar areas. In full flower, however, they are unique and extremely dangerous mechanisms of destruction. Mature hurricanes consist of a disk of rotating air perhaps 500 kilometers in diameter surrounding a central calm core or "eye" of roughly 10 kilometers in diameter. Pressure is quite low within the eye, perhaps 5 per cent below normal atmospheric pressure, or more, and under the influence of surface friction, air in the planetary boundary layer spirals

245

sharply inward toward the center. The convective clouds of the hurricane are arranged in spiral bands marking the boundary layer flow direction. Hurricane development is a fairly rare event (about sixty develop per year), which occurs when a number of factors together lead to unstable growth. The requirements evidently are an inflow in the planetary boundary layer, the consequent release of latent heat in convective clouds, a fall in surface pressure caused by the release of latent heat, enhanced inflow, and a repeat of the cycle at greater intensity. As inflow increases it is essential that increased evaporation and warming occur at the sea surface, and it is also critical that the heat released in the convective clouds not be swept away by strong winds. The theory of hurricanes has developed considerably in the last few years, but the subject is difficult and many obscure points remain.

Individual hurricanes occupy only a very small proportion of the atmosphere, but they are so vigorous that, for example, in the course of their lifetime most of the air in the planetary boundary layer over the North Tropical Atlantic may be pumped through such a storm. Obviously, hurricanes dominate the transfer processes for these periods, but they are sufficiently rare that they are probably not crucial elements in running the global circulation system.

The intertropical convergence zone, on the other hand, is such a crucial element. This is a region of dense convective clouds perhaps 100 kilometers in north-south extent that runs more or less east-west across the tropical ocean areas. It lies in a region of easterly winds and forms the boundary region between the northeast tradewinds of the Northern Hemisphere and the southeast tradewinds of the Southern Hemisphere. However, the intertropical convergence zone wanders in latitude between about 10 degrees N and 10 degrees S; and it may disappear in one area for a time and reappear in another area. On occasion, twin zones may form on either side of the equator with a markedly clear, dry region at the equator. The role of the intertropical convergence zone in the global circulation system is not yet entirely clear, but there is little doubt that it dominates the process that transfers water vapor and thermal energy from the planetary boundary layer to the free atmosphere. It will require an elaborately coordinated series of observations made from the surface, from aircraft, and from satellites to elucidate the mechanism of the intertropical convergence zone. Some of these observations were made in 1969 in the Barbados Oceanographic and Meteorological Experiment, which is referred to as BOMEX; and further observations are being planned by an international group under United Nations auspices.

An important consequence of the latent heat released in the tropical free atmosphere through condensation in the intertropical convergence zone is the generation of storms in middle latitudes and the resulting global circulation. To understand these processes, we may think of the atmosphere as a rotating disk of fluid heated in the tropics and cooled in the polar regions. Expansion of the warmed air and contraction of the cooled air tends to set up air flow at high levels toward the pole and toward the tropics at low levels. But because of rotation of the earth, the air cannot flow along these simple paths; conservation of angular momentum requires that the poleward-moving air increase its rotation toward the east while the air moving away from the pole decrease its rotation. Thus the easterly trade winds of low latitudes and the prevailing westerlies of middle latitudes are formed. This arrangement of winds and temperatures, however, is unstable to small disturbances. Mathematical analysis shows that disturbances having horizontal dimensions of several thousand kilometers will grow more rapidly than either smaller or larger disturbances. For this reason storms of this size are common features of the middle latitudes. They depend upon the free atmosphere temperature difference between tropical and polar regions, so that they are not as intimately related to the planetary boundary layer as are the tropical systems mentioned previously. Consequently, they may form in many places; however, they develop most often in winter in the regions where cold air flows from the continents over warm ocean areas. Under these conditions evaporation is especially rapid and energy is fed into the developing storm in large quantities. Therefore, the Gulf Stream off the east coast of North America and the Kuroshio Current off the east coast of Asia are the regions of greatest middle latitude storm development.

The characteristic response time of the upper part of the ocean is long as compared to the lifetime of storms. For this reason, atmospheric scientists often treat the ocean as an infinite heat reservoir, and we assume that the ocean surface temperature remains unchanged at least for periods of a month. However, if we are interested in changes occurring from one season to the next, or one year to the next, or even longer climatic changes, then we must consider changes in ocean properties. Ocean surface temperatures are influenced by the amount of solar radiation falling on the surface, by evaporation, by upwelling currents that bring deep cold water to the surface, and by surface waves and turbulence that mix warm surface water with colder water from depths. Solar radiation is controlled largely by clouds; evaporation is controlled by winds, as are surface waves and surface currents. Thus we see that the atmosphere and ocean constitute a single system of two coupled fluids. Response times for the two are different, and as a result they may interact in very complicated ways. Subtle resonances between the slowly responding ocean and the faster responding atmosphere might conceivably occur. We could imagine the annual cycle of ocean temperature as applying a regular impulse to the atmosphere. Under one circumstance the configuration of atmospheric properties might be such that in a particular ocean region clear skies and light winds prevailed during a period of rapid increase in solar radiation, with the result that ocean surface temperatures increased markedly. In another year at the same season the configuration of the atmosphere might be such that a storm was energized. Clouds would cut off the sun's radiation and high winds would increase surface evaporation and stirring of the surface layer of ocean; each of these effects would tend to prevent warming of the ocean. Thus, substantially different surface layer temperatures might be developed in these two cases. These conditions might prevail for extended periods with a marked effect on the seasonal climate, or they might possibly initiate quite different trains of weather events.

These are largely speculations. However, Jerome Namias noticed that in 1962 a period of unusually warm North Pacific surface water corresponded with a subsequent colder than normal winter in both North America and Europe, and he has proposed a plausible explanation linking these observations. Examination of interactions of this sort is one of the objectives of the international program known as the Global Atmospheric Research Program. Under this program we hope to obtain the global data needed to extend the range of useful weather prediction from the present limits of a few days to periods of two weeks or even longer. This goal is closely coupled to an improved understanding of air-sea transfer processes. Through BOMEX and other research programs, we are improving the design of mathematical prediction models of the ocean and atmosphere. These models in turn will teach us new things about how the two fluids interact and hopefully will lead to a further extension of the range of prediction and to an understanding of how climate changes. Experimentation with mathematical models should help reveal the long-term effects of pollution or the modification of the earth before these changes become dangerous or irreversible.

19 THE ORIGIN AND EVOLUTION OF LIFE IN THE SEA

Alfred Sherwood Romer

In our current explorations of outer space, we are attempting to enter regions in which neither man nor his ancestors has ever lived and in which, as far as we know today, no living thing exists. Quite different is the situation regarding our attempts to learn more about the oceans that surround us. For in contrast to the seemingly bleak sterility of most (although we hope not all) of the heavenly bodies, the seas swarm with living things. Furthermore, although man and his ancestors have dwelt on land for well over 200 million years, this period is only a small fraction—perhaps 10 per cent—of the time during which life is known to have existed on this planet. The early careers of our biological ancestors and, indeed, of all life, began in salt water.

For the relatively recent history of living things, we have recourse to the fossil record, because many life forms have hard structures capable of being preserved as fossils. But fossil records are not available to help us decipher the earlier parts of the story, for quite surely all the earliest forms of life were tiny and soft-bodied little creatures.

The problem of learning the way in which the first living things came into being is largely a matter for the chemist rather than the biologist. Some data regarding the conditions under which life may have first appeared, some thousands of millions of years ago, were given by Harold C. Urey in Chapter 2. It seems reasonable to believe that life gradually evolved from complex molecular structures that became capable of performing the chemical activities characteristic of living matter and, finally, became capable of reproducing themselves.

This fundamental advance certainly occurred in water that contained a considerable quantity of material in solution, without which the complex chemical structure of living matter could never have been created. But this fundamental evolutionary process could not have taken place in the open oceans; rather, it probably occurred in quiet environments such as the pools along the shores of very ancient seas. How long it took for chemical evolution to produce the first primitive living thing is not known, and probably will never be known. Before the last 600 million years or so, the record of the rocks has yielded only very sparse evidences of life, but recent discoveries have revealed the existence of true living cells as long ago as about 3,000 million years.

We tend to sharply divide all living things into animals or plants. The first living cells must have been plants because while plants can exist without animals, animals cannot exist without plants. Plants alone are capable of manufacturing the organic molecules of which living matter is formed. Animals may obtain some materials, such as oxygen and simple salts, needed for their sustenance, from air and water, but the basic food supply for an animal comes from the plant world, either directly by eating plant food or eating other animals, which, in turn, subsist on plants. Plants are largely factories that can take simple chemical materials, such as carbon dioxide, water, and nitrogen and combine them into organic compounds (in which carbon is the most essential element) to form living protoplasm. Once these compounds are formed by plants, they can be utilized by animals, which may break them up and modify them into new chemical forms; but animals themselves cannot make them.

To combine materials into complex compounds requires energy; and although at the very beginning there was probably some variation in the methods, nearly all plants have found their energy source in the rays of the sun. An early "invention" of plants was the compound chlorophyll, which gives the green color to every living leaf and blade of grass on the surface of the earth and most of the seaweeds and primitive plants of the sea. Radiant energy from the sun is captured by the chlorophyll and utilized by the plant in its manufacturing activities.

For a long time primitive single celled forms of life were exclusively plants, by definition. But even among unicellular forms of life, such as we see under the microscope today, a differentiation has evolved between those that manufactured their own food, and remained plants, and those that existed by devouring or scavaging from other organisms. These forms, fattening upon their plant cousins, became the first animals. From then on, animal and plant kingdoms began independent evolutionary histories.

This early evolutionary history took place in the sea. All early life was water-dwelling, and sea water, containing a modest concentration of salts in its solution, is the sort of environment in which living cells flourish best. Today, of course, almost every land surface is covered with an abundant and varied vegetation, amidst which is found a wealth of animal life. This is not the case in the older eras of the earth's history. As far as can be determined, for much of the history of the world, the lands were bare and rocky, without the slightest vestige of any living thing upon them. It is only within the last few hundreds of millions of years—a long time for us to comprehend but only a modest fraction of the total span of the earth history—that life invaded terrestrial streams, and invasion of the land took place at a still later date.

It is not until the Paleozoic era, whose beginnings date back about 600 million years, that we find in the geologic record any adequate representation of fossil animals and plants. Much had happened before that time. Our lack of knowledge of earlier history may be attributed to a combination of two causes —one, that most earlier forms of life were so soft-bodied that they were not ordinarily capable of fossilization; second, that even if traces of them had been left in the rocks of earlier ages, later geological activity has in great measure destroyed or modified the rock strata in which they were recorded.

Much of the interesting evolutionary history of the plant world took place after members of this kingdom had become plants that could live on land. Even today the plant life of the sea is restricted almost entirely to relatively simple forms that botanists usually group together under the term "algae." Some of these, such as the familiar seaweeds, may grow to considerable size, but remain relatively simple in structure. Most algae, however, are very much smaller and still simpler in nature, consisting only of small clusters of cells or single cells alone. Their distribution in the sea is worldwide although it is mainly limited to the sun-lit surface waters. They depend upon sunlight for the support of their vital functions, and even in clear ocean waters, sunlight can penetrate but a short distance—20 or 30 meters—below the surface. Thus, the growth of ocean plant life is restricted to near-surface waters. But despite this limitation, marine plant life, mostly of microscopic forms known as "phytoplankton," is the basic food on which all animal life in the sea ultimately depends. The nature and importance of this phytoplankton is more fully discussed by John H. Ryther in Chapter 20.

Animal evolution in the sea was much more varied than that of the plants. At the beginning of the Paleozoic era about 600 million years or so ago, the curtain lifted, so to speak, to give us a view of how far animal evolution had progressed by that time. Some of today's soft-bodied groups of animals are little known from ancient times. But with the exception of the assemblage to which man and his vertebrate relatives belong, remains of every important major group of animals are to be found in the rocks of the oldest period of that Paleozoic era, the Cambrian. A large fraction of the entire evolutionary story of animal life had already occurred—and all of it had taken place in marine waters.

In this limited space, we can attempt only a brief outline of the evolution of animals in the sea. As in the case of the plants, the animal kingdom began with single-celled forms, the Protozoa, which are still abundant today. But long before we find our oldest animal fossils in the Paleozoic era, there had occurred the advance toward larger, more complex, multicellular organisms. A first, rather imperfect step in this direction resulted in the clustering together of masses of cells into the forms called sponges, with an imperfect organization of their structure. This seems to have been a blind sideline, which led to nothing higher. At about the same time, the evolution of a well-organized if simple type of multicellular animal apparently began, in the form of a little two-layered creature. This animal probably (although not surely) lived attached to surfaces with a differentiation of tissues so that its outer layer was concerned with protection and "external relations," whereas the inner layer served as a digestive tract for food materials brought in by a mouth opening at one end. No such simple animal exists today, although some of the lowly marine animals usually termed coelenterates (hydroids, corals, and so forth) are similar in many ways. An animal of this sort, with a multicellular organization and differentiation of tissues is defined as a metazoan, and all animals other than single-celled protozoans and the aberrant sponges are classified by zoologists as members of the great subkingdom Metazoa. These primitive animals have evolved and differentiated into a score or so of subdivisions termed phyla, most of which had already assumed characteristic structures when they first appeared in the fossil record of marine life.

A few important general features characterize the history and mode of life of these varied marine forms. Considered broadly, a sea animal has two ways of making a living—he may actively seek out his food or he may sit passively and wait for food materials to come to him; he may be either a "go-getter" or a "sitter." There are, to be sure, intermediate courses of action, but for the most part animals fall fairly readily into one category or the other. (See Figure 19–1.)

Most likely, sitting motionless and waiting for food particles to come to him in water currents flowing past was the mode of life of the oldest and most primitive metazoan. "Sitters" generally lack the bilateral symmetry, with right and left sides, characteristic of more active animals. Essentially, they only

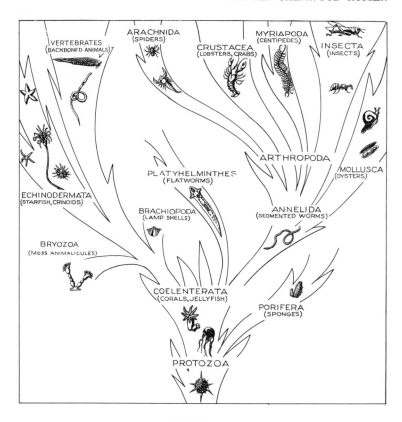

FIGURE 19–1.

A simplified "family tree" of animal groups. (From A. S. Romer, *Vertebrate Paleontology*, University of Chicago Press.)

know top and bottom; their lower end attached to the sea bottom, either directly or by a stalk, and their upper end opening to the world. The animal is arrayed around a vertical axis and it makes little difference to him as to where, around the circuit of the body, any structures are placed. Animals of this type tend to acquire a more or less radial kind of symmetry.

Food seekers are fundamentally different. Movement—primarily in the search for food—is their keynote. A lengthwise horizontal build is the best type of body plan, with front and

255

back ends, top and bottom sides, and bilateral symmetry, one side of the usually slender body being a mirror-image of the other; an arrow-like shape is the ideal.

Of these "go-getters," the more primitive forms are the varied worms. Some worms have an extremely archaic structure, and some have wandered off any main evolutionary line to become parasitic. The most progressive of the worms are those in the phylum Annelida. Some of the annelid worms came ashore as the familiar earthworms. However, they are aberrant and rather degenerate types. More highly organized and typical worm forms are abundant in the oceans, and are often found at rest beneath a rock or in a burrow, but are alert for prey and able to swim about freely. Unlike the earthworms, marine annelids are supplied with sense organs as aids to navigation, and their wriggling propulsive motion, made possible by the musculature of their strongly segmented body, is aided by their possession of pairs of small limblike paddles on every segment.

From advanced worms of this type, it seems certain, arose what in many ways is the most successful of all the animal groups, the phylum Arthropoda. The arthropods, of which the crustaceans in the seas and the insects of land are familiar modern representatives, have a basal segmental structure similar to that of their annelid ancestors, but they have become modified and advanced in many ways. In the worm ancestors, each of the numerous segments was just like every other; in arthropods many of the segments have been consolidated into compact head and thoracic structures, and only in the "tail" do we see a preservation in the adult of free segments. A second major progressive feature is that arthropods are armored; there is no internal skeleton, but the body is completely covered by a hornlike substance, chiton. A third major advance is that on nearly every segment (at least in primitive forms) there is a pair of jointed legs (the name "arthropod" refers to this), which were primitively used for swimming or crawling along the bottom. Arthropods are present in the oldest rocks in which fossils are at all common, as bottom dwelling trilobites. Long abundant, the trilobites eventually died out to be succeeded in the seas by other related groups. Today the crustaceans, such as lobsters and crabs, are the major arthropods of the oceans.

We now turn to forms that belong to the general category of "sitters," sessile organisms. Highly primitive in most structural features are the members of the phylum Coelenterata, including such sessile sea-bottom forms as the sea-anemones, hydras, and coral animals—with the jellyfishes as a free-floating side branch. Most sessile animals depend for their food on small particles floating by them in the currents. The coelenterates, however, have one specialization that has made them moderately successful in an unusual fashion. They have developed peculiar stinging cells, which can be thrust out like tiny harpoons to capture creatures of relatively large size, even small fishes.

A second major phylum of which most members are sedentary is that of the Mollusca. The oysters, clams, and snails are representative. Most are sedentary forms, subsisting on food particles drawn by a current into the shell-covered body. The Mollusca illustrate, in complex fashion, the way in which radical changes in modes of life may occur during evolutionary history. Their mode of development suggests that the sedentary molluscs had evolved in ancient days from active, swimming, annelid worms. That this theory, seemingly unlikely at first sight, is true has been in great measure confirmed by the discovery, a few years ago in the depths of the Pacific Ocean, of an archaic mollusc type in which there are traces of the original annelid body segmentation, which has been altogether lost in typical molluscs. A second quirk in their history is that, after becoming sedentary, some of the molluscs swung again into activity. This is the case with the mollusc subdivision termed the cephalopods, represented by the squids and octopi. We know from fossil evidence that the ancestral forms of cephalopods had well developed shells; the modern types have reduced the shell, thus decreasing their weight, so that they have become among the most active and aggressive inhabitants of the oceans.

Apart from a few odds and ends that we will not stop to consider, there remain several phyla that are (or were to begin with, ancestrally) "sitters" rather than "go-getters." In each case the primitive members were simply built little animals, sedentary and often with a stalk above which was a blob of body containing little but a digestive cavity. At the top was a mouth and, above this in all primitive members of each group, arms, termed lophophores, usually two to six or so in number, stretching up and out to gather food particles; each lophophore has a band of cilia to carry these particles down to the receptive mouth.

Two relatively unimportant phyla of this type are the Bryozoa, often called "moss animalicules" because clusters of tiny individuals on stones or wharf pilings give a mossy appearance, and the Brachiopoda, or lamp shells, which look superficially like stalked clams but have a very different organization; the shell encloses the lophophores. A third, more important, phylum of this group is that of the Echinodermata, of which the star fishes and sea urchins are familiar forms. These are not stalked; but the most primitive of echinoderms, the crinoids or sea-lilies, are stalked forms and have the basic construction that was described for a typical "sitter."

One animal phylum is that to which we and our vertebrate relatives belong, that of the Chordata. Fishes, reptiles, birds, mammals, and man are vertebrates—essentially active animals, bilaterally symmetrical in structure. One would think that this group would have been discussed earlier, along with other phyla of "go-getters." But here again (as in the case of the Mollusca) we find a remarkable change in the life of the ancestors of the vertebrates.

The most primitive members of this phylum present today are tiny rare deep-sea creatures, more or less colonial in nature, called pterobranchs. In these little animals are found the typical structures seen in other food-gatherers; a simple lump of body set above a stalk, with a set of ciliated lophophores around the mouth. But there are two seemingly minor items that give a clue as to pterobranch relationships—the presence of a constriction, a type of collar, between body and lophophores, and a projecting blob of tissue, a sort of nose, projecting above the mouth between the lophophores. These features tie the ptero-branchs to the next higher level in the chordate series, the balanoglossids, or acorn worms, not uncommon residents in burrows in shallow waters. These forms look somewhat like annelid worms in superficial appearance, but there is not the slightest resemblance to true worms internally; instead they are like the pterobranchs in the presence of a collar and a "nose" or proboscis, so highly developed that in some forms proboscis and collar have somewhat the appearance of an acorn in its cup.

But here there is a notable shift from other lowly "sitters" in the method of gathering food particles. The forms previously mentioned depend upon ciliated bands on the lophophores to carry food to the mouth. In acorn worms lophophores are aban-doned for an improved method; a current of water, produced by ciliary action, brings food particles directly into the mouth. On either side of the pharynx, or throat region, there are open-ings through which the water can pass out to the surface. Here we have the first strong indication that in these lower chordates we are dealing with vertebrate relatives (Figure 19-2); these openings are internal gill slits, structures which, apart from lower chordates, are found in no animals of any sort except vertebrates. In fishes the internal gills are the major breathing organs rather than food filters. In land vertebrates they are succeeded by lungs as breathing structures, but in every high vertebrate, including man, the primitive gill pouches occur invariably in the embryo although they are not functioning in the adult.

A third stage upward toward true vertebrates is seen in the little marine animals known as ascidians, tunicates, or sea squirts. They are usually attached and are frequently colonial but some-times free-floating. In these little animals this food-filtering device of gill slits is so highly developed that the greater part of the animal consists of a relatively enormous barrel, a "throat" region surrounded by a complex series of gill openings. This could have been an end type of the food-filtering animals, if it were not that in some tunicates there is a larval form, which

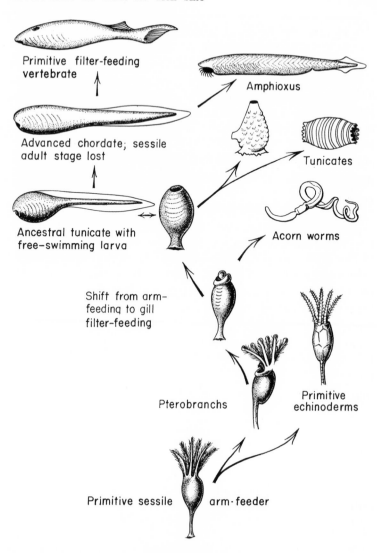

Primitive filter-feeding
vertebrate

Amphioxus

Advanced chordate; sessile
adult stage lost

Tunicates

Ancestral tunicate with
free-swimming larva

Acorn worms

Shift from arm-
feeding to gill
filter-feeding

Pterobranchs

Primitive
echinoderms

Primitive sessile arm-feeder

FIGURE 19–2.

Evolution of vertebrates from simple sessile primitive chordate ancestors.
At the stage of ancestral tunicates, there appears to have developed a
motile larva, from which arose the true vertebrates. (From A. S. Romer,
The Vertebrate Story, University of Chicago Press.)

was presumably present in tunicate ancestors and shows the initiation of a radically new evolutionary direction. In this larva there are structures that allow the little animal to swim about freely for a short time in tadpolelike fashion. In contrast to adult tunicates, this larva has a primitive brain and sense organs. Running down the back of the body is a nerve cord of the sort found in all true vertebrates. Beneath this nerve cord is a stout longitudinal structure, the notochord, which is present in the embryo of every vertebrate and is the predecessor of the backbone. In a modern tunicate this larva persists for only a few days or hours before settling down to become a degenerate adult form. But it seems quite certain that in some early Paleozoic stage, a larva of this sort persisted to become a sexually mature form, and thus began a new evolutionary series of active animals from which the vertebrates arose and forgot their lowly sessile ancestry. (See Figure 19-3.)

The oldest known vertebrates, which date from 400 million or so years back, in the Ordovician period of the Paleozoic era, had not actually progressed far beyond the stage seen in a tunicate tadpole, except that they had put on bony surface armor, presumably as a protection against invertebrate enemies. Like their lower chordate relatives, they were still filter feeders, obviously making a living by filtering food materials through an enormous pharynx.

These earliest vertebrates, termed ostracoderms, became extinct well before the end of the Paleozoic era. Their closest living descendants are the lampreys and hag fishes of modern waters. These forms are no longer filter feeders, as were their ancestors, but like them they lack the jaws characteristic of more advanced fishes. They have, however, invented something "equally effective" in evolving a rasping tongue, which enables them to bore into the flesh of other fishes upon which they feed.

Beyond this most primitive vertebrate stage, the major advance in the history of aquatic vertebrates was the development of biting jaws armed with teeth, which allowed the main stream of vertebrate evolution to become carnivores, living on large types of food and thus being able to abandon the primi-

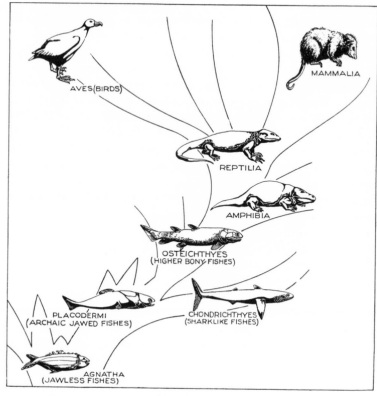

FIGURE 19-3.

A simplified "family tree" of the vertebrates. (From A. S. Romer, *The Vertebrate Story*, University of Chicago Press.)

tive and restrictive mode of life of the ancestral filter feeders. The exact way in which jaws came into the evolutionary story we do not yet know, but in the early Devonian period, well over 300 million years ago, there appeared in the ancient waters a great variety of fishes with well-developed jaws. Some of the early jaw-bearing forms (such as arthrodires, prominent in Devonian seas) have long since disappeared, but other groups have continued to flourish to the present day. Sharks appeared well before the end of the Devonian period, and continue to form a modest percentage of the present marine fish fauna.

From the sharks, apparently somewhat over 100 million years ago, developed the skates and rays, with flattened bodies and dentitions suitable for mollusc-crushing.

The most highly developed types of fishes are the forms usually termed the Osteichthyes, or bony fishes, not because bone was their exclusive property (it was present in many of the oldest known fishes) but because in most members of the group the internal skeleton was highly ossified in addition to their having a dermal armor of bony plates and scales. Although the sea was the home from which the fish ancestors came, it is probable that much of fish evolution, particularly that of the higher bony fishes, took place in fresh waters. In fact, of the three major divisions of the bony fishes, two have had little to do with the sea. The dipnoans, or lungfish, rare today, were abundant in lakes and streams in Paleozoic days, but few of them entered the sea. Somewhat similar has been the history of a second group, that of the Crossopterygii. This type of fish is of great interest because it gave rise to land vertebrates. But as fish, the typical crossopterygians, at first abundant in fresh waters, soon decreased in numbers and became extinct before the close of the Paleozoic era. Fossil evidence reveals that a specialized side branch of the crossopterygians, termed coelacanths, left the fresh waters early for the ocean. But the fossil record led us to believe that they had become extinct by the end of the days of the dinosaurs. Hence it was a matter of great scientific interest when, a few decades ago, a last coelacanth survivor, named *Latimeria*, was discovered in the deep waters of the western Indian Ocean.

Far different has been the history of the third group of bony fishes, termed the Actinopterygii, or ray-finned fishes, because their paired fins, unlike those of lungfishes or crossopterygians, have little flesh or skeleton in them but are, instead, mainly webs of skin stiffened by horny rays. In the earliest days of bony fish history they were relatively rare. Later, however, they increased rapidly in numbers and variety. Although, like other bony forms, they may have originated in fresh waters, they soon invaded the sea and have swarmed the ocean ever since making up the greatest part of the fish population. The modern representatives of this group, termed the teleosts, probably include 30,000 or so different species of marine fishes, and the number of individuals must run to many thousands of millions.

Let us now turn to the development of life on land. Plants, with animals following, invaded fresh waters and then dry land. Plants apparently progressed from the sea into inland waters by at least the Silurian period, about 400 million or so years ago, if not earlier, and by the following Devonian period had progressed so far that we know of fossil forests of those days. Animal progress toward and onto land, however, was not on so broad a front, for in general it is only active types that could enter fresh waters and withstand the constant downward flow of continental streams. Two animal groups that have made the most remarkable contributions to land life are the arthropods and vertebrates. Of the arthropods the outstanding invaders were the insects, which appeared during the Carboniferous era, the age of the coal swamps, and ever since have swarmed the world in countless numbers of species and individuals. Following then, came the vertebrates. From crossopterygian fishes there evolved the amphibians, still represented today by frogs, toads, and salamanders; from them descended the reptiles, and from reptiles, in turn, the birds and mammals that dominate the terrestrial scene today.

But although the reptiles, and their avian and mammalian descendants are fully competent to be purely terrestrial in habits, many of them returned to the seas. Among the ancient reptile forms now extinct, there developed a number of remarkable types that had returned to a life in the ocean, and even today there are such marine reptiles as turtles and the poisonous sea snakes of the Indian and Pacific oceans. Some birds, too, such as the penguins, are ocean dwellers. Mammals as well have felt the attraction of a marine life, and we find that a number of members of this group have reverted to the sea—whales and porpoises, sea cows, seals and walruses, and sea otters.

Man is a terrestrial animal (although with aspirations toward the sky) and quite surely will never revert to water dwelling.

But today scientists look longingly toward the ocean. Much of what goes on there, in both physical and biological aspects, is little better known to us land-dwellers than what goes on on other planets and distant stars. Exploration of the oceans can be of both scientific and material benefit to us. It is many hundreds of millions of years since our ancestors left the sea, but we long to become better acquainted again with our ancestral home and its plant and animal inhabitants.

20 PRODUCTIVITY OF ORGANIC MATTER IN THE OCEANS

John H. Ryther

Organic matter is produced in the sea, as on land, by the photosynthetic action of green, chlorophyll-bearing plants. We are all familiar with the organic producers of the land—the trees, grasses, the various cultivated crops, and so on. The larger marine plants—the seaweeds and sea grasses—are also well known to anyone living near the seashore. As is true with their terrestrial relatives, these aquatic plants must grow rooted or attached to the bottom. Since they require sunlight for their photosynthetic activity and since enough sunlight for this process can penetrate no more than about 100 meters of seawater (often as little as 10 meters if the waters are turbid), their occurrence is limited to an extremely narrow fringe around the very edge of the sea—a total area which is probably no more than 1 per cent of the total world ocean.

Not only are the larger aquatic marine plants relatively insignificant from the point of view of their total distribution and abundance but they are also ecologically of minor importance in the sea. Few animals feed directly upon them, and thus they are not major constituents of the so-called "food chains," which sustain the higher forms of marine life.

The source of life in the sea, the principal producers of organic matter are the community of microscopic, unicellular algae that occur in the surface waters of all the oceans of the world. Highly diverse in form, structure, and taxonomic position, these minute organisms, collectively known as the "phytoplankton," have the photosynthetic pigment, chlorophyll, in common and share with the higher plants on land and in the sea the ability to utilize solar energy in the photochemical reduction of carbon dioxide to organic matter.

Invisible to the naked eye, the very presence of these organisms, not to mention their critical role in the economy of the sea, goes largely unsuspected. Only in rare cases do they become abundant enough to produce a green, brown, or reddish discoloration of the water, the color depending upon the species present and its particular pigmentation. Certain species have the property of bioluminescence and may give a bluish-green phosphorescence to the sea. These visible manifestations of the phytoplankton are rare, however. Nevertheless, phytoplankton are present everywhere in the surface waters of the sea. There is no naturally occurring combination of temperature, salinity, or any other chemical or physical property of seawater to which a community of these micro-organisms is not adapted. The species that make up these plant associations are highly variable from one type of environment to another, but all occupy the same ecological niche of producing the organic matter of the sea.

As they are true plants and require sunlight for their photosynthetic activity, the phytoplankton are restricted to the surface layer of the ocean. Sufficient solar radiation of photosynthesis penetrates to no more than 100 meters in the clearest ocean water, as little as 10–20 meters in the more turbid coastal waters. Paradoxically, as the plants grow and their numbers increase, they absorb an increasingly large fraction of the incident solar radiation, thereby reducing its penetration into deeper water and cutting off their own light supply. In the most productive regions of the ocean, the phytoplankton are so dense that they absorb all of the incoming solar energy within the upper 5 meters or less. Thus the process of organic productivity is limited to an extremely thin layer of the sea surface, a volume of the order of $\frac{1}{100}$ that of the entire ocean.

In the process of photosynthesis, plants utilize solar energy in a complicated series of biochemical reactions to convert carbon dioxide and water to a simple carbohydrate, producing molecular oxygen as a by-product. In the terrestrial environment, the supplies of both carbon dioxide and water may be limiting to the growth and even, in some places like deserts, to the very existence of plants. This is not the case in the sea, where water is obviously no problem and where there is also a great reservoir of carbon dioxide in the form of dissolved carbonates and bicarbonates. Thus neither of these essential substances limit the production of organic matter in the sea. Other characteristics of the marine environment, however, may severely limit organic production, as we shall see.

As has been noted, light energy, water, and carbon dioxide are needed for the photosynthetic production of carbohydrate. However, plants are not made of carbohydrate alone. A whole host of chemical substances are needed for the metabolic conversion of the primary products of photosynthesis to the proteins, lipids, and other compounds that make up the stuff and substance of living organisms. Most of these essential plant nutrients are present in seawater in great excess of their needs, but a few elements such as nitrogen and phosphorus, and certain metals and organic growth factors needed only in trace amounts may be assimilated by the plants so completely that they become reduced to undetectable concentrations in the surface waters of the sea. When this occurs, further growth of the phytoplankton community and the production of organic matter become nutrient limited and may be almost completely arrested. Since organic production is restricted to the surface layers of the sea, as we have seen, nutrient depletion also is limited to this upper, illuminated or so-called euphotic zone.

As the phytoplankton or the animals that feed upon them die or as they excrete or otherwise eliminate waste products, this nonliving organic matter is quickly attacked and decomposed by bacteria and the essential nutrients are regenerated to a form in which they can again be utilized by the plants. In a closed system, this complete cycle can run indefinitely with photosynthesis proceeding continuously, though with no net production of new organic matter. But the productive part of the sea is not a closed system, since it overlies a vast reservoir of nonproductive deep water. Any organisms that sink or are carried out of the euphotic layer represent a net loss of organic matter together with its content of bound, essential nutrients. This loss may represent an extremely small fraction of the total organic production, but may, over a sufficiently long period of time, lead to the complete impoverishment of the surface waters. Clearly some mechanism must exist for returning nutrients from the depths into the euphotic layer or the sea would become sterile. Molecular diffusion across the existing concentration gradient is one such mechanism, but it is extremely slow and inefficient. Physical mixing of the water itself is far more effective, and it is mainly by this process that nutrients are restored to the surface layers of the sea. Vertical mixing, however, is a function of both hydrodynamic and meteorological conditions that are highly variable, seasonally and geographically. It is the variability of these physical factors, more than anything else, that cause some parts of the ocean to be extremely rich in marine life while others are virtually biological deserts.

In tropical seas, and in temperate regions during the summer months, solar radiation warms the surface waters and establishes a rather sharp temperature gradient between the surface and the colder, deeper water. Because the warm water is less dense than the cold water beneath it, this thermal stratification, once it is established, tends to persist and resist vertical mixing, even from the force of high winds and tropical storms. Under these conditions, nutrient-rich subsurface water is not readily transported up into the euphotic layer by physical mixing processes and, as a result, the surface layers are nutrient impoverished and maintain extremely low levels of organic productivity.

This impoverishment is a permanent characteristic of most tropical seas and explains why the major commercial fisheries of the world are not located in such regions, with a few notable exceptions. It also explains the clear blue color of tropical seas, which is simply a manifestation of the lack of planktonic life and organic matter in general.

In the temperate regions of the ocean, the type of thermal stratification just described is a seasonal phenomenon. In fall, when solar radiation decreases and the air temperature falls, the sea surface cools, and, through the action of winds, the waters become vertically mixed to considerable depths. These conditions persist throughout the winter and early spring with mixed, homogeneous water extending sometimes to depths of several hundreds of meters. Under these conditions, the nutrient levels of the surface waters are thoroughly and effectively replenished.

One might think that this situation would set the stage for vigorous growth of the phytoplankton. But now another factor becomes limiting to organic production. The unicellular algae are nonmotile or, at best, very weak swimmers that are carried passively by water movements, a characteristic for which the name "plankton," meaning "wanderer," was derived. The same mixing process that brings nutrient-rich water to the surface carries the light-dependent phytoplankton organisms down into the dark subsurface waters where photosynthetic production cannot take place. If continual wind mixing occurs between the surface and some intermediate depth, the organisms will of course spend some of their time in the euphotic layer. But if, for example, the mixed depth is ten times the depth of the euphotic zone, the plants will spend on an average only $\frac{1}{10}$ of their time in the light. This does not permit them to photosynthesize enough new organic matter to compensate for their own metabolic requirements, so that no net growth or production of organic matter can take place. This situation is aggravated by the fact that there is less incoming solar radiation in the winter months, thereby reducing the depth of the photosynthetic layer. The extreme example of this last factor is, of course, the polar winters where perpetual darkness precludes the possibility of any organic production irrespective of the vertical mixing effect or any other limiting factors.

In the temperate-polar regions where nutrients and light alternate seasonally as limiting factors of organic production, there is one brief period of the year when neither of these factors is critical. In spring, after the water has been well mixed and the nutrients restored to the surface layers, and when the water first begins to stabilize with the onset of thermal stratification, conditions become favorable for organic production. There then occurs a sudden outburst of phytoplankton growth which is known as the "spring bloom" or "spring flowering." The density of microorganisms may be so great at these times as to discolor the water. The bloom, however, is doomed to a short life of a few days, or at most, a week or two, for it depends entirely upon the supply of dissolved nutrients that have accumulated in the euphotic zone over the winter. Once this reservoir is exhausted, the supply from below is again cut off by thermal stratification and the resulting lack of mixing. Occasionally the spring bloom is intermittent and appears as several successive blooms if the weather is such that thermal stratification develops and breaks down several times during the spring. In general, however, this annual pulse of organic production is a short-lived phenomenon. It is nonetheless an important event in the annual cycle of biological activity, for as much organic matter may be produced in that brief period of activity as during the entire rest of the year. For this reason, the productivity of temperate and polar oceanic regions may be twice or more that of the permanently nutrient-impoverished tropical seas. That the latter do not become sterile is evident of the fact that some slight amount of mixing and diffusion of nutrients into the surface water does, in fact, take place, although it does so at an unmeasurable and undetectable rate.

It is clear from what has been said thus far that the open ocean is not a particularly favorable environment for the production of organic matter. In fact, almost the entire region beyond the edge of the continental shelf, an area representing nearly 90 per cent of the world ocean and well over half of the surface of the earth, can be well described as a biological desert. There are, to be sure, occasional "oases" of moderate to high productivity in this desert, and there are sparsely populated plant and animal communities that are adapted to live throughout this unproductive environment. But this vast oceanic area cannot, by any stretch of the imagination, be considered a major food resource, existing or potential, for a hungry world.

What, then, of the remaining 10 per cent of the ocean that

lies within the borders of the continental shelf? For several reasons it is considerably more productive than the open sea and, generally speaking, the more shallow the water the more productive it tends to be. For one thing, mixing often extends to the bottom in shallow coastal waters and brings the rich nutrient supply associated with bottom deposits into the photic layers. In addition, coastal currents and tidal action often prevent the development of thermal stratification in the summer months, thereby insuring a continual replenishment of nutrients during this favorable time of year. Finally, in shallow coastal regions, the water cannot be mixed vertically to great depths below the photic layer, so photosynthesis can and does occur throughout the year. On the average, the coastal zone within the boundaries of the continental shelf is five to ten times more productive than the open sea. Since the former is roughly one-tenth the area of the latter, this means that nearly as much organic matter is produced in coastal waters as in the rest of the ocean.

In view of the concentration of biological activity within this small and shallow area, it is not surprising that the major commercial fisheries of the world are also concentrated on the shelves and banks of the nearshore environment. It is not just a matter of convenience or economics or sea-keeping ability that keeps the fishing fleets close to land—experience has shown that this is where the fish are.

One particular type of near-shore environment, the coastal region of the world where there are strong and persistent off-shore winds, deserves special mention here. These winds and the associated currents carry surface water away from the shore. Since a hole cannot persist in the sea surface, this water is replaced by nutrient-rich subsurface water from beneath the euphotic layer and this water, in turn, enters into the surface circulation. In these coastal upwelling systems, as they are called, a continual supply of rich water is thus brought into and retained within the shallow, photosynthetic surface layer. These are the most productive regions of the ocean—perhaps 100 times more productive per unit of area than the open sea. Indeed they are among the most productive regions on earth, rivaled only by the most intensively cultivated and heavily fertilized land crops.

The most well-developed areas of coastal upwelling occur on the west coasts of continents just north and south of the equator, where the system is driven by the Trade Winds—the most persistently prevailing winds of the world. Of these the most familiar and by far the most productive is the coastal upwelling system off Peru. The incredible growth of phytoplankton in this one small area, no more than 800 miles long and less than 50 miles wide, gives rise to an annual harvest of 10 million tons of anchovies—20 per cent of the total commercial fish landings of the world.

Other centers of upwelling associated with the Trade Wind system are located on the west coasts of the United States and Mexico and both the northwest and southwest coasts of Africa. In the Arabian Sea, coastal upwelling occurs in connection with the monsoon winds, and its geographical location changes with the direction of this reversing wind system. There is also a large but poorly defined and poorly understood region of upwelling off the Antarctic Continent. The high organic productivity of this region gives rise to dense populations of Antarctic krill—small, shrimplike creatures—which in times past provided the food for the once-tremendous herds of whales that man has all but made extinct. The high productivity of this region is, of course, limited to the summer months, since no photosynthesis can take place in the perpetual darkness of the Antarctic winter.

There are numerous other regions of upwelling in the sea—mostly small, local phenomena but some rather extensive in size—that are not necessarily coastal in location or associated with offshore wind systems. These may be caused by a variety of hydrodynamic features such as, for example, the divergence of two adjacent surface currents flowing in opposite directions and acted upon by the Coriolis effect or the turbulence produced when a prevailing surface current flows over a region of shoal water or through an island group. In every case, the effect is to bring nutrient-rich subsurface water into the photo-synthetic zone and thereby stimulate organic production. These scattered regions of off-shore upwelling are much less productive than the regions of coastal upwelling. In terms of annual productivity, they are comparable to the coastal waters.

Until quite recently, we had no reliable method of quantitatively measuring the rate of production of organic matter in the sea. In 1952 the Danish oceanographer, Einer Steemann Nielsen, developed a method whereby the rate of uptake of carbonate by phytoplankton—in other words the rate of photosynthesis—can be measured under natural or simulated natural conditions by using a radioactive carbon tracer technique. This method is both highly sensitive and easily adaptable to routine oceanographic exploration and it was quickly adapted by all of the major oceanographic laboratories of the world. In the intervening years, a considerable body of information on the productivity of all the major oceans has been accumulated.

The total productivity of the oceans is now estimated to be about 5×10^{10} tons of dry organic matter per year—a large and almost incomprehensible number. To put it in its proper perspective, one must also consider the size of the ocean. Almost exactly the same figure has been derived quite independently for the productivity of the land—an area roughly one-quarter the size. The average productivity for the sea is a little better than one ton of dry organic matter per hectare per year, certainly not very impressive when compared to the best agricultural yields of 25 to 50 tons per hectare per year.

But averages can be quite misleading in such a large and highly variable system as the ocean. As was mentioned earlier, the open sea, with some justification, can be considered a biological wasteland while the productivity of small, localized areas of coastal upwelling may equal that of the most intensively cultivated land crops on earth.

A small amount of the organic matter produced as unicellular algae at the surface of the sea is excreted by the microorganisms as dissolved organic compounds which are quickly attacked and decomposed by bacteria. A small fraction of the cells sink out of the euphotic layer and die and decompose in the deep water or on the bottom. An even smaller fraction may become incorporated as organic constituents of the bottom sediments. Generally speaking, the more shallow the water the greater is the fraction of the organic production that reaches the bottom. Petroleum deposits, for example, are believed to have originated in shallow coastal regions probably of exceptionally high productivity, such as the upwelling areas that have been described.

These losses of organic matter by excretion, natural death, and sedimentation, taken together, are probably very small—at most a few per cent of the total production. It is the fate of most of the phytoplankton in the sea to be eaten. In the open ocean, the consumers of phytoplankton are tiny grazing animals of many different kinds, known collectively as the "zooplankton." In shallow coastal waters, the cells that sink to the bottom are, for the most part, eaten by a wide variety of bottom organisms. Some species of fish, like the menhaden and anchovy, are especially adapted to filter the unicellular algae directly from the water.

The details of the complex "food-web" of the sea, which leads from the phytoplankton—the pastures of the sea—through the herbivorous animals that graze on the plants, and ultimately to the predators that feed on the grazers and upon each other, will be the subject of Chapter 21. It is sufficient to say here that, with the exception of the small losses from excretion, natural death, and sedimentation, the plants and animals of the sea are in a steady state of dynamic equilibrium. Most of the organic matter and the entrained essential nutrient materials are rapidly recycled through the animal populations, regenerated to the inorganic form by bacterial action, and again made available to the plants.

In the terrestrial environment, many of the most important organic producers, such as trees, accumulate their organic matter for many years with no appreciable loss to predation. It has been estimated that the standing crop of living terrestrial plant material present at any one time on earth is of the order of 10^{12} tons. Despite the fact that the annual rate of production of organic matter in the sea is roughly the same as that on land, no such organic accumulation occurs in the oceans of the world. The standing crop of marine vegetation is probably never in excess of about 10^9 tons, one thousand times less than that of the land.

The explanation of this difference clearly lies in the rapid turnover of the marine as compared to the terrestrial organic matter. This is an important distinction to keep in mind when considering the productivity of the sea which is measured by short-term tracer experiments of a few hours or at most a day. Annual rates of production are then calculated from these measurements, which may have to be repeated several times a year if pronounced seasonal variations occur. But what is the significance of the annual production of organic matter in a system in which the material is almost completely recycled every few weeks? It is much like the distinction between annual income—the total of the weekly paychecks—and annual savings. In our eagerness to fully exploit the food resources of the sea, man may quickly overdraw nature's bank account if we are not careful in our interpretation of the organic economics of the sea.

21 THE FOOD WEB OF THE SEA

Gordon Riley

The casual observer, looking out over the ocean, sees a green or gray or blue wasteland, seemingly barren of life. It is hard to believe that there is active life hidden away in this ocean—that the ocean is very nearly as productive as the land—but this is so.

The general pattern of life in the sea is basically like what is found on the land. Green plants are the primary producers of food in the sea. Animals in the sea eat the plants and are in turn eaten by other animals, and bacteria use up the organic remains. The needs of the green plants for sunlight and fertilizing nutrients are much the same as those of land plants, and the cycling of mineral elements through the system is similar.

However, the differences between land and sea plants often seem more striking than their basic similarities. The most important green plants are primitive poor relations of our highly developed land plants—algae, so-called—of microscopic size, which have a free-floating existence in the surface layers of the oceans. Lacking a microscope, we have no awareness of their presence except as a greenish or brownish discoloration of the water in places in which they are relatively abundant.

An important thing to realize about the growth of green plants in the sea is that they require light in order to grow, just as land plants do, and the depth of penetration of sunlight in the sea is distinctly limited. The maximum limit of growth of sea plants is thus 300–400 feet, and is often less. One consequence of this is that kelp and other large algae that are attached to the sea bottom only grow in shallow coastal waters. There they are more productive as well as more conspicuous than the microscopic floating forms. However, the latter are at least ten times more important in any over-all consideration of oceanic productivity, for they grow everywhere in the surface layer of the ocean rather than being limited to the shallow margins of the sea.

The term "plankton," literally meaning "the wanderers," applies to the small floating life of the sea that has little power of locomotion and simply drifts where ocean currents take it. The little algae are called phytoplankton, and an associated population of animals is known as zooplankton. Most of the latter are quite small, although a few larger animals such as prawns and jellyfish are logically included under this term. One of the most common members of the zooplankton is a small and primitive relative of the prawns, known as the copepod. Most species of copepods are less than a tenth of an inch long, and most of them feed primarily upon phytoplankton. Their mouthparts have hairlike growths that interlock, forming a little filter basket that serves to sieve out phytoplankton cells from the water.

The zooplankton population as a whole consists of many different kinds of animals, most of which feed on phytoplankton and have some kind of mechanism for concentrating these small cells, which are rather thinly dispersed through the water. Some phytoplankton, to be sure, are carnivorous, and some are capable either of indiscriminant filtering of phytoplankton or selective capture of larger organisms.

The zooplankton is eaten by herring and other small fishes and by many other animals, who are in turn caught by larger fishes. The larger animals have no means of capturing the microscopic phytoplankton, and a series of predations serve to package the food into bite-size morsels for successively larger animals.

In the older oceanographic literature one sometimes sees the term "food chain," a general term for the chain of predations that has just been described, in which phytoplankton is consumed by herbivorous zooplankton, and the latter in turn by a first level of carnivores; they are consumed by larger carnivores, and so on. This concept has served a useful purpose in its time, but it is a distinctly oversimplified picture of the food relations that exist in the sea. Few animals are so limited in their diet that they can be assigned to a rigid, arbitrary level in the food chain. Things are more complex and interwoven than that. Hence another catch phrase—"food web"—has largely replaced the older term "food chain," as being a more accurate description of the complex food relations that exist in the sea.

Almost any animal in the sea feeds on a variety of creatures and often on markedly different kinds of creatures at different stages in its life history. The codfish can be regarded as an example. A mature codfish is primarily a fish eater, and by the older way of looking at things, one would say that there are at least four steps in the food chain between phytoplankton and codfish. However, it really is not that way. A codfish egg hatches into a larva that begins to feed upon phytoplankton and zooplankton. Later it goes to the bottom and begins to feed on small bottom animals. A codfish of moderate size has a varied diet of bottom invertebrates and small fishes, and frequently it swims up well above the bottom to capture some of the larger zooplankton. The fish-eating habit becomes more pronounced as the codfish becomes older. However, on heavily fished commercial grounds there are few of these large, old fish. The majority of the commercial catch consists of fish which have been supported during their growing period by all of the so-called food chain levels and which are still eating a variety of foods.

Part of the food that an animal eats is used for its body growth; another and larger proportion must be used up in supplying the energy for basal metabolism and movements in search of food. The growth efficiency of an animal—that is, the proportion of its total food consumption that goes into tissue building—is seldom more than 10–20 per cent, and may be less in the case of old and slow-growing animals. Thus, the productivity of a predator population is limited to a small fraction of the production of the prey on which it feeds.

This basic fact of life is well known and is the obvious reason why land-produced animal protein is scarcer and more costly than vegetable products. In the ocean, with its complex food relationships, the disparity is likely to be even greater between basic plant production and any animals that are large enough to provide useful food for people. There are exceptions to this, as there are to almost any broad generalizations that one makes about a subject as complex as the ocean. However, the fact is that most of the great commercial fisheries of the world have been based on fish stocks that have a very low rate of production compared with basic plant production.

Let us suppose that we have an oceanic area that is capable of producing a quantity of phytoplankton amounting to 300 grams of dry organic matter per square meter of sea surface in a year, or about 600 pounds per acre. This is about average for the ocean. There are considerable regional variations in productivity; some areas are more and some are less productive than this. Of course phytoplankton is continuously being produced and continually being consumed by zooplankton, just as cows graze the grass in a pasture as fast as it grows. If the growth efficiency of the zooplankton is 10 per cent or somewhat higher, we can suppose that zooplankton production might be about 60–100 pounds per acre in a year. On up the "ladder" of the ocean's food web are the herringlike fishes that feed upon zooplankton and the larger fish such as tuna and cod that prey upon small fish. At each step, according to the old food chain concepts, there would be another tenfold reduction in productivity. Modern concepts of food webs would indicate that the reduction is less extreme than this. In the few cases that have been carefully examined food webbing can shorten the so-called food chain by about half a step, which means that the production through several steps can be about five times as much as would be indicated by the older estimates. Even so, the computed production of cod or tuna is less than 1 per cent of the basic plant productivity.

This discussion may seem of little interest except to specialists, but from it come some important practical considerations. At a time when the world desperately needs more protein food, we have to take a close, hard look at what the ocean has to give us. We cannot assume that marine resources are unlimited, nor is a given area of ocean likely to yield as much food, on the average, as an equivalent land area. Neither the oceans nor the land can support an unlimited increase in world population. The present population increase must be slowed down by other means, and hopefully by more intelligent and humane methods than wholesale starvation.

On the other hand we must do our utmost to increase the yield of marine foods. In order to do this we must understand something about marine productivity, and we must go along with nature and operate within the edicts of the natural food web. It is important to find out more about production efficiencies in order to help us determine what the yield of a particular fishery is likely to be and how much fishing effort should be put into it. Detailed information of this kind cannot be obtained easily; however, some of the general food-web concepts can be put to immediate use.

One rather simple basic premise is that in order to get a maximum yield we should operate as closely as possible to the primary levels of production, where the efficiencies of production are relatively high. Furthermore, we must not take such a large harvest that it seriously depletes the population although if we operate close to the primary level, the return may be high enough so that we can afford to put some effort into artificial cultivation in order to maintain the stock.

Some guidelines for marine culture have already been laid down. The Japanese have been leaders in this kind of endeavor, although to single out one people is perhaps unfair to others who have also made significant progress along these lines. Certain marine algae are used directly in the Japanese diet, and the artificial propagation and culture of these algae has reached the state of a fine art. In Japan, and elsewhere, the harvesting of marine algae is becoming more and more important, both for direct food use and as processed food additives.

A few herbivorous marine animals such as oysters, clams, and mussels have been important items in man's diet since prehistoric days. Unfortunately, natural oyster beds are not equal to the strain of intensive harvesting by modern methods. However, artificial culture can give enormous yields; partly because they are low in the hierarchy of life in the sea and hence are relatively efficient in production. Also, artificial plots are established in areas where tides and currents provide a continuous flow of water, so that a continuous supply of plankton food sweeps through the area. Thus, in effect, such plots collect the basic production of a much larger area. And finally, methods have been developed for culturing these organisms in racks well off the bottom, thus protecting them from starfish and other bottom-crawling predators.

One might ask at this point why we do not harvest plankton directly rather than getting oysters to do it for us, thereby losing a major part of the potential food. Aside from the fact that oysters taste better, the answer lies in economics and technology rather than biology. We have no simple, cheap method of catching food of microscopic size. In this respect we are only slightly better off than the codfish. The energy required to filter a usable amount of plankton from the water is much more costly than the value of the product. Until the efficiency of our own technology improves, we must leave that task to nature.

A few other types of artificial culture of marine organisms have been developed, although further study and experimentation are needed. Our shallow coastal waters and embayments are more productive than most open seas areas. Here the development of artificial culture methods can vastly increase the yield of marine food.

The most productive fishes are the ones that are close to the primary source of production—namely, the plankton feeders. One of these, the menhaden, provides the basis for one of our most productive fisheries. It is a remarkable fish in that its gill rakers are so fine that it can feed directly on phytoplankton. Most of the other herringlike fishes are zooplankton feeders, but they too are much closer to the basic source of supply than are the larger carnivores. This does not mean, however, that we should not continue to take what we can of cod, haddock, and the many other important commercial stocks that are relatively inefficient producers. However, the development of new fisheries for plankton feeders has been mainly responsible for the large increase in the world fish catch that has been achieved during the last two decades, and further developments along these lines are needed.

These are a few of the immediate applications of food-web principles. Admittedly the investigation of food-web problems has not got very far beyond first principles. The number of species and life habits is so large and their relationships so complex that we do not have very precise knowledge of what eats what or of the rates of production or production efficiencies. Oceaographers continue to work on these problems, mainly out of scientific curiosity but also with the feeling that this kind of knowledge is essential in order to make the most of our marine resources.

The evaluation of any commerical fishery is a most amazingly complex problem. There are, to begin with, large variations from year to year in the number of young fish that are produced. Most of these fishes are temporary members of the plankton for a brief period after hatching. It is a critical period during which they are an easy prey for larger animals and are at the mercy of winds and currents that may sweep them far away from any area that is suitable for their later development. The size of a given year-class is likely to depend more on chance events during this early critical period than on the size of the parent stock.

At a later stage the problems of survival of the growing fish are less severe but there are still predators to contend with along with competition for the available food, and frequent fluctuations in the abundance of certain food species. It is no exaggeration to say that the whole food web must be examined in order to understand the problems of any one of the component species.

The food webs are, of course, very different in different parts of the ocean. Phytoplankton and zooplankton occur everywhere, differing only with respect to species composition and relative abundance. The larger animals in the food web differ more. For example, the populations that develop in shallow coastal waters are vastly different from the ones found in the open ocean where the depth of water is several miles.

In a coastal area where the depth of water is little more than the zone of active growth of phytoplankton, some of the phytoplankton will sink to the bottom, and zooplankton will also be found in the vicinity of the bottom. There is an abundance of food to nourish a variety of bottom animals. One finds a large population of clams, worms, shrimp, and other crustacea, and many other invertebrates on these shallow bottoms. Some of these animals are adapted to filter plankton from the water just above the bottom; others scrape off the surface layer of the sediment, which is rich with the organic remains of recently deposited plankton. Still others burrow through the sediments, feeding indiscriminantly as earthworms do. Some bacteria exist everywhere in the ocean, and are particularly abundant in bottom sediments. They obtain a share of the organic remains, and in turn provide food for sediment feeders. And finally, fishes and carnivorous invertebrates prey upon the other bottom animals.

As indicated earlier, about 10 to 20 per cent of the food that is eaten will be utilized in animal growth. Most of the remainder is burned to supply energy for metabolic processes, and waste materials are excreted. Such things as phosphate and ammonia are waste materials as far as animals are concerned, but they are fertilizers for the growth of green plants. Thus the animals and bacteria use the organic matter produced by green plants and turn back excess mineral nutrients for reuse by green plants, and this keeps the wheels of the system turning.

There are wheels within wheels. A small part of the waste

products of the animals are simple organic compounds such as amino acids, which can be used directly by the bacteria for cell growth, and they in turn can be eaten by animals. A fraction of the organic matter produced during phytoplankton growth is also liberated as dissolved organic substances that similarly can be used by bacteria. Moreover, it has been demonstrated experimentally that these dissolved substances are adsorbed on bubbles and converted into particles of about the size of phytoplankton cells, and other experiments have shown that the particles so produced with support the growth of filter feeding animals. There is little doubt that this process of particle formation can occur naturally wherever breaking waves produce foam and subsurface bubbles, but as yet we have little knowledge of the relative importance of these phenomena.

Obviously we are dealing with a very complex system, which has gradually evolved through geological ages in such a way that every creature in it is in competition with other creatures for the essentials of life, but at the same time, through its processes of activity and growth and death, is providing things that are essential for the well-being of other creatures. It is precisely this combination of survival of the fittest and the presence of a variety of creatures of complementary requirements that make it a stable and enduring system.

In these respects the biological system of coastal waters is no different from that of the open ocean, but the latter has evolved in some interestingly different ways. Whereas in coastal water the whole population lives together in a fairly shallow depth of water, the open ocean has an average depth of about two and a half miles and a maximum depth of nearly seven miles. All of the phytoplankton production takes place in the upper few hundred feet, and most of it is consumed there. However, some phytoplankton and organic remains sink into deeper water, and there are animals feeding on these remains and on each other. Directly or indirectly, through the complexities of the food web, there is some food available at all depths in the sea although it is all ultimately dependent upon surface production. Thus one finds animals and bacteria in the ocean deeps and on the bottom, far from the original source of food supply. Food consumption by these organisms leads to the release of inorganic nutrients that tend to accumulate in fairly large concentrations in deep water. They serve no useful purpose until they can be transferred back to the surface layer where they can again be used in phytoplankton growth. The return of these nutrients to the surface by mixing processes tends to be slower than in the shallow waters. In general, the wheels of the cycle in the deep sea turn very slowly, and the productivity of the open ocean generally is less than that of the coastal zone, although a few special exceptions could be cited.

The surface layer of the open ocean has the usual assemblage of phytoplankton, zooplankton, and bacteria. There are also plankton eating fishes such as the herrings, mackerel, and flying fishes, and larger predators such as tunas, marlin, and sharks. This near-surface population extends down a little deeper than the maximum limit of phytoplankton growth, but 1,000 feet is about its limit. It intergrades into the so-called middepth population, which has a different species composition and a distinctive behavior pattern.

The middepth group includes copepods and other crustaceans, small fishes, and lesser numbers of a variety of other organisms. During the daytime these animals can be found at depths of the order of 1,000 to 3,000 feet, near the limits of penetration of natural light into the water. At sunset they move up toward the surface and return to deep water in the early morning.

The smaller members of this population are plankton eaters, and undoubtedly they can feed more effectively in the surface layer than at their daytime level, although small amounts of food are available for them at middepths. Organic particles sinking from the surface layer contain some usable food, and are colonized by bacteria, algae, and small animals. These middepth algae are, of course, well below the zone of active plant growth, but they are able to exist by absorbing dissolved organic matter in much the same way that bacteria do. This population of very small organisms is more abundant than has been realized until fairly recently. Even so, it appears to be a minor source of food for filter feeders as compared with surface populations.

The larger animals at middepths are mainly carnivorous, feeding on smaller members of the middepth population as well as on surface forms at night. Most of this population as we know it consists of small fishes, squid, and prawns. There may be larger animals that we know nothing about because they are swift enough to elude our nets. We know that there are giant squid at middepths that are eaten by deep-diving sperm whales, but they have never been caught in middepth trawls. There may be other large animals that remain unknown.

There have been estimates that of the total food production of the sea, about 75 per cent is used up by the near-surface populations and perhaps another 20 per cent by the middepth animals, leaving only about 5 per cent or less for the ocean deeps and the bottom populations. These figures may not be completely accurate, as precise estimates are difficult to make, but certainly the ocean deeps have a very sparse population. Again the major components are copepods, prawns, and fishes, but it is a different group of species from those found at middepths. Most of these deepwater forms appear to be adapted to a carnivorous life, eating each other and any dead bodies that come down to them from above. The scarcity of food is epitomized by amazing adaptations that permit these fish to accommodate to any food that is available. Some of them have great jaws and expandible bellies that permit them to engulf an animal that is literally as large as they are. Even mating is a problem in this scantily populated world. There is an angler fish in which the male is a tiny creature that attaches itself to the female and becomes parasitic upon her, ensuring fertilization at a time when her eggs are ripe, but performing no other function.

We really know almost nothing about the life habits of these deep-sea creatures except what can be inferred from the structure of captured specimens. Some of the copepods have mouth parts which imply a filter feeding habit, or, more likely, they combine filter feeding with a selective capture of larger particles. However, a large proportion have grasping claws rather than filter baskets, implying carnivorous feeding.

Plankton tows in the deep sea generally catch a significant quantity of dead organisms. This is not ordinarily the case with surface collections. Animals in the deep sea that die of starvation or old age are not likely to be found and eaten immediately, because the living animals are so sparsely distributed. Hence these dead animals, sinking into deeper water, are a means of distributing food to deeper layers and can supply nourishment to larger animals at the deeper layers that capture them.

Particles of nonliving organic matter that are present in the deep sea and colonized by a small population of algae and bacteria, are a possible source of food for small animals. These particles are commonly supposed to be detrital remains of surface living organisms, sinking slowly toward the bottom. The total quantity of these particles in the deep sea is large—considerably in excess of the amount of organic matter in living organisms—but the concentration per unit volume of sea water is small, and the quality is poor. Indeed some oceanographers have assumed that this material is completely unusable as food; however, laboratory tests with digestive enzymes indicate that at least 20 per cent of it might be usable.

Experiments also have shown that particles can form spontaneously in sea water and can grow by gradual accretion of smaller particles and dissolved substances. This is a process that could and probably does take place in the ocean, and it is conceivable that some or most of the particulate matter found in the deep sea has developed there rather than being derived directly from the surface layer. However, this is another question that does not yet have an answer.

The bacteria of the deep sea are largely found in association with these organic particles and may derive sustenance from them or from amino acids or other dissolved organic matter. Such substances are known to be present in amounts that will support that kind of life habit, but only marginally. In turn these organisms can supply some sustenance to animals. This food web of the deep sea probably is nearly as complicated as that of the surface layer and is much more difficult to study. The food requirements and behavior of deep-sea organisms are still relatively unknown, and there is no easy way of observing these creatures in their normal environment nor of creating an artificial environment for them that is sufficiently like their own world for good experimentation. There are complicated interrelationships between organisms and nonliving organic matter that we are only beginning to learn.

The last leavings of the food web sink to the bottom of the deep sea. Present indications are that something of the order of 1 per cent of surface production is deposited on the deep-sea floor, and if that is true, the surprising thing is that so much of the surface production survives the manipulations of the food web in the miles that intervene between the surface and bottom of the sea. Part of the reason for this is simply that the food supply in the deep sea is so scanty and so poor in quality that it does not support a population large enough to use it up before it reaches the bottom.

The material that is sedimented on the deep sea floor is the same kind that is observed in the water column above—organic particles and animal remains. Collected and concentrated on the bottom, it is more vulnerable to attack by both animals and bacteria than in its thinly dispersed condition in the water column. It supports a population of bacteria and sediment feeders that is considerably more abundant than the population in the water column above the bottom, although hardly a thousandth as much as the rich assemblage that one finds on shallow ocean bottoms. The bottom population in the deep sea also includes carnivores and sometimes filter feeders. Although the total quantity is not large, it is highly diverse as to species. Many of the smaller forms have not been fully described and classified as yet. The reason for this species diversity is a problem that biologists are still struggling with. We find this diversity in places where the environment is very stable—places as different as warm, tropical surface waters and the cold depths of the deep sea. Most biologists think that the presence of a large number of species in an environment is a natural evolutionary development in any place where conditions are constant enough to permit it, and that this kind of species diversity has real evolutionary significance, in making the population more resistant to any disturbing influences, such as the climatic changes associated with the glacial periods. However, there are places such as the Arctic Ocean, where conditions are reasonably constant and yet in which the animal population is quite limited in species number. One highly respected marine biologist has proposed the idea that the Arctic Ocean is quite new, geologically speaking, and has not had time for evolutionary development to reach its climax. This may be so, although the available evidence is not completely convincing.

In terms of sheer volume, the deep sea is the largest biological environment on earth and the one that we understand the least. It is an environment of near-freezing temperatures and eternal darkness except for occasional flashes of the luminous organs of some of its inhabitants. These creatures exist despite near-starvation conditions and enormous pressure caused by the weight of the overlying mass of water. We know little about pressure effects or the kinds of adaptations that animals must make in order to live in that kind of environment. The basic principles of the food web are still a matter of debate, and the deep-sea creatures themselves are still imperfectly known. Probably there are many kinds of animals in the deep sea that have never been captured. If there are large, swift ones, they have thus far eluded our nets. The deep-sea fishes that we know are monstrous in appearance, but they are tiny monsters less than a foot long. It is amusing to note, though, that a Danish expedition of some years ago captured an eel larva about four feet long, and it is amusing to speculate as to what size the adult would be.

The deep sea is the last great oceanographic frontier, and its mysteries are intriguing to layman and scientist alike. Investigation of the deep sea is not likely to yield anything of practical value in the way of food resources, yet it would be remarkable indeed if the study of such an unusual way of life did not uncover biological principles that would be valuable to us in one way or another, to enable us to gain a better understanding of the problems of life on our earth. That, after all, is the mission of scientists. We pursue knowledge out of curiosity. However, most of us, in this modern world, also work in the hope that our research will be of some use to a world that needs much help.

22 FISHERIES OF THE WORLD

Wilbert McLeod Chapman

From the dawn of history man has taken part of his food from the waters, and particularly from the ocean. Kitchen middens, some as old as 10,000 years, mark the sites of long-forgotten villages where Paleolithic man gathered clams, mussels, fish, and other sea animals, leaving their bones and shells in the mounds of kitchen refuse that marked his passage.

There has been an unprecedented growth in man's use of living resources from the world's waters since the end of World War II. World fish landings have tripled in that brief period and were more than 65 million metric tons in 1968. The value of landings at the fisherman's level (about $10 billion per year) is much greater than that of all other resources taken from the ocean put together, including oil and gas. Tonnage landed has increased at a rate of about 6 per cent per year for the last twenty years—a rate of increase that should continue until the end of this century because the resources are available and the demand continues to grow.

While living resources are harvested from most waters, the ocean produces by far the greater amount, and marine fish dominate production. Roughly speaking 90 per cent of fish and shellfish are taken from the ocean, or as they come out of the ocean to the rivers to spawn. This has been so since world records began to be kept, and the percentage of fish taken from the ocean is likely to increase a little as time goes on.

THE FRESH WATERS

Although fresh-water fish production has remained a relatively small and stable percentage of the total world catch for a long time, it is an important element of the protein food supply in several sections of the world where it is particularly needed. In all of the Far East, from Japan around to West Pakistan, aquaculture in ponds of all sorts, ranging from rice-paddies to temple ponds, is an important provider of animal protein for the human diet. Aquaculture is practiced in particularly sophisticated and productive manners in Taiwan, Mainland China, Java, and the Philippines (as well as Thailand), where the fertilization of ponds, and the use of several sorts of fish in the same pond, often brings production per hectare to a relatively high level.

Although there is much scope for increases from freshwater pond-culture, aquaculture is by no means a panacea for the world's protein needs. It is quite sophisticated animal husbandry, and does not respond well in the hands of people who are not disciplined to the care of animals. Its production cost is rather high and its semiluxury products do not reach the very poor unless they live close to the area of production so that transportation, processing, and marketing costs are minimal. Aquaculture also tends to compete with other crops for the use of land, as well as for the use of water, which limits the potential area for its economic use.

THE NATURE OF FOOD FROM THE OCEAN

The production of food from the ocean begins, as it does on land, from plants and their ability to synthesize living matter from inorganic salts, water, and the energy derived from sunlight. The difference is that plant production in the ocean is predominantly in the form of single cell plankton of microscopic size that does not yield seed, root, or fiber crops as do the multicelled plants.

The ocean does produce considerable volumes of multi-celled land plants including some rather large plants, such as the kelps and algaes of the near-shore area. These are grown by aquaculture in large volume in Japan and Korea where certain kinds are used more or less as a condiment in direct human consumption. Others are gathered in large volume in the United States, Canada, Western Europe and elsewhere, and are manufactured into products that go into a wide variety of food and other use products, but their main contribution is their ability to assist in forming gels rather than their nutritive qualities. But the relative importance of these large plants is very small compared to that of the microscopic plant plankton that collectively produce about 2,500 times more than all of the larger kelps put together.

The one-celled plankton usually are not large enough to be seen individually by the human eye, but they are often so abundant that they color acres of ocean red, brown, green, or yellow. Even where they are in such enormous quantities, their dry-weight volume is such a tiny fraction of the total weight of the water mass in which they are included that no serious student of the ocean anticipates that they will be the object of economic harvest in the foreseeable future. The energy cost of removing them from the water is entirely out of line with the value of any product that could be made from them. Besides, single cell algae can be cultured in volume ashore on such abundant and cheap substrates as agricultural wastes, sulphate paper plant wastes, petroleum, and the like, at much lower cost for equivalent nutrition value. Lastly, man cannot digest those plants any better than he can grass; his digestive system is of the wrong sort.

Thus the enormous plant production of the ocean is not of much use to man until it is concentrated into larger sized pieces that can be economically harvested. This is done for him by animals, and the result is mainly animal protein and edible oils, although considerable and useful quantities of some vitamins are also produced. The smallest sized animals that man presently harvests from the ocean are about 2 centimeters long and large volume production is presently made on animals about 10 centimeters long or longer. Although this animal production in the ocean includes the blue and sperm whales, which are the largest animals that have ever lived on earth, by far the greatest volume of animal production in the ocean is naturally of organisms less than 2 centimeters long and thus smaller than man can presently harvest and use in an economic manner.

Thus mankind must continue to depend indefinitely on the production of land plants for the bulk of the calories in its diet, the carbohydrates secured from land crops. From the ocean man can only expect increased crops of animal protein and edible animal oils, in addition to minor quantities of vitamins and other odds and ends. It happens that low cost, large volume sources of animal protein are what man now needs, and thus ocean food production assumes a greater prominence than heretofore.

THE CHANGING USES OF AQUATIC FOODS

The basic trouble with fish and shellfish as foods is that they spoil rapidly after the animal's death, and quickly lose that "sea flavor," which is their chief gustatory quality if they are not promptly preserved in some fashion. This has nothing to do with the nutritive value of fish because the proteins that form the main part of their nutritive value are only slightly changed even in rather badly spoiled fish, and can be recovered from the latter rather cheaply.

But it is taste, appearance, and texture that give fish and shellfish their prime commercial value and these qualities are evanescent. No sooner is the animal dead than its own enzymes begin digesting it, its own bacteria begin to decompose it, and the highly unsaturated oils of its body begin to oxygenate and become rancid. There are few foods that bring higher prices than fresh lobsters, shrimp, crab, salmon, tuna, and sole, because of their fine taste, appearance, and texture; on the other hand, there is hardly anything less appetizing than a stale fish.

Fish and shellfish, thus, have been marketed in a fresh state or in a number of traditional preserved conditions, such as pickled, dried, salted, and cured. Even as recently as 1938, 80 per cent of the world's fish production was in these forms, and another 7 per cent of fish used for canning.

Historically, fresh fish could only be marketed along the coast close to the centers of production, although during the last generation shelf life has been extended for a few days in countries where ice has been plentiful and cheap, and transportation into the interior was both cheap and easily available. Fish preserved in the traditional ways for later use could be kept for some months and thus transported into the interior, or even in world trade (dried and salted cod, for instance). But the taste and form of the preserved product was different from that of the fresh, and these preserved forms had a limited market appeal. Even their consumption was highest in coastal areas where they formed the off-season animal protein part of the diet. The canning of fish preserves them indefinitely, but it is rather costly and thus restricts the market. In many parts of the world the cost of the can is actually higher than the cost of the fish raw material included in it.

With the spread of freezing and cold-storage facilities to all levels of the food chain, from the fishing vessel to the consumer's kitchen (whether restaurant or home), frozen fish and shellfish maintaining a good resemblance to the taste, texture, and appearance of the ocean-fresh product can be stored for months without serious deterioration in many cases and transported with ease to the interior of large land masses. Thus the use of frozen fish in the world has gone up from substantially zero in 1938 to 5 per cent of world production in 1948, and a little more than 12 per cent in 1967.

Freezing has stimulated world markets for three major commodities (frozen shrimp and lobster, frozen tuna, and frozen fish blocks), which bring these foods from distant production to consuming centers on a worldwide basis. There they are frequently further processed into new and varied products that reach ever increasing markets. This use of food from the sea in frozen forms seems certain to increase as freezing and cold storage facilities continue to increase over the world. While these processes began in North America, they are now spreading out widely as facilities for their handling proliferate and food habits change to accommodate these new tastes, textures, and appearances.

By far the most rapid increase in the use of fish and shellfish, however, has been for fish meal. In this form most of the water and oil is removed from the fish, the water is discarded, and the oil is used for making margarine or other products, and the resultant dried, whole fish meal is used for feeding domestic animals, chiefly poultry. In 1938, 8.1 per cent of world fish and shellfish production was used in this form, and most of that was the by-product of other fish manufacturing uses. By 1968 more than a third of all fish and shellfish production in the world was used for this purpose, and the largest single species fishery in the world (anchovy in Peru and Chile) was devoted almost exclusively to this use.

TABLE 22–1

Estimated Use of World Catch, 1959–1968 (Live weight basis)

Year	Reduced to Meal oil, and so on (billion pounds)	Other Purposes (billion pounds)	Total (billion pounds)
1959	13.89	66.14	80.03
1960	16.75	70.23	87.08
1961	21.38	74.30	95.68
1962	26.46	77.16	103.62
1963	26.42	79.84	106.26
1964	33.95	79.81	113.76
1965	33.73	81.79	115.52
1966	39.02	86.20	125.22
1967	44.75	88.63	133.38
1968	50.26	90.83	141.09

Animals, including man, suffer from the deficiency that in order to maintain their health and growth they must have a relatively steady amount of protein in their diet, which is composed of a balance of amino-acids, some of which they are unable to synthesize from other food. The average human, for instance, needs about 80 grams of protein per day and of this amount about 15 grams must be either animal protein or plant protein to which suitable amino-acids have been added. Domestic animals (other than ruminants, such as cattle, that have made other digestive arrangements) have similar dietary needs.

In the past generation poultry raising has approached the level of a manufacturing operation with all facets of the bird's needs, and particularly its diet, being given close attention. The bird's daily ration is closely calculated by the use of a computer to give it that diet that will keep the bird in vigorous health, so that it will produce meat and eggs at the lowest cost. In the diet 3 to 7 per cent by weight of fish meal has been found to promote health, growth, and egg production that is more than adequate to cover its costs. Thus the poultry and fish meal businesses have expanded together at a very sharp rate. This chicken-raising practice has spread from North America to Japan and Western Europe, and is now spreading on literally a worldwide basis through the developing world. The raising of turkeys follows the same pattern, and in some countries such as Thailand, ducks are raised in the same fashion.

Fish meal can be made, stored, and shipped in bulk or dry bags cheaply and conveniently. Modern selected breeds of poultry convert the essential amino-acids in the fish meal to chicken meats and eggs on a nearly one to one basis. Chickens, by modern methods, can be produced cheaply in nearly all climates and under nearly all conditions. They are almost universally accepted in the human diet (with turkeys in North America, quail in Japan, ducks in Thailand).

Thus the food value of the smaller sea animals is translated through fish meal and poultry into readily acceptable flesh for direct human consumption at a cheaper price and on a broader basis than any other way yet devised. It is the ever growing demand for animal protein in an acceptable form at low prices in all societies and nations that has boomed the poultry business on a worldwide basis and the fish meal industry with it. This is still going on and at this writing there is no end in sight. In the past decade and a half, the world production and use of fish meal has increased nearly ten times.

Fish meal is a fish protein concentrate that is stable in dry storage for months. The addition of antioxidants to the fish meal at manufacturing time so that the remaining oils in the fish meal stay nonrancid and edible is an increasingly common practice. Much engineering research is now going on to perfect a colorless, odorless, flavor-free fish protein concentrate that can be made from whole fish under human food hygiene conditions so that the product can be mixed in with breads, beverages, gravies, and other formulated foods for direct human consumption. The idea is to short circuit chickens and other domestic animals by bringing this cheap, highly nutritious animal protein directly from the highly abundant, and low-cost, small animals of the sea in to the human diet on a very broad basis. This has already started, in publicly supported emergency feeding schemes at several areas in the world, and is likely to be on a commercial scale within the next decade.

THE SHAPE OF THINGS TO COME

The traditional fish market of history was made up of fishes about 25 centimeters or longer in length—as is the market today. Fish meal is made quite satisfactorily of fishes half that length, and the proportion of fish in the world catch of this smaller size has been increasing in the past thirty years, and especially for the past ten, as the production of fish meal in the world has zoomed. Fish meal can also be made quite nicely (fish protein concentrate as well) from animals as small as two centimeters in length, but these are not yet quite so economic to concentrate, catch, and handle as are the larger animals.

Some small animals (for instance many kinds of shrimps and related crustacea) are so delicious, and take freezing so well, that demand for them keeps their prices high enough to warrant the labor in picking meats and freezing them for later consumption, plus the freight bill of getting them to market from production centers.

Thus the tiny, boreal, Pandalid shrimps of Alaska and the Norwegian Sea, the longostino of Chile, and some others, are beginning to come on the world market in good volume. It seems likely that the very large resources of red crab off Mexico and the krill of the Antarctic may do likewise in a relatively few years. The bulk of the small animals of the sea, in the range from 2 to 25 centimeters in length, however, are unable to bear these costs, and if they are not used in fish meal or fish protein concentrates they simply die in the sea at the end of their lives, unused by man, and recycle in the ocean's vast web of life.

But the muscle proteins of all fish and crustacea have about the same amino-acids composition, and thus the same nutritional value, whether it is anchovy that brings the fisherman $10 per ton in Peru, or large shrimp that bring him $2,000 per ton in Texas, or blue-fin tuna that bring him $3,000 per ton in Tokyo. Accordingly if these small animals can be brought to harvest at low cost and into the human diet through chicken meat, eggs, or fish protein concentrate, great new food resources of the ocean will be brought to the use of man.

The major advantage of this move toward the utilization of small sea animals is their enormous abundance. Roughly speaking there are about ten times as many edible animals in the ocean in the range from 10 to 25 centimeters long as there are in the range of 25 centimeters and longer. There are also at least ten times as many edible animals in the ocean in the range from 2 to 10 centimeters long as in the range from 10 to 25 centimeters long. Thus the move toward the harvest and use of smaller and smaller animals, which goes on apace, brings ever larger amounts of human food resources into availability.

There is general consensus among fishery scientists acquainted with these matters that as each fishery resource comes to maturity in its use (that is, as the fishing effort applied upon it reaches the level corresponding to its maximum sustainable yield) the resources of the sorts now used will only yield on a sustainable basis three or four times the amount now taken, or, roughly 200–250 million tons from the whole ocean. If demand keeps increasing for the next thirty years as it has for the past twenty, double that quantity of living resources will be needed each year from the ocean by the year 2000. This is possible from the known resources if the trend continues toward the use of smaller forms. Of these sorts an annual harvest of a thousand million tons, or more, is possible on the basis of sustainable yield, from the wild things in the ocean. Such goals depend upon technology decreasing costs at all levels from production, through processing, to distribution and marketing.

One of the better social aspects of sea fisheries and their growth is that the major part of the cash flow generated by them stays in the hands of the fishermen and cannot be drained off effectively by larger business enterprises. The rapid development of the Peruvian fisheries has, for instance, revolutionized the coastal economy of Peru. The present fishermen's income of $9 billion per year is of enormous social importance in many remote parts of the world. By the turn of the century, this should rise to somewhere between $30 and $40 billion per year.

Another beneficial aspect is that localized fisheries on coastal stocks are more economically efficient in most cases than are the long-range fisheries. The statistics bear this out. The three countries (Japan, Russia, Spain) that have increased their long-range fishing activity most strongly in the 1960s came well short of doubling their combined catches in the last decade. Ten selected highly industrialized countries (United States, United Kingdom, Germany, France, Canada, Netherlands, Italy, Denmark, Belgium and Sweden) increased their combined catches by a bare 10 per cent during that time. But thirty selected countries of the developing world (Morocco, Senegal, Ghana, Sierra Leone, Tanzania, Uganda, Zambia, Liberia, Madagascar, Cuba, Mexico, Panama, Argentina, Chile, Colombia, Guyana, Peru, Venezuela, Ceylon, Taiwan, Hong Kong, India, Indonesia, Korea, Malaysia, Pakistan, Philippines, Thailand, South Viet Nam, and Poland) more than tripled their combined catch from 6 million tons in 1958 to 21 million tons in 1967.

In the period from 1958 through 1968, all of the "developed" countries increased their catches by half (from 17.2 to 24.9 million tons); the countries with centrally planned economies did not quite double theirs (from 7.8 to 13.8 million tons); but the "developing" countries all put together tripled their catches (from 8.2 to 25.3 million tons) and actually surpassed the "developed" countries in total catches.

A good deal of this sharp progress in fish production in the developing world can be attributed to great need, to assistance programs from industrialized countries (both bilaterally and through the Food and Agricultural Organization and the United Nations Development Program), to the fact that there is free entry into high seas fisheries without tenure problems, and other factors. But a major factor in this program is that relatively small and simple vessels, plus shore freezing and nearby processing plants are economically more efficient in most fisheries than large vessels plus factory ships. The trend of future developments in the sea fisheries is likely to continue to favor the countries of the developing world.

CONCLUSIONS

The ocean is capable of producing more animal protein than a human population several times the size of that now existing in the world could use if every man, woman, and child had a daily ration equivalent to either its needs or desires. It is, in fact, producing such volumes steadily, without the aid of aquaculture. Most of its production dies a natural death and is absorbed back into the ocean's web of life unused by man. There are such large known stocks of underutilized wild fish and shellfish in the ocean that the products of aquaculture in the ocean to fill the large volume, low cost animal protein market will not be able to compete economically with the wild stocks for the foreseeable future. Ocean aquaculture is useful in producing luxury and semiluxury foods, but not cheap ones.

The first thing that is needed in man's over-all diet is not new means of food production but more equitable distribution of what is now produced, or of which the production can be easily expanded. Most people who suffer from protein malnutrition do so because they have nothing to trade (money or otherwise) with those who have more edible protein than they need. The problem at this stage of history is one of distribution and economics, not of basic productive capability. The role of advancing science and technology in food from the sea is to lower cost of production so that a wider range of products that the consumer will want can be put on his plate at a price he can afford to pay.

The reason why ocean fish and shellfish production has been expanding so rapidly over the past twenty years is that considerable progress has been made in this application of science and technology to ocean food production, processing, and marketing. The application is now being speeded up in the developing world on a large scale through activities not only of industry from the industrialized world, as has been the case mostly in the past, but by the Department of Fisheries of the Food and Agricultural Organization of the United Nations supported financially jointly by the Special Fund of the United Nations Development Program and recipient countries. The International Bank for Reconstruction and Development (World Bank) and the Regional Development Banks are now beginning to assist with capital for investment.

The production of food from the sea has been increasing at a much more rapid rate than the human population, or than land agricultural production, for the past twenty years and there is every likelihood that this will continue for the next twenty years. The demand and markets are available, underutilized resources to meet the demand are known; ocean-oriented science and technology are producing new understanding of the ocean and its resources at a rapid rate; and this new knowledge is being applied to improve the range, as well as the volume, of available sea food, and thereby lower its unit cost.

Fisheries are already not only the largest extractive industry from the ocean in terms of value, but are larger than all others (gas, oil, water, minerals) put together. It appears likely to hold this place for some time to come.

23 THE MULTIPLE USE OF THE COASTAL ENVIRONMENT

Nelson Marshall

The relationships between man and the oceans are focused primarily along the coastal zones of the world, that is, along the river-mouths, the shorelines, and the oceanic waters near the coast. It is here that man and man's activities interact with the estuarine and oceanic environment, and it is from here that man sets forth to harvest the resources of more distant waters or sets sail on his journeys to overseas places.

The coastal regions vary so greatly over the face of the globe that generalizations are difficult. Almost everywhere the shore slopes seaward gradually to form a relatively shallow continental shelf with water depths of less than 200 meters. The shelf may be little more than a narrow strip or may be over 150 kilometers wide. Thus, when one stands on the shore and looks out to sea, he is usually scanning a vast expanse of relatively shallow continental shelf water.

The coastal land may consist of a relatively low plain sloping seaward to a shoreline of sand bars, sand dunes, and extensive bordering swamplands. Other coastal lands are more elevated, in some cases with mountains seeming to drop precipitously into the sea. We tend to speak of the mountainous shores as emergent and to refer to the low coasts as submergent or drowned coastlines, thereby suggesting the contrasting geological histories of these distinctly different coastal features.

The water that falls on the continent in the form of rain or snow drains across the coastal areas as it returns to the oceans.

Along an emergent coast the river mouths carrying this seaward flow may be quite narrow. Along the drowned coastlines the rivers may expand into large bays. Whatever the pattern, that portion of a river system that meets the open ocean and is directly affected by the saltwater and the tides is known as an estuary.

The properties of the coastal and estuarine waters differ as greatly as the geological features previously mentioned. Since, even over the continental shelf, there is some mixing of river and ocean waters, these areas are almost always somewhat less salty than the open sea. There is no need to explain in detail here the complex circulation patterns generated by the mixing of river and open coastal water but it should be noted that dissolved nutrient chemicals may be added to these waters, both from river drainage and from the deeper waters offshore. These nutrients usually become well mixed in the shallow coastal waters and effectively fertilize the microscopic plant life that supports larger forms of life. Accordingly coastal waters are often extremely productive and, being varied, they provide conditions that support numerous and diverse forms of life. As a result most of the important fishery areas of the world are concentrated along the coasts and estuaries.

Not only because of the many uses made of the coastal areas but also for reasons of preference or personal choice, people tend to construct their homes and business buildings along the shore of these coastal zones. This can be noticed almost anywhere and is well illustrated along the northeastern coast of the United States, one of the more densely populated sections of the world. The coastline, the river shores, and the borders of the waterways extending inland are relatively crowded, busy, and, in some areas, highly industrialized. By contrast, when one drives inland, only a short distance from the populated coastal areas, he is soon traveling through a less crowded landscape with much more open space between the houses, the towns, and the cities.

We are not always aware of how intensively and in how many different ways we use our coastal areas. For example, my home town, South Kingstown, Rhode Island, and the neighboring towns have grown around an estuary about 7 kilometers long by 1 kilometer in width, called Point Judith Pond (Figure 23–1). One quickly notes many different ways in which this estuary is used. First, at the mouth of Point Judith Pond there is a small, but very busy, commercial fishing port. The fishing fleet consists of about forty-five boats with an average length of 20 meters. In addition to the piers where fish are landed for the wholesale seafood market, there is a fish-meal processing plant on the shore where part of the catch, not used for sale as human food, is made into meal to feed poultry. Deep-sea sport fishing also is a rapidly growing business out of Point Judith. Every day from early spring to late fall private and commercially operated sport fishing boats leave for the nearby ocean fishing spots. Two tournaments are held each summer where sport fishermen compete to catch large tuna fish. Some of the tuna caught weigh from 200 to 350 kilograms.

Except on a few remaining large tracts, kept intact by local families through generations, the suitable building sites along the shores of the estuary are dotted with houses. Many of these are homes occupied all year, others are cottages used only in the summer months during vacations, or on weekends. A boys' camp is located on the west shore of Point Judith Pond and two tourist camp areas are being developed on the east shore. A large motor hotel has been built near the harbor mouth.

Pleasure boating on the estuary involves a sailing fleet of more than 100 boats, many power craft, and seemingly countless outboard motor boats. Many of the smaller boats are used in water skiing. Other recreation includes swimming, sport fishing, and shellfishing in the estuary. It is not uncommon to see 100 persons digging for clams on a summer day.

Colorfully enough, one town at the mouth of Point Judith Pond is called Galilee, whereas across the harbor mouth is the town of Jerusalem. Galilee is a freight and passenger port, only for an off-shore island to be sure, but vital and important to the island population.

Boat maintenance and boat-chartering services constitute a prosperous small business on the Point Judith estuary, with

POINT JUDITH POND
inlet of estuary is through
jetties at bottom of picture

FIGURE 23–1.

more than four boatyards along the shore and many additional pier facilities. Obviously, with features such as I have discussed, the Point Judith area attracts many people who are sightseeing and visiting the enjoyable southern New England shores.

And, finally, not to be overlooked, this estuary carries off the excess domestic sewage and household wastes seeping from septic tanks of the surrounding homes, plus a burden of organic wastes from small factories on the watershed. In the future there will be a sewage system for much of the Point Judith Pond drainage basin and, after treatment, wastes will be discharged at the mouth of a nearby and much larger coastal bay. If sewage treatment is adequate, waste disposal via our coastal waters may not be an abuse but one of the vital uses of a waterway, essential wherever there are large concentrations of people and their industries with wastes and excesses that must be carried off.

My account of this local estuary did not include two resource uses that have been declining as other uses have developed; namely, the commercial harvest of shellfish and the hunting and trapping of former years. We have the knowledge needed to revive the shellfisheries, but our state law does not provide for water leases or other rights required if a grower is to practice advanced fishing methods. This would involve demands for space that is not readily found where other uses such as the boating, fishing, swimming, and the diverse requirements associated with living along the estuary seem to take precedence. Similarly hunting and trapping require extensive, large, open areas no longer readily available in such populated regions. Thus one finds that, while we can develop many different and intensive uses for an estuary of this sort, we cannot expect to concurrently provide for all interests.

Of the resource uses mentioned, several depend upon the natural assets of the estuary. We hope that such resources can be sustained and will prosper but we must never lose sight of the fact that they depend upon the ecological well-being of the total environment and will suffer drastically if the natural qualities of the area are not maintained. In addition, offshore commercial and game fishing are indirectly highly dependent upon favorable estuarine conditions since many of the offshore fish migrate into the estuaries for spawning and early growth.

Almost all the uses I have discussed are bound to show some patterns of conflict with other uses as the shoreline is further and more intensively developed. Stated another way, if we wish to develop such an estuarine or coastal environment as a total resource and wish to use a region to the fullest extent possible, we are bound to face numerous conflicts in resource use interests.

My home is also close to another and much larger estuary, Narragansett Bay, where the same resources occur, added ones are found, and all uses have developed on a much larger scale. Narragansett Bay is about 50 kilometers from the headwaters to the sea and about 25 kilometers across. One of my associates at the University of Rhode Island, Niels Rorholm, of the Department of Food and Resource Economics, has considered the different uses made of the resources of the Bay and has discussed the conflicts that develop as these uses grow. Of the twelve resource uses that he selected for discussion, every one conflicts with at least one other as we increase our utilization of these assets. Perhaps the most serious conflicts come from those businesses or interests which pollute the waters and seriously damage the shellfisheries, the residential properties, the beaches, and the other shorefront recreational areas. As Rorholm points out, "A multiple-use resource is probably not producing services efficiently unless use-conflicts occur." And he adds, the most conflicting resource use interests unfold first along the shoreline and may, more than anything else, involve competition for the available shore space. Rorholm recommends continued serious attention to shoreline planning and points out that the way we use the shore is basic in determining the kind of open water activity that will follow.

Whereas various marine use interests will conflict, others might develop without affecting one another; still others might supplement one another. Waterfront and beach recreation do not compete with intensive sport fishing; businesses that cause pollution do not conflict with commerce, ship navigation, and commercial port activities. As such activities develop concurrently, one may find that conditions that favor one activity simultaneously favor the other; however, resource developments that strengthen each other in a very substantial way are not as evident. Although fisheries interests sometimes conflict, they do at times support one another. Fishing concurrently for food fish and for trash species, such as the type used for various animal feeds, not only increases the total yield but protects the fishing grounds from domination by either group and thus provides a check against the crowding out of desired species. The developing threat of rising water temperatures, as we use the estuarine waters for cooling the much needed power plants being built along the shore, may even lead to enrichment as we attempt improved shellfish culture and other aquaculture programs utilizing the warmer waters. Certainly the power plant warmwater outfalls are well known as areas of improved sports fishing. To extend such examples we might note that household pollution, primarily human wastes, may be handled so as to avoid health hazards and uncontrolled growth triggered by excess nutrients and may serve to beneficially fertilize our estuaries. Certainly examples of increased shellfish growth where such wastes are present are quite common. Imaginative suggestions of this sort, for the handling of development and use conflicts to our eventual advantage, are extremely difficult to bring to reality without serious management errors, but success in such ventures may be very rewarding. Such imaginative and constructive solutions will become more and more necessary as multiple-use conflicts increase.

Power plants and the problems in meeting additional power needs vividly illustrate the conflicts in a resource development. As pointed out, population growth and industrialization tend to be concentrated in the coastal areas. This in turn creates a concentrated and growing demand for energy sources, often best met with electric power. Not only in the United States but in distant countries throughout the world, we are attempting to meet this demand by building large power plants, usually driven by nuclear energy. However, these large power plants threaten natural conditions rightfully defended by the very people who need the electricity. Large, economically favorable power plants release enormous volumes of warm water, creating a stress on the marine environment. They may lead to high mortalities of tiny plankton, fish larvae, and the like, passing through the cooling systems of the plant generators. And large power generators on a beautiful stretch of shoreline certainly do not enhance the scenic features of an area. Thus our power needs lead to intense conflicts, even within the minds of individuals concerned who want both the luxury of more electricity and the pleasures of an unspoiled environment. As with other resource-use conflict problems, we should resolve the differences through a clear understanding of the problems and the options available to us.

There is a pressing need for well-conceived planning and management as we strive to reach the great potential of our coastal areas through ever increasing, complex, and conflicting uses. For many of the decisions to be made in situations of conflict, advisors, planners, and finally the people who use the estuary must choose between tangible and substantial economic assets on the one hand, and highly abstract, often esthetic values, on the other. Although there have been attempts to report the esthetic and the abstract in monetary terms for direct comparison with tangible economic assets, it is almost impossible to do this. Economists today encourage us instead to consider critically the very different nature of our assets and to attempt to make wise choices with a frank awareness of the alternatives. For example, there are those who would fill vast areas of our tidal marshes to provide land for homes, boatyards, and waterfront commerce, all of which promise substantial money returns. Others fight to save the limited marsh tracts for their wildlife or esthetic values and their general contributions to the total natural environment. Often the cost of adequate sewage treatment looms as an excessive burden, almost impossible to justify in terms of direct financial returns gained from cleaner water but readily justified in the cumulative subtle benefits, some bearing on health, some showing long-range money returns, and some purely esthetic. Thus we have choices to make that involve, on the one hand, our need to develop the economy of a shoreline town or city and, on the other hand, our appreciation of our natural surroundings. With economic growth we become concerned over the growing pollution and ecological decline of the densely populated areas along the coastline and the realization that over the years this economy cannot flourish in a degraded environment.

Economists sometimes speak of the multiplier effects of the different enterprises we encounter in the marine resource development of a region. For example, Rorholm and his colleagues, in studying the economics of marine-related businesses in southern New England, have calculated that for every $1 of increase in fresh-fish processing over $3 is realized in total earnings and enterprises associated with this activity. Thus fish processing exerts a multiplier effect of about three and one third, This is high and probably results from the fact that the basic resource, the supporting activities and the manpower are mostly found within the region. By contrast, if the ship and boat-building industry, which depends in part on resources from outside the area, is increased the multiplier is slightly less than two. One must not hastily conclude that we should, in our resource planning, encourage the fishing more than the ship construction businesses. Among other things the immediate and long-term possibilities for growth of the various enterprises should be considered. It is interesting to note, however, since a concern for the environment is being stressed in this discussion, that in the analysis by Rorholm and his coauthors, use enterprises drawing directly on the production of the environment, namely fish catching, fresh-fish processing, frozen-fish processing, and charter fishing, consistently have a large multiplier influence on the economy.

Unfortunately we may pay little attention to a valuable resource until conflicts with others or independent difficulties arise. Important assets may be taken for granted and their use may move forward appreciably without attracting widespread attention until a critical problem develops. And as problems have arisen we have tended to deal with them as isolated issues, failing to recognize conflict and interactions. For example, traditionally we have fisheries administrative divisions within our state governments with responsibilities to the fisheries but lacking the powers, directives, or motivation to adequately consider the fisheries as related to other problems. At the same time, we also find, in most of our states, departments of health that are concerned with problems of pollution and sanitation. These health groups are usually entrusted with responsibilities to prevent and to correct pollution in our natural waters. Seldom do they have adequate power nor are they suitably encouraged to work toward finding solutions for the conflicts and interrelated problems faced by businesses and towns and cities in managing their wastes. Once the total picture of the resources and the very complex interrelations are recognized and encompassed in complete administrative programs of coastal management, we will be in a far better position to form balanced resource use plans for our coastal regions.

Looking ahead to days of more comprehensive management of the multiuse coastal areas, it is encouraging to note that some resource use conflicts can be easily resolved when recognized, while for certain other conflicts we are confronted with alternatives not difficult to accept. Sometimes the conflicts are just imagined, as in numerous cases of supposed conflict between sports fishermen and commercial fishermen. The former may accuse the latter of overfishing and thus causing a decline in the resource, although there may be no evidence to support such charges. Accurate information and educational efforts often resolve such issues. It is also possible that, in many situations, we might take advantage of the interactions, as in the aquaculture programs considered for the warm water discharged by power plants. Thus we can be angered by conflict, sometimes for good reason, sometimes out of ignorance. We can and should be encouraged to understand the true nature of the options available to us and even challenged to seek interesting and beneficial solutions to this conflict.

Along some stretches of the coastline the growth and spread

of populations in the large cities and into the residential areas
has led to a continuous populated area that amounts to a
supercity or megalopolis. Such regions, where the densely
populated expanses of one city may merge with those of another, place a tremendous stress on the environment and may
result, particularly around the large cities and ports, in an
almost complete deterioration of the natural features of the
coastal waters. Of late, and hopefully not too late, we are
becoming increasingly concerned with these effects over such
broad areas. In the megalopolis that extends from Norfolk, Vir-
ginia, to Portsmouth, Maine, on the eastern seaboard of the
United States, some well-preserved expanses of estuarine and
coastal areas still remain between the major cities. For the
marine environment, these are the counterparts of the parks,
open land, and cherished countryside stretches of our land
areas. The severe strain on the environment that occurs around
the cities is partially offset by the remaining fish-breeding sites,
wildlife habitats, and other natural features of the coastal area
that are provided by this aquatic open space between the densely
populated areas. But how much added strain can be placed on
this system before the environment collapses? When one speaks
of the world's overpopulation he usually points first to existing
or threatened food shortages. The serious threat of mass environmental destruction from cumulative effects, some very
subtle and overlooked, tends to grow and is seldom adequately
checked.

Although I have discussed the region that is of personal interest to me, the basic points that have been made can be
applied to other shoreline and coastal areas. In regions that
are in the relatively early stages of their commercial development some of the more idealistic and involved dimensions of
an over-all resource use program may seem beyond present
needs. A region primarily concerned with food that might
come from its coastal fisheries may not be confronted with problems related to pleasure boating. Often such areas have little or
no recreational boating interests. Yet conflict and interplay in

resource use always exist to some degree. For example, no one can ignore the pollution question, and few coastal areas are free from competing demands for space along prime sections of the shoreline. There are always conflicts. There is a vital need in almost every coastal area to look at the total picture and to develop a comprehensive plan for coastal resource use. Every country must aspire to the fullest development and realization of its coastal assets, which, as I have emphasized, leads to added conflict and an added need for planning.

There are basically three steps in attaining desired planning and management capability. The first is an appreciation of the resources and their potentials and an awareness of the intensive, multiple use interactions stemming from a greater resource use development. Next, an area must have the proper management provisions in its government. Finally, research capability must be encouraged to deal with these complex development problems. In the United States we speak today of coastal zones, defined arbitrarily and for governmental convenience as the coastal waters, the estuaries, and the adjacent shore areas of each state. Our goal, progressing more rapidly in some states than in others, is to create the administrative structures needed to plan and to oversee proper management programs for these coastal zones. This goal obviously requires that planning and administration groups use the work of research scientists capable of studying the numerous resource questions and of searching for effective management and development techniques. Their studies certainly will involve pollution, its effects and how it is controlled, the potential and the ways of managing the fisheries, and economic problems caused by the sharing of the waterfront areas by competing interests. They will include other countless problems we encounter in living by and using the waterfront.

In my own state of Rhode Island we are following the three steps just mentioned. We are very conscious of our resources, their use and the interactions involved; we have organized a state coastal zone authority or official management group; and we are strengthening our marine research efforts, particularly at the state university where work is progressing in such important areas as marine economics, coastal engineering, coastal law, inshore oceanography, and fisheries.

Finally, I would like to comment briefly on the effect of the marine environment on man rather than man's effect on his surroundings. Water, for all of its vital importance to our economic well-being, serves another need—basic and very difficult to define. Man is constantly attracted to the coast. He is relaxed, comforted, soothed, and, in a sense, restored as he looks out over our bays and oceans. This attraction is beyond definition, but it certainly influences our living habits and choices.

24 SHORE PROCESSES

Douglas L. Inman

The transition between sea and land occurs in the shallow nearshore waters that cover the drowned shelves and estuaries of the world. Here shore processes begin the mixing, sorting, and transportation of sediments and run-off from the land. Waves, winds, and currents mold the shorelines of the world, and their interaction with the land and its run-off determine the configuration of the coastlines and adjacent bathymetry. The longshore movement of sediment is surprisingly large. Along many ocean coasts the transport of beach sand may have a volume in excess of 1 million cubic meters per year.

The nearshore and estuarine waters are the part of the sea that overwhelmingly dominates the everyday affairs of mankind. About two-thirds of the world's population lives near the coast. Here, waves, storm surges, tides, and secular changes in sea level attain their greatest height. Nearshore waters impinge on the beaches, harbors, and estuaries that are so important for industry, recreation, and human habitat. The nearshore zone is the part of the sea that mostly concerns sailors because of its dangerous shoals, strong currents, and destructive waves. The continental shelf is the site of rich oil and mineral deposits, and the shallow waters covering it contain much of the plant and animal life of the sea. Man's rapidly expanding use of the ocean and his increasing traffic upon and entry into the ocean, are mostly concerned with processes that take place in shallow water. Conversely, it is mostly within the nearshore waters that the acts of man, such as waste discharge, fishing, dredging, and coastal structures, have their greatest impact on the ocean.

THE COASTAL ZONE AND SHORE ZONE

The oceans and seas have a profound effect on the continents, exerting the controlling influence on weather and climate. In fact, the presence of the sea completely dominates the environmental aspects of the land bordering the sea. In this connection it is useful to describe coastal areas in terms of a "coastal zone" and a "shore zone" (Figure 24–1).

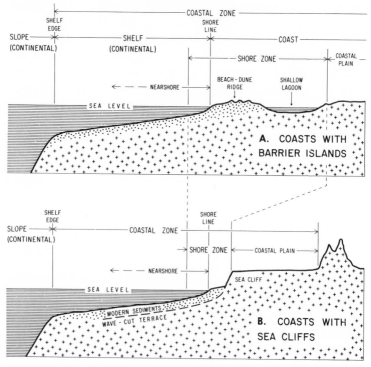

FIGURE 24–1.

Definition sketch for coastal zone nomenclature (from Inman and Nordstrom, 1971).

The coastal zone is defined in terms of the large-scale tectonic and erosional-depositional features that have linear dimensions along the coastline of the order of 1,000 kilometers and on offshore dimensions of the order of 100 kilometers. The coastal zone consists of the coastal plain, the continental shelf, and the waters that cover the shelf; it also includes other major features such as large bays, estuaries, lagoons, coastal dune fields, river estuaries, and deltas.

The shore zone is the sedimentary and solid surface associated directly with the interaction of waves and wave-induced currents on the land and its run-off. The shore zone includes the beach, the surf zone, and the nearshore waters where wave action is effective in moving bottom sediments. The shore zone extends landward to the sea cliffs that border the backshore of a beach, and where wave deposited structures such as barrier islands and spits are narrow, across these features to the cliff or coastal plain bordering shallow lagoons. All water bodies have shore zones, their extent and size depending upon the length and height of the waves, the range of the tide, and the size of the wave deposited structures.

In a practical sense the waters of the coastal zone can be considered as including the shallow seas and the waters covering the continental shelves of the world, an area of 29 million square kilometers, or about 5½ per cent of the surface area of the world and about 8 per cent of the area of the world's oceans (Table 24–1). The nearshore waters are bounded on the landward side by shorelines that total about 400,000 kilometers in length, and to the seaward by the break in slope at the shelf edge, marking the change from the relatively horizontal shelf to the steeper continental slope. The continental slope marks the topographical and structural edge of the continents and is the boundary between the relatively shallow water covering the shelf and the great depths of the true oceans. The continental slopes are one of the striking geographic features of the earth and have a combined length of about 150,000 kilometers.

Conventionally, the depth of the shelf edge is taken as 200

TABLE 24–1
Dimensions of Major Topographic Features *

	Area 10⁶Km.²	Length of Coastline or Shelf Break 10³Km.
Continents	138.8	210
Large islands (98 islands larger than 2,500 km.)	9.3	136
Small islands (25 to 2,500 km.)	0.8	93
TOTAL LAND	148.9	439
Oceans (depths greater than 200 m.)	332.1	
Continental Shelf (0–200 m.)	29.0	149
TOTAL MARINE WATER	361.1	
TOTAL AREA EARTH	510.0	

* Area of land mass from National Geographic Atlas of the World, 1966; area of continental shelf and oceans is from Sverdrup, et al., 1942; length of coastline of South America, Australia, Africa, Madagascar, and Great Britain were measured from charts 1:6,000,000 scale, other coastline lengths were calculated, assuming them equal to 6.5 × area of the land mass. Length of the shelf break was measured on a world bathymetric chart 1:39,000,000 scale (From Inman and Nordstrom, 1971).

meters or 100 fathoms, although in some localities the depth may be as great as 400 meters. On a worldwide basis, the average depth of the shelf edge is about 130 meters. The width of the shelf ranges from zero to over 1,300 kilometers, and averages about 74 kilometers (Shepard, 1963).

THE NEARSHORE:
A ZONE OF AIR-SEA-LAND INTERACTION

The nearshore zone is a complex region of intense interaction among waves, tides, currents, river run-off, and the erosion products from the land. The energy for nearshore processes comes from the sea, and is produced by the force of winds blowing over the ocean, by the gravitational attraction of the moon and sun acting on the mass of the ocean, and by various impulsive disturbances at the atmospheric and terrestrial boundaries of the ocean. These forces produce waves and currents that transport energy toward the coast. The configuration of the land mass and adjacent shelves modifies and focuses the flow of energy, and determines the intensity of wave and current action in coastal waters. Rivers and winds transport erosion products from the land to the coast, where they are sorted and dispersed by waves and currents. The dominance of erosion or deposition is determined by the nature of these complex interactions between the air, the sea, and the land (Figure 24–2).

FIGURE 24–2.

Aerial photograph of rip currents along a beach. The spacing between rip currents determines the longshore dimension of the nearshore circulation cell (DLI Photograph 571–12).

Most energy from the ocean waves and tides is ultimately transmitted into the nearshore waters of the coastal zone. In the nearshore zone, the energy is dissipated in various ways, including reflection, generation of turbulence and longshore currents, transportation of sediment, and the formation of other kinds of waves. Some energy appears to become "trapped" against the coast, thus leading to an increase in the energy level at the coast. The trapped energy may take the form of edge waves, which are special modes of surface waves that travel along the coast, or long period resonant oscillations called shelf seiche.

The many forms of energy flux and the high rates of energy dissipation over the shelf and in the surf zone further complicate the processes within the nearshore environment. Although the mutual interaction of waves in deep water is relatively weak, in shallow water the interaction of waves with other waves, of waves with currents, and of currents and waves with the bottom can produce strong interchanges of energy. For example, the waves in shallow water produce bottom-boundary currents flowing in the direction of wave propagation, and these play a significant role in the transport of sediments over the shelf. Pressure fields produced by waves traveling in shallow water change the average water level, reducing it near the breaker zone, and increasing it where the waves run up the beach face.

The interaction of surface waves moving towards the beach, with edge waves traveling along the shore, produces alternate zones of high and low waves that determine the position of seaward flowing rip currents (Figure 24–3). The rip currents are the seaward return flow for the longshore currents that flow parallel to the coast inside of the surf zone. The pattern that results from this flow takes the form of a horizontal eddy or cell, called the nearshore circulation cell (Bowen and Inman, 1969).

The nearshore circulation system produces a continuous interchange between the waters of the surf and offshore zones, acting as a distributing mechanism for nutrients and as a dispersing mechanism for land run-off. Offshore water is transported into the surf zone by breaking waves and particulate matter is filtered out on the sands of the beach face. Run-off from land and pollutants introduced into the surf zone are carried along the shore and mixed with the offshore waters by the seaward flowing rip currents.

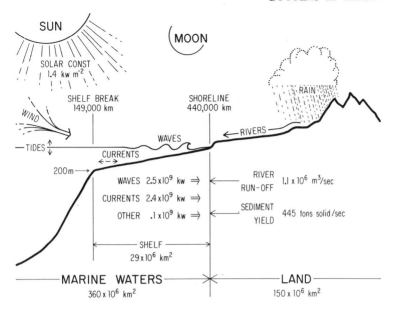

FIGURE 24-3.

Schematic diagram of the marine and terrestrial contributions to the near-shore waters.

Coastal circulation on a much larger scale but of less intensity occurs over the entire shelf. This circulation may take the form of eddies and counter currents from the permanent ocean current systems that flow across the shelf; the circulation may be caused by tidal currents; or, it may be induced locally by the wind, in the form of the upwelling of deep water, and the horizontal flow of water along the coast.

In addition, coastal circulation cells of large dimension are associated with the submarine canyons that cut across the shallow shelves of the world. The submarine canyons act as deep, narrow conduits connecting the shallow waters of the shelf with deeper water offshore. At times, strong seaward flows of water occur in the canyons, so that they resemble large-scale rip currents. The canyon currents produce circulation cells having the dimensions of the shelf width and the spacing between the submarine canyons. These strong currents in submarine canyons seem to be caused by a unique combination of air-sea-land interactions consisting of:

1. A pile-up of water along the shoreline caused by strong onshore winds.

2. Down-canyon pulses of water caused by the surf beat of the incident waves.

3. A shelf seiche excited by the waves and by the pressure fluctuations in the wind field.

4. The formation of steady down-canyon currents as the weight of the sediment suspended by the currents overcomes the density stratification of the deeper water.

The pile-up of water by the wind is less over the canyons and causes the shallower waters over the shelf to flow along the coast toward the canyons and, as in the case of rip currents, to flow seaward over the canyons. The surf beat waves and the shelf seiche are very long waves, whose interaction with the shelf and canyon produce current pulses capable of suspending sediment. When these pulses are of sufficient velocity to suspend sediment and to maintain a suspended load of sediment, auto-suspension results and the pulsating current is converted into a self-maintaining turbidity current that travels down the canyon into the adjacent deep waters of the ocean.

Despite these intense interactions, it is becoming increasingly clear that the closely interrelated driving forces, although masked by a high level of background noise, are essentially of low frequency and regular in form. The background noise is random and largely associated with the processes of energy dissipation, while the driving mechanisms are regular. Thus, the nearshore circulation is governed by a fundamentally simple incident wave-edge wave interaction, while shelf and canyon currents are related to the oscillating fields associated with waves and winds. Furthermore, the processes operative in the near-shore waters of oceans, bays, and lakes all appear quite similar, differing mainly in intensity and scale, variables that are determined primarily by the wind systems and the size of the water body over which they blow.

BUDGET OF ENERGY DISSIPATION
IN SHALLOW WATER

One approach to understanding the relative importance of nearshore processes is to compare the sea's potential to erode the land with the land's potential to supply terrestrial erosion products. Such a comparison ultimately resolves itself into the balance between the budget of power in waves and currents and the budget of sediments available for transport. Of course, this balance varies widely from place to place, and even in the best studied areas, is but poorly understood. However, order of magnitude estimates can be attempted on a worldwide basis, and their consideration here gives some overall perspective for the relative importance of the driving forces that are operative in nearshore waters.

The current systems of the world's atmosphere and ocean are solar powered, and together, maintain the earth's heat budget by accounting for a poleward transport of energy at the rate of about 10^{13} kilowatts. Solar energy heats the earth's surface unevenly and generates winds. Its direct effect on the oceans is to stratify and stabilize the surface water. As a consequence, the ocean responds much more to wind, even though the intensity of thermal energy from the sun greatly exceeds the mechanical energy from the wind at the water's surface. Averaged over the earth's surface, the intensity of thermal energy is about 200 watts per square meter, while a wind blowing 10 meters per second dissipates about 1.3 watts per square meter.

The wind systems are the direct link between atmosphere and ocean, and through momentum exchange at the ocean's surface, dissipate kinetic energy at the rate of about 10^{11} kilowatts. (Malkus, 1962, p. 98). Winds plus ocean and earth tides are directly or indirectly responsible for most of the energy dissipated in the nearshore zones of the oceans. By far, the most common form of nearshore energy is that associated with the wind-generated surface waves, which will be considered first.

A three-meter high surface wave at sea transmits 100 kilowatts for every meter of wave crest, or 100 megawatts per kilometer. This is roughly equivalent to the power of a solid line of automobiles, side by side, at full throttle.[1] On an oceanwide basis, wind-generated waves probably have an average height of about one meter, and transmit power at a rate of about ten kilowatts per meter of wave crest. If these waves were to break continuously along the 400,000 kilometers of the world's shoreline, they would dissipate energy at the rate of 4×10^9 kilowatts. This is probably too high for the world's average dissipation because all shorelines are not exposed to the open ocean. However, even Hue, on the Viet Nam coast of the South China Sea, receives wave energy at the average rate of 8 kilowatts per meter of beach during the four monsoon months, and at an average annual rate of half this amount. Therefore, a reasonable estimate of the world's average rate of dissipation for wind-generated wave energy would be about one-half to two-thirds of the previous calculation, about 2.5×10^9 kilowatts, which is the equivalent of 10,000 large power plants (Table 24–2).

TABLE 24–2

Estimates of the Rate of Dissipation of Mechanical Energy in the Shallow Waters of the World; in Units of 10^9 Kilowatts = 10^{19} Ergs Sec^{-1}

Wind-generated waves breaking against the shoreline (assuming power of 6¼ kw. per meter times 400,000 km.; Kinsman's, 1965, p. 154, G# estimate is 1.9 to 2.2)	2.5
Tidal currents in shallow seas	2.2
Large-scale ocean currents in shallow seas (Guiana, 0.13; Falkland, 0.03; etc.)	0.2
All other sources (wind stress on the beach, 0.01; internal waves, 0.01; edge waves; shelf seiche; tsunamis; rivers entering ocean; etc.)	0.1
TOTAL	5.0

[1] Assuming that the wave period is 11.3 seconds and that the power of an automobile is 268 horsepower per 2 meter width = 100 kilowatts per meter = 10^{10} ergs per second per centimeter.

The tides, having wavelengths that are very long compared with the depth of the ocean, produce some motion even in the deepest water. However, this motion is usually only a few centimeters per second so that the energy dissipation by tides against the deep sea bottom is negligible. The principle tidal dissipation results from the flow of strong tidal currents in shallow seas. The energy dissipated by currents against the shallow sea bottom is one of the major factors that causes the rotational deceleration of the earth. Much of our present knowledge of this dissipation results from investigations by geophysicists into the possible causes of the deceleration in the earth's rotation (Jeffreys, 1962; Munk and MacDonald, 1960). It is estimated that tidal currents in shallow seas dissipate energy at an average rate of 2.2×10^9 kilowatts, or at a rate only slightly less than that from wave action. (See Table 24-2.) About half of the tidal current dissipation occurs in five shallow seas having a total area of only 10 per cent of the shelf area of the world.

The most impressive waves in the sea are those generated by submarine earthquakes and volcanic eruptions. These waves, called tsunamis, are well known because of the loss of life and great damage to coastal structures associated with their passage. Of the many types of surface waves, tsunamis contain the highest instantaneous power surges. They are reported to have caused run-ups to heights as great as 30 meters above sea level. Detectable tsunamis have occurred about once a year. However truly large tsunamis with energy contents as high as 5×10^{15} joules occur only about five times each century (Van Dorn, 1965). Averaged over long periods of time, tsunamis dissipate energy at the rate of about 8×10^4 kilowatts. Thus, because of their relative infrequency, these catastrophic waves contribute little to the worldwide budget of power.

There is good evidence that some of the energy in the long surface waves such as tides and tsunamis is transferred to other kinds of wave modes, including internal waves and edge waves. Cox and Sandstrom (1962) found that internal waves were coupled to surface waves, and estimated that the rate of conversion of tidal energy into internal wave energy in the Atlantic Ocean is roughly between 6 and 69 per cent of the power of the surface tide. From this, Munk and MacDonald (1960, p. 220) estimate that the conversion of energy from surface to internal modes on a global scale may be about 1.5×10^9 kilowatts. Most internal wave energy is contained in the areas of deep ocean, but some of the energy travels into shallow water and is dissipated against the sea bottom. La Fond (1962, p. 735) measured internal waves from a tower in 18 meters of water off San Diego, California that had heights over 6 meters and periods ranging from a few minutes to over two hours. Owen Lee (personal communication) studying data from the same tower estimates that the average energy of the internal waves in this area is about 18 joules per square meter, and that the waves propagate shoreward with a velocity of 25 centimeters per second. At this rate, the total power for internal waves crossing over the 150,000 kilometer length of the continental shelves of the world would be about 7×10^5 kilowatts. Since the internal waves have traveled across most of the width of the continental shelf before reaching the tower, it seems reasonable to estimate that the power available at the seaward edge of the shelves of the world may be about 10^7 kilowatts.

The kinetic energy associated with the large-scale ocean currents is very large compared with the energy in surface waves and tidal currents. Stommel (1958, p. 148) estimates that the average kinetic energy of currents in the North Atlantic Ocean is about 2×10^{17} joules. Flows such as the equatorial and Antarctic Circumpolar currents transport water at rates of 50 to 200 million cubic meters per second. Even the relatively small California current transports 25 million cubic meters per second, a discharge nearly two-and-one-half times greater than that of all the rivers in the world. Whereas the flow of major ocean currents is predominantly in deep water, some of their boundaries overlap the continental shelves, and the currents dissipate some of their energy against the shallow sea bottoms. For example, the Guiana Current flows with velocities up to one meter per second over the one-half million square kilometers of shelf off the coastlines of the Guiana's and northern Brazil. The

Falkland Current flows with velocities of one-quarter to one-half meter per second across the one million square kilometers of shallow shelf off Patagonia. If the Guiana Current averages one-half meter per second and the Falkland Current averages one-quarter meter per second, they would dissipate energy at the rate of 0.13×10^9 and 0.03×10^9 kilowatts, respectively.[2] Therefore, it seems likely that the worldwide dissipation of energy from the flow of ocean currents in shallow water may be about 0.2×10^9 kilowatts.

In addition to generating the ocean's waves, atmospheric winds and pressures have important local effects near shore. Pressure fronts generate shelf seiche, and the combination of pressure and wind stress on the water's surface produces local anomalies in sea level that induce circulation of water over the shelf and in the submarine canyons. Shelf seiche up to a meter or more in height are common along the Argentine coast (Inman, et al., 1962), while the sea level anomalies associated with storm surges may exceed three meters for severe storms (Neumann and Pierson, 1966, p. 372). Also, winds blowing over the coastal zone dissipate energy on beach and sand dunes. On a worldwide basis this dissipation may be about 10^7 kilowatts, and because of the prevalence of sea breeze winds, this results in a net inland transport of beach sand.

From the foregoing discussion, it appears that the total rate of dissipation of mechanical energy in the shallow waters of the world is about 5×10^9 kilowatts. (See Table 24-2.) Dissipation by one process or another occurs over the entire shelf. The wind-generated surface waves primarily dissipate their energy nearshore, especially in the breaker zone, while tidal and other ocean currents and internal waves dissipate energy mostly over the outer portions of the shelf. Internal waves, edge waves, shelf seiche, and local winds may produce water motion over the continental shelf and submarine canyons. Thus, it is apparent that understanding of the processes in the nearshore environment requires a careful assessment of the amounts of

[2] Assuming that the power is given by kpu^3 where the drag coefficient k has a value of 2×10^{-3}.

energy in the various kinds and modes of wave current motion; a determination of the mechanics of interaction of waves, currents, and sediments, as well as the careful evaluation of the rates of energy transfer into the formation of turbulence and heat and into the longshore transport of water and sediment.

BUDGET OF SEDIMENT

The shoreline is the junction of the realms of terrestrial erosion and marine deposition. Thus it is the unique singularity between air, land, and sea, and is the critical datum for dynamic geology. In 1955 James Gilluly calculated that sediment is now being carried across this boundary at a rate great enough, if continued, to "erase all the topography above sea level in less than 10 million years. . . ." This is a very short time on the geological time scale.

The principal sources of beach and nearshore sediments are the rivers, which bring large quantities of sand directly to the ocean; the sea cliffs of unconsolidated material, which are eroded by waves; and material of biological origin, such as shells, coral fragments, and other skeletons of small marine organisms. Occasionally, sediment may be supplied by the erosion of unconsolidated deposits in shallow water. Beach sediments on the coasts of Holland are derived in part from the shallow waters of the North Sea. Windblown sand may be a source of nearshore sediment, although winds are usually more effective in removing sand from beaches than in supplying it. In tropical latitudes many beaches are composed entirely of grains of calcium carbonate of biogenous origin. Generally, the material consists of fragments of shells, corals, and calcareous algae growing on or near fringing reefs. This material is carried to the beach by wave action over the reef. Some beaches are composed mainly of the minute skeletons of foraminifera that live on the sandy bottom offshore from the reefs.

Streams and rivers are by far the most important source of sand for beaches in temperate latitudes. Cliff erosion probably does not account for more than about 5 per cent of the material on most beaches. Wave erosion of rocky coasts is usually slow, even where the rocks are relatively soft shales. On the other hand, erosion rates greater than one meter a year are not uncommon in the unconsolidated sea cliffs. As early as 1873, C. Lyell showed that the Ganges and Brahmaputra Rivers carry a load of sediment into the Bay of Bengal each year that is 780 times greater than the material eroded by wave action from the thirty-six-mile stretch of cliffs near Holderness, England. The Holderness cliffs, which are on the exposed North Sea coast, are noted for their rapid rate of erosion; they are forty feet high and recede at the rate of about seven feet per year.

Surprisingly, the contribution of sand by streams in arid countries is quite high. This is because arid weathering produces sand-size material and inhibits the growth of vegetation that would protect the land from erosion. Therefore, in arid climates, the occasional flash floods transport large volumes of sand. The maximum sediment yield occurs from drainage basins where the mean annual precipitation is about 30 centimeters per year (Schumm, 1963).

Following the initial deposition at the mouths of streams entering the ocean, much of the sand-size portion of terrestrial sediments is carried along the coast by waves and wave induced longshore currents. The sand carried by these longshore currents may be transported to deeper water by submarine canyons that cut into the continental shelf and effectively divert this supply of sand into deeper water offshore. Since submarine canyons occur along most coasts, except those bordered by shallow seas, they probably account for most of the sediment lost into deep water from the nearshore zone.

Notable among the major sediment transporting submarine canyons of the world are Cap Breton Submarine Canyon on the Atlantic coast of France; Cayar and Trou Sans Fond, and Congo Canyons on the Atlantic coast of Africa; the Indus and the Ganges Submarine Canyons in the Indian Ocean; and the Monterey Submarine Canyon on the Pacific Coast of North America. Observations by H. W. Menard (1960) suggest that most of the deep sediments on the abyssal plains along a 400 kilometer section of the California coastline are derived from two submarine canyons: the Delgada Submarine Canyon in northern California and the Monterey Submarine Canyon in central California. These canyons cut the continental shelf almost to the shoreline, and consequently they trap almost all of an estimated volume of 10^6 cubic meters per year of sediment transported along the coast.

The budget of sediment for a region is obtained by assessing the sedimentary contributions and losses to the region and their relation to the various sediment sources and transport mechanisms. Determination of the budget of sediment is not a simple matter since it requires a knowledge of the rates of erosion and deposition as well as an understanding of the capacity of the various transport agents.

Historically, the budget of sediment has been estimated in a number of different ways. Geologists have estimated long-term erosion and deposition rates from the amount of material deposited during geological time. More recently, other estimates of the sediment budget have been made possible by the increasing number of geophysical measurements that have led to a better understanding of sedimentation rates in ocean basins, erosion rates on land, the load and discharge of rivers, and the longshore transport rates of littoral sediments. These new measurements permit estimates to be more closely associated with the various transporting agents. This has resulted in a marked improvement in our understanding of nearshore processes and the relative importance of variables such as climate and coastline configuration.

Estimates of the sediment yield from the erosion of land by water vary from 20 tons per square kilometer per year for the Appalachian region of North America to 2,600 tons per square kilometer per year for the Himalayan Mountains of Asia (Table 24–3). In terms of the volume of particulate solids, assuming that 40 per cent of the material is dissolved in the processes of erosion, these yields would be equivalent to 8 and 1,000 cubic meters of sediment per square kilometer per year, respectively.

TABLE 24–3

Estimates of Sediment Yield from Land Erosion by Water

Investigator and Assumptions	Region	Area 10^6Km.^{2}	Erosion Rate * Tons/ Km.^{2}	Erosion Rate * Cm./ 10^3Yr.	Total Vol. for Earth at Rate Shown Km.^{3}/Yr.
Gilluly (1955) based on Kuenen's (1950) estimate of 12.0 km.^{3}/yr. solids from rivers and 0.12 km.^{3}/yr. for coastline erosion; Clarke's (1924) est. of 1.5 km.^{3} for dissolved loads of rivers.	Land area of world	149.	237	9.1	13.6
Menard (1961) *present rate*, using suspended load from rivers	Mississippi	4.8	109	4.2	6.3
	Appalachian	1.0	21	0.8	1.2
	Himalaya	1.0	2,600	100.	149.
Menard past rate, from dep.					
150×10^6yrs.	Mississippi	4.8	120	4.6	6.9
125×10^6yrs.	Appalachian	1.0	161	6.2	9.2
40×10^6yrs.	Himalaya	1.0	546	21.	31.2
Schumm (1963) from gauging stations for drainage basins averaging 3,900 km.^{2}	United States		78	3.0	4.5
Schumm from reservoirs for drainage basins averaging 78km.^{2}	United States		240	9.2	13.7
Gibbs (1967) measurements of dissolved and suspended load	Amazon River Basin	6.3	116	4.5	6.7

TABLE 24–3 (cont'd)

Investigator and Assumptions	Region	Area 10^6Km.^{2}	Erosion Rate *		Total Vol. for Earth at Rate Shown Km.^{3}/Yr.
			Tons/ Km.^{2}	Cm./ 10^3Yr.	
Goldberg (personal communication) using dissolved and sus- pended loads from major rivers listed in Leopold et al. (1964) and Holeman (1968).	World		104	4.0	6.0

* Based on assumption that solid rock, $\rho_s = 2.6$ gm./cm.^{3}, is eroded to form 40% dissolved load, and 60% particulate solids; solids at rest have porosity of 40%. The erosion rate is in tons of solid plus dissolved load:

$$\frac{1 \text{ cm}}{10^3 yr} = \frac{26 \text{ tons(solid} + \text{dissolved)}}{km^2\, yr} = \frac{15.6 \text{ tons solid}}{km^2\, yr} = \frac{10 m^3}{km^2\, yr}$$

Assuming an average land erosion rate of 6 cm. per 1,000 years gives an annual yield of 9×10^9 m^3 of particulate solids plus 9.4×10^9 tons of dissolved material.

The data is obtained mostly from rivers with large drainage basins, which have been shown (Schumm, 1963) to have a lower yield per unit area than small drainage basins. Also, the sediment yield of glaciers and wind is neglected so that the data may be conservative. Excluding the Himalayan data, which is anomalously high, and the Appalachian, which is anomalously low, the remaining data give ranges from about 30 to 92 cubic meters per square kilometer per year. Therefore, on a worldwide basis, the total yield from continental erosion must be about 9 cubic kilometers of particulate material plus 9.4×10^9 tons of dissolved material. This is equivalent to the erosion of a 6-centimeter thick layer from the surface of the continents in one thousand years, or about 445 tons of sediment in one second.

In the nearshore waters the sediment is dispersed and transported by waves and currents. Since energy is the capacity for doing work, the flux of energy associated with the waves and

334

currents is a measure of their potential to transport sediment. The efficiency of utilization of energy in transport is, of course, generally low and depends upon the source of energy and the nature of the coupling between the source and the sediment. If the bottom slopes, the force of gravity acting on the excess density of the sediment constitutes an additional source of potential energy for the down-slope transport of sediment. While the details of the coupling between the fluxes of energy and sediment vary widely from place to place, the net balance between them will determine whether the coast erodes or accretes.

Thus, it is of interest to compare these fluxes on a worldwide basis. The flux of energy from the oceans into the nearshore waters is estimated to be 5×10^9 kilowatts, while the flux of sediment from the land to the oceans is estimated to be 445 tons per second. The sediment flux, when converted to immersed weight in water, is about 2.5×10^6 newtons per second. The energy flux stated in comparable units becomes 5×10^{12} newton-meters per second. Since the sediment flux is proportional to the rate of dissipation of energy per unit of distance transported, dimensional considerations indicate that the distance transported is proportional to the ratio between the energy flux and the sediment flux, a ratio of 2×10^6 meters. If the energy were expended only in sediment transport, the dissipation of the energy would require that each sediment grain be transported a distance of 2,000 kilometers![3] Even under the inefficient coupling that exists in nature it is apparent that the potential for sediment transport in nearshore waters is great.

TECHNOLOGY AND ENGINEERING
FOR THE COASTAL ZONE

Our understanding of shore processes is still in a very rudimentary stage. Most important phenomena and their interactions can-

[3] The general relation is $I = K\Omega$, where I is the rate of sediment transport (immersed weight in newton/seconds), Ω is the energy flux per unit of distance transported (watt/meters), and K is a dimensionless constant of proportionality, assumed to be unity for this calculation (Inman and Bagnold, 1963; Inman, et al., 1969).

not be described by rigorous theory. It is only during the past five years or so that experiment and measurement have progressed to the point where general concepts can be formulated and tested. As a consequence, engineering and technology for the coastal zone have not advanced to the point where the problems of today can be adequately handled.

In contrast, there are ever increasing demands on the world's coastal zone for habitation, recreation, industry, shipping, marine resources, and the disposal of many kinds of wastes. In short, our increasing demands are far exceeding our technological ability to deal with them. This presents a most serious problem, having worldwide proportions.

It was once thought that the ocean was an infinite sink for waste of all kinds, and that pollution was a local problem concerned only with maintaining sufficiently rapid dispersion of the effluent so as to keep the count of ecoli bacteria to acceptable levels. We now know that there are very definite hazards associated with an entire spectrum of waste products ranging from DDT to detergents to thermal pollution. The problem is no longer just that of local dispersion, but the more serious one of background level over large coastal and oceanic areas. As an example, coastal power plants circulate sea water for cooling, and require the power equivalent of 1.4 watts coolant for each watt of electrical power generated.

The predicted California coastal power plant requirements for 1980 is 37,000 megawatts. This will use coolant at the rate of 1.2×10^{10} calories per second, and is equivalent to a flow of sea water of 12,000 cubic meters per second heated by 1° Celsius. This flow is one-one-thousandth of the total flow of the California Current, one of the oceans' permanent current systems.

From the standpoint of beach erosion, the most frequent and most obvious coastal problems have resulted from the interruption of the longshore transport of sand by coastal structures such as jetties and breakwaters. These structures often act as dams that intercept the longshore movement of sand, causing sand to pile up on one side of the structure and to erode on the other (Inman and Frautschy, 1966). Santa Barbara Harbor on the

California coast is the most studied structure of this type. The harbor acts as a giant sand trap, intercepting most of the long-shore flow of sand, which averages about 230,000 cubic meters per year. For the first ten years following its construction in 1927–1930, the harbor caused erosion of the beaches that progressed down coast from the harbor at the rate of about one mile per year, and resulted in damage to the coast of about 1 million per year.

From the standpoint of beach preservation, the most serious conflict results from the loss of beach sand by dams constructed for flood control, water supply, and hydroelectric power. There seems to be no simple solution to this problem; the specific objectives of the flood control dams are to prevent the occurrence of floods, which are the principle sediment transporting agent. The sediment carrying capacity of streams increases, as the cube of the flow rate, so that the same total volume released over longer periods does not produce the same sediment transport.

Coastal communities are in the curious position of rapidly acquiring and improving beach frontage without criteria for evaluating the likelihood of the beaches' existence in ten or twenty years. It is imperative that we develop the means to preserve the beaches and harbors that we now have and that we develop practical techniques for creating new beaches and shoreline facilities.

References

Bowen, A. J., and Inman, D. L. 1969. Rip currents; Part 2: Laboratory and field observations. *Jour. Geophys. Res.* 74: 5479–5490.

Cox, C. S., and Sandstrom, H. 1962. Coupling of internal and surface waves in water of variable depth. *Jour. Oceanographic Soc. of Japan,* 20th Anniversary Vol., 499–513.

Gibbs, R. J. 1967. The geochemistry of the Amazon River system; Part 1: the factors that control the salinity and the composition and concentration of the suspended solids, *Geological Soc. of Amer. Bull.* 78: 1203–1232.

Gilluly, J. 1955. Geologic contrasts between continents and ocean basins 7–18 in A. Poldervaart, ed., *Crust of the earth*. Geol. Soc. Amer. Special Paper 62: 762 pp.

Holeman, J. N. 1968. The Sediment yield of major rivers of the world. *Water Resources Research*, 4, No. 4: 737–741.

Inman, D. L., and Bagnold, R. A. 1963. Littoral processes. *The Sea: Ideas and observations* 3, The Earth beneath the sea, M. N. Hill, ed. Interscience Publ., 529–553.

Inman, D. L., and Frautschy, A. J. 1966. Littoral processes and the development of shorelines. *Coastal Engineering*. Santa Barbara Specialty Conf. Amer. Soc. Civ. Engrs., 511–536.

Inman, D. L., Komar, P. D., and Bowen, A. J. 1969. Longshore transport of sand. Eleventh Conf. on Coastal Engineering. London: *Amer. Soc. Civil Engrs.* 1: 298–306.

Inman, D. L., Munk, H. W., Balay, M. 1962. Spectra of low frequency ocean waves along the Argentine shelf. *Deep-Sea Research* 8: 155–164.

Jeffreys, H. 1962. *The Earth; its origin, history and physical constitution*. Cambridge: Cambridge Univ. Press, 438 pp.

Kinsman, B. 1965. *Wind waves; their generation and propagation on the ocean surface*. Englewood Cliffs, N.J.: Prentice-Hall, Inc., 676 pp.

LaFond, E. C. 1962. Internal waves. *The Sea: ideas and observations*, 1, Physical Oceanography, M. N. Hill, ed. Interscience Publ., 731–751.

Leopold, L. B., Wolman, M. G., and Miller, J. P. 1964. *Fluvial processes in geomorphology*, Freeman and Co., 522 pp.

Malkus, J. S. 1962. Large-scale interactions, *The Sea: ideas and observations*, 1, Physical Oceanography, M. N. Hill, ed. Interscience Publ., 88–294.

Menard, H. W., 1960. Possible pre-Pleistocene deep-sea fans off Central California. *Geological Soc. Amer. Bull* 71: 1271–1278.

Menard, H. W. 1961. Some rates of regional erosion. *Jour. of Geology*, 69, No. 2: p. 154–161.

Munk, W. H., and MacDonald, G. J. F. 1960. *The Rotation of the earth; a geophysical discussion*. Cambridge: Cambridge Univ. Press, 373 pp.

Neumann, G., and Pierson, Jr., W. J. 1966. *Principles of physical oceanography*, Englewood Cliffs, N.J.: Prentice-Hall, Inc., 545 pp.

Schumm, S. A. 1963. The Disparity between present rates of denudation and orogeny. *U.S. Geological Survey*, Prof. Paper 454-H, 13 pp.

Shepard, F. P. 1963. *Submarine geology*. New York: Harper and Row, 557 pp.

Stommel, H. 1958. *The Gulf stream: a physical and dynamical description*, University of California Press and Cambridge University Press, 202 pp.

Sverdrup, H. V.; Johnson, M. W.; Fleming, R. H. 1942. *The Oceans; their Physics, Chemistry, and General Biology*, Englewood Cliffs, N.J.: Prentice-Hall, Inc., 1087 pp.

Van Dorn, W. G. 1965. Tsunamis. *Advances in Hydroscience*. New York: Academic Press, 2: p. 1–48.

25 FISHERY FORECASTING FOR FOOD FROM THE SEA

Glenn A. Flittner

Since time immemorial, man has used the living resources of the sea for his food and commerce. Before Aristotle's day, our ancient ancestors explored the edge of the sea, and began harvesting those living sea resources that were most easily accessible. As they gained experience in building nets, traps, and fishing craft worthy of the sea's elements, men began to push farther from shore in their search for food. And, as they began to multiply in population centers about the world, men began to experience the consequences of overfishing—and pressed ever farther into the offshore zone and into the depths.

By 1800 distant-water fisheries began to evolve in several areas of the world, each developing quite different methods according to the character of the species being pursued. By 1970 we witnessed an explosive expansion of high-seas fisheries into all the world's oceans—such that by the year 2000, Wilbert Chapman, author of Chapter 22, on the fisheries of the world, believes that up to 690 million metric tons of fish, shellfish, and other edible materials will be harvested annually.

This explosive expansion is being aided by a rapidly expanding marine science and technology community that will develop the means of exploiting virtually every living marine resource now known to man. Paradoxically, this expansion will continue to depend primarily upon the wild stocks of the world oceans; the competition between sovereign nations for the harvest of these so-called "common property" resources will multiply by at least a factor of ten. At such time as the world community of nations presses the natural resilience of these wild stocks to the fullest capacity, practical management and regulatory systems, as well as the fishery industrial system itself, will require a wide variety of forecasts so as to harvest at an optimum level and yet maintain these living resources in perpetuity.

To better understand the breadth of the forecasting challenge, one must first take a look at the nature of the problem.

Two general kinds of problems arise with the rapid expansion of the development and exploitation of the living resources of the sea. One problem concerns the rational management and use of these common property resources so as to reduce or minimize conflict between nations and societies and yet maintain the stock's yield in perpetuity. The second problem arises from major fluctuations in the availability and abundance of the stocks being fished. Rational solutions to both problems require specific kinds of forecasts so that man may make orderly use of his marine resources.

All fishes and aquatic invertebrates are hungry prisoners of their environment. Each species requires specific kinds of food and is physiologically and behaviorally suited to a specific range in the aquatic realm. Each species is also suited, to a greater or lesser degree, to a relatively limited range of physical oceanographic and meteorological conditions. Their requirements change during their lifetime as they hatch, grow, mature, spawn, and die; their requirements also vary with the seasons because of changing physical and biological conditions which bring about migrations, spawning and other characteristic forms of behavior.

The world's major fishery resource areas are generally known for each season of the year. This knowledge has been assembled over centuries by a lay fishermen's community having little understanding of the reasons for the occurrence of a resource in a specific region. The knowledge is retained on a personal basis through the experience of the individual fisherman and his forefathers, and is oftentimes regarded as trade secrets among fellow fishermen. Consequently, local concentrations and behavior are often poorly known because of the lack of specific detail and accumulated knowledge of the relation of the fishes and invertebrates to their day-to-day environment. The required detail for such understanding has not yet been accumulated for many of the well-established fisheries, despite research that has been conducted on them for many years.

Today fishermen must still search ocean areas on the basis of memory and past practice to find concentrations of fish suitably available to their equipment. Most fishermen have little understanding of the interrelations of the biology of the resource with oceanography and meteorology.

Fishermen have long experienced the frustration of being "on the fish" one day and "off" the next. When schools of fish move away and cannot be relocated, fishermen are faced with the challenge of deciding where to look next. Then, without knowing why the fish have disappeared, and their most probable behavior during the interval, the fisherman must begin a search of the district until he finds the same fish reassembled in another place, or another aggregation of the same species. This procedure is tantamount to hunting, and becomes highly inefficient when it is conducted in secrecy by individual vessels.

In some fisheries, vessel operators exchange information concerning catches, locations, and fishing strategy. In highly competitive fisheries where the effort is high and the catch relatively low, fishermen are commonly reluctant to work cooperatively and to divulge information to others. Some fisheries have evolved intricate code systems to pass intelligence on to favored friends.

As a consequence, a hard-headed, single-minded, fatalistic philosophy has evolved among professional fishermen: they think that they alone can catch most of the fish in an area, and that they must fill their vessel first before other vessels arrive on the scene. Luck becomes paramount: they further hope that, having filled their vessels with fish, they can run to port, unload their catch and return to the same aggregation again. Experience has shown this to be contrary to fact: most aggregations of fish are transient. They move or disperse for natural reasons before they can be fished again, and it is seldom that a fisherman finds a school of fish where he last left it. He must commence his hunt all over again.

Based on evidence that there are sufficient stocks of fish and invertebrates to support a greatly expanded world fishing industry, many fishing companies, some with national government subsidy support, are constructing larger, better equipped, and more expensive vessels having ever-larger appetites for the tonnages required to yield an adequate return on their investment. When one considers the narrow profit margins in many commercial fisheries, it becomes essential that the fleets operate more efficiently, spending far less time traveling to and from the fishing grounds and searching, and much more time in fishing than they do now.

Another major problem facing the entire fishing industry relates to fluctuations in the availability and abundance of the stocks being fished. Neither fishermen nor processor can plan their operations efficiently when major disruptions in supply occur. Thus, it is essential to the proper management and conservation of the stocks that we know when there will be good and bad spawning years and good and bad growth years, so that conservation measures can be altered to suit the changing events within the fishery resource. No longer can we treat each species on an exclusive basis: we must have sufficient data on all major fishery stocks so as to be able to recommend the point in time when it would be in the best interests of the industry to shift from one kind of fish to another. By knowing when a given stock is being overtaxed, either by fishing pressure, environmental pressure, or both, the fishing industry would be better served if it were advised to move from stock to stock as scientific findings and predictions warrant.

Recognizing the two general problems mentioned previously, what are the major kinds of forecasts that must be made, and what are the prospects for achieving these objectives?

Two kinds of forecasts are required by the world fishing community and its regulatory bodies: first, long-term forecasts; second, short-term forecasts and information services. Furthermore, each of these forecasts has two basic components, one biological and the other environmental (or physical). Thus, each specific forecast will deal with trends within the resource and within its food base, its relation to environmental trends, and a mixture of meteorological and oceanographic predictions. In addition to these components, each forecasting system requires sociological and economic inputs, depending upon a particular society's needs.

Governmental agencies and processors—but also fishermen and boat owners—have an urgent need for long-term predictions and advisory information. Distant-water fisheries having tremendous capital investments must know how much a fish stock can be expected to yield. For example, in the Pacific Ocean the question now being asked is whether or not the annual yield of skipjack tuna can be sustained at the 100,000, 200,000, or 500,000 ton level. In addition, the nature of a particular season, that is, good or bad production levels, early or late, big fish or small fish, shortage or abundance of preferred species—seriously affects the entire fish industry. The ultimate objective of such long-term predictions would be to enable better planning and operations, and to permit improved treaty agreements and management and regulatory measures to be taken.

Both the fisherman and the processor benefit from the constant updating of present conditions and short-term projections of the trends of several variables. Environmental conditions, such as sea temperature and especially weather, seriously alter the course of daily events. Fishing operations and strategy are planned over intervals of one month down to about five days, depending upon boat characteristics and the kind of fish being hunted. Tactical decisions are made from day to day, and even on an hourly basis. For example, the Pacific Coast tuna fishery may elect to move 300 to 1,000 miles during a 4- or 5-day interval to exploit new grounds. Processors, by having constantly updated information, can plan for surges in landings caused by boats seeking refuge from the weather or coming upon unexpected aggregations of fish, and can make better decisions affecting day-to-day unloading, storage, canning, and marketing operations.

The long-range forecast is the most difficult. We must obtain much more knowledge than is presently available to establish a basis for long-term projections of the biological, environmental, social, and economic variables that are part of the system.

The short-term forecast is the more practical of the two. Advances in communications and computer technology provide the means for constant contact with daily events on a worldwide scale; short-term forecasts are now considered the "state of the art." One example is the albacore and bluefin tuna forecasting system that I have helped to develop at La Jolla, California, over the past nine years.

Four species of tuna support the United States tuna fishery in the eastern Pacific Ocean. The California-based industry fishes from Vancouver Island on the north, at about 50 degrees N latitude, all the way south to Antofagasta, Chile, at about 25 degrees S latitude. The fishery operates in both the tropical equatorial region and the temperate zones at both the northern and southern limits of the range. The species harvested are the albacore, the bluefin, the yellowfin, and the skipjack. The yellowfin and skipjack are tropical species comprising the bulk of the harvest, which is taken in the district from upper Baja California, Mexico, down to Peru. The yellowfin is the major tuna species in value and tonnage, and the skipjack is the secondary species. The albacore tuna is the only species accepted for the fancy white-meat pack, and commands the highest price at the dockside, whereas the bluefin is a lesser-valued species, but commands a higher price than skipjack and is harvested in the smallest quantities of the four. Albacore are found along the North American coastal region from southern Baja California, Mexico to Vancouver Island, British Columbia, Canada. Bluefin range from southern Baja California to the Columbia River, but are most common south of central California.

One of the problems that has persistently plagued the tuna fishing industry has been availability. Of the four species, yellowfin tuna appear to be most uniformly available to fishermen, whereas albacore and skipjack appear to be most unpredictable from year to year and season to season. Bluefin appear to be less problematical.

Our best record of fluctuations in distribution has been observed for the albacore tuna. Since 1940, landings of albacore have varied widely, and California, Oregon, and Washington have experienced large fluctuations. In 1953–1955 California waters produced almost all the albacore, whereas in 1966–1969 Oregon and Washington waters yielded up to 75 per cent of the total albacore production, reflecting major dislocations of as much as 1,000 miles in the centers of the distribution and availability of the species.

The tropical tuna fishery characteristically moves northward into Baja California waters during the Northern Hemisphere summer, and exhibits similar but less noticeable movements to southern latitudes during the Southern Hemisphere summer. Fish are found intermittently all through the year in the region of the meteorological equator, about 5 degrees N latitude, but one readily observes that the coastal and offshore region visited by the tropical tuna fleet exceeds a distance of 5,000 nautical miles. Finding fishable concentrations in this vast region becomes a major problem at times.

All the major tuna fisheries move rapidly from place to place during a given season. For example, in the temperate tuna fisheries, albacore may be found near Guadalupe Island, about 30 degrees N latitude, in June when the fishery usually commences, but may occur as far north as Cape Flattery, about 49 degrees N, by early September. Bluefin usually appear just north of Cape San Lucas, Baja California, about 22 degrees N in June, and later appear off southern California, about 33 degrees N by early September. Yellowfin and skipjack may be found at 20 degrees N off the coast of Mexico in January but occur off Baja California at 30 degrees N by mid-August. In each instance, the movement is highly variable from year to year and is related to changes in oceanographic conditions.

The general coastal migratory patterns thus follow a poleward course from winter to summer, depending upon whether one is

345

in the Northern or Southern Hemispheres. One of the factors that dictate this cyclical pattern of movement is sea surface temperature. We know that the 21 degrees C limit is significantly correlated with the summer appearance of both yellowfin and skipjack off Baja California. The degree of northward movement varies from year to year: the farther north the limiting temperature occurs, the farther north the tropical species are found. A similar situation prevails for albacore and bluefin tuna.

One of the other important features is the vertical temperature structure of the upper layer of the sea. Temperature characteristically declines with increasing depth; the zone of sharp decrease is called the thermocline. A purse seine's efficiency is affected by the depth and intensity of the thermocline—when the thermocline is shallow and the waters underneath are cold, the yellowfin and skipjack tend to stay up in the net. As the rings are closed and the net is pursed, the fish do not dive down and are captured. When the thermocline is deep, the fish are willing to dive down and escape during pursing operations. Thus, good fishing strategy in the tropical tuna fishery is to look for areas where the first set of conditions prevails; when schools are found and the net is set, the probability of catching the tuna is significantly enhanced.

The albacore tuna, the most cold-tolerant of the four species, exhibits a similar kind of temperature relationship: a 5-year tabulation of albacore logbook data for approximately 7,000 tons of troll-caught fish landed in California shows that the modal temperature is about 17 degrees C and the upper and lower two-thirds limits are about 15.5 degrees C and 20.0 degrees C.

The same situation prevails with bluefin tuna. This is a purse seine fishery, and excellent logbooks maintained by the fleet have provided similar information. Analysis of a 3-year record including approximately 20,000 tons of bluefin has shown that the bulk of the catch is taken near the modal temperature of 19.5 degrees C, and the upper and lower two-thirds limits are 16.7 degrees C and 21.7 degrees C.

It should be apparent at this point that the tuna fishing industry would benefit considerably by having the right kind of sea temperature information. Furthermore, not only analyses of present temperature conditions, but forecasts of future temperature conditions would be extremely useful.

One of our most difficult problems in forecasting the sea temperature structure for the tuna fisheries is that we have insufficient hydroclimatological data for the world oceans on which to base forecast models. The thermal cycle in the upper layer of the sea has been only generally described and is still poorly understood. In the tropical seas, too little useful data are available even to describe existing conditions, especially in the Southern Hemisphere. In the Northern Hemisphere, sufficient data are now at hand, particularly in the Pacific Ocean, but forecast models are largely empirical and have little statistical or physical basis.

Up to now our only successful applications of temperature forecasts have been for albacore and bluefin tuna. Until more observational data become available, forecasts of thermal conditions in the tropical seas inhabited by yellowfin and skipjack tuna cannot be attempted.

The first step in our forecasting program was to analyze and publish charts of average sea temperature conditions for the eastern Pacific Ocean on a monthly basis. The second step was to commence publication of average sea temperature conditions for the west coast of the United States on fifteen-day intervals each year starting on April 15 and ending on October 31. These charts have been most useful to the albacore and bluefin tuna fleets who operate in districts where the temperature conditions vary considerably over short intervals. The third step was to recognize that these publications most often failed to reach the primary producer who most needs to see them—but is at sea—so in 1966 we commenced a series of daily albacore fishing information broadcasts from a radio station located on the Scripps Institution of Oceanography campus at La Jolla, California. These broadcasts commence on June 1 and terminate on October 31, and include the latest albacore information obtained from research vessels, fishing vessels, and unloading station operators. They also contain sea temperature reports, regional weather

347

information, and current market prices and unloading information whenever it is pertinent.

The fourth step is still in progress. In the past four years we have heard a common reply: ". . . don't tell us what it was like during the last interval, but give us forecasts for the next period, so that we can plan where to operate next . . ."

In 1966 we first attempted to forecast sea surface temperatures off the Pacific Coast. Using our own five-year data base, we determined the average temperatures for each fifteen-day chart, and the average temperature differences as well for the season. Then, starting with the existing analysis for the initial period we added the average temperature change of record and graphically constructed a "prognostic" chart which served as a first approximation to the new sea surface temperature field to be realized two weeks later. At the close of the calendar interval, we then graphically compared the actual analysis with the prognostic chart and computed the error field. Our first experiment proved to be disappointing. Our experience subsequent to this first experiment has shown that accurate climatological forecasts up to fifteen days in advance are required before meaningful progress can be made in sea surface temperature forecasting.

From this discussion, it should be clear that our fishery forecasting challenge is manifold: to give meaningful sea surface temperature prognostic charts to the tuna fishermen, we must first have accurate climatological forecasts for periods of up to fifteen days. In the absence of workable models that can predict weather so far in advance, it has been necessary to shorten the forecast interval and to increase the day-to-day reporting of synoptic information.

In 1966 we established a connection to the U.S. Navy's environmental data network. The Navy's master computer facility at Monterey, California, assembles meteorological and oceanographic information from all over the world, and processes the data into convenient charts and other interpretive formats on a regular time schedule. In exchange for this service, we have collected environmental data from research, fishing, and other cooperating vessels for transmission to Monterey for incorporation into the charts. Today we receive regularly about 30 to 40 oceanographic and meteorological products selected from the Fleet Numerical Weather Central's portfolio of over 150 scheduled analyses produced each twelve hours. Certain charts are updated at 1-, 3-, 12-, and twenty-four-hour intervals, thus enabling our staff to monitor environmental changes almost as they occur. Significant changes are reported by daily radio advisories or bulletin as soon as trends are discernible.

Our forecasting capability has been substantially advanced by the activities of the Fleet Numerical Weather Central at Monterey. For the first time we have the capacity to assimilate and interpret large masses of synoptic data on an orderly basis, and to relay our interpretations to the fishing community while the information still has value.

The experience of the albacore tuna fishing seasons in 1966 through 1969 seems to indicate some measure of success. In 1966, just as we were observing the poorest July start in over twenty years in southern California, Oregon was experiencing the earliest opening since 1950. Our first bulletin was broadcast by radio on July 15, noting that weather and sea conditions had favored early movement of albacore into Oregon, bypassing California waters. In about ten days, a large part of the California fleet moved north on the basis of our daily radio broadcasts and arrived on the northern grounds at least two weeks earlier than previously. The result was an estimated 1,800 tons of albacore valued at about $780,000, which was caught at the beginning of a season, which, even though the fishermen operated at peak capacity the remainder of the year, fell short of the 1945–1966 average production by almost 15 per cent.

In 1967 the fishing community accepted our advisory information very early, and consequently it was difficult to tell just how much our activities may have added to the catch. However, we do know that our monitoring of the unusual oceanographic warming off Oregon and Washington successfully foretold another unusual northern year. We issued our first bulletin of the season on July 14 and published a follow-up bulletin on July 31, which alerted the industry to the rapid changes that were

349

taking place. Despite the latest start in several years, virtually 90–95 per cent of the albacore production was subsequently taken off Oregon and Washington in the seventy-day interval between July 21 and September 28. All-time record catches were logged by southern California baitboats operating far north of their usual range, and even though the entire albacore season lasted between eighty and ninety days, almost 19,000 tons were produced, placing 1967 right on the 1945–1966 production average.

In 1968 the albacore fishery was centered in Pacific Northwest waters again, which we first reported in our bulletin on July 15. Subsequently, despite persistent bad weather, an early-season price dispute lasting more than two weeks after the albacore appeared off southern California, and unloading delays in northern ports, a near-record production year followed. Catches off Oregon set an all-time record since albacore were first landed there in 1935–1936, and the combined United States–Canadian landings totals placed 1968 in the third highest position for all years since the fishery first started in California in 1915.

In 1969, subsequent to the issuance of our preseason forecast statements, we attempted to vector the fleet onto the first fish of the season off Cape Mendocino by assisting a fishing vessel via nightly radio-telephone patches through our radio station at the Scripps Institution. In the June 15–30 interval, the boat took the first fish of the season 450 miles WSW of Cape Mendocino. Despite a longer season, widespread fishing effort and the most information yet available to the fleet, 1969 production totals only pulled up to average in the November-December period. The reasons for this poor production record are not clear, but one factor may be overfishing in an unregulated fishery. We did conclude, however, that the industry would have fared even worse without our assistance.

We know that the tuna fishing industry now depends heavily on our services. The sea temperature chart series provides the basic information, but the radio broadcasts have permitted the fishermen to cope more effectively with environmental "unknowns." Changes observed in vessel design and fleet operation strategy in the past four–five years also suggest that the impact of these services is substantial.

In the future, as the maritime nations push to the sea with ever-growing needs for animal protein, fishing competition for the common property resources of the sea will become extremely keen. At that point, fishermen, in their search to maintain competitive advantage, may have the need for special kinds of services that will help them to use their fishfinding devices, such as sonar, to better advantage. When this day comes, we plan to provide them regularly with information on temperature and sound velocity profiles, ranges, sound ray envelopes, and the like. The technology of these problems has already been explored, and it will be a relatively simple task for us to adapt these techniques to fishery needs.

Other new problems will arise as we push farther along on the road to better fishery forecasts. Other major fisheries besides tuna could well benefit from forecasting and monitoring activities performed in much the same manner as has been described above. Each regional fishery will present a somewhat different set of problems—but as we begin to understand the relation between meteorological, oceanographic, and biological events, so also will we become capable of providing meaningful information to the entire fishing industry.

Until the time comes when we have developed sufficient knowledge and experience to begin to manipulate the gene pools of most of the wild stocks of marine fishes, and to begin "farming" on a truly oceanwide scale, we must continue to be the hunters. Refinement of a truly global marine environmental monitoring and prediction system patterned along the lines that have been described will enable the world community of fishermen to carry out their hunting operations on a more rational basis, maximizing production and yet maintaining fishery resource stocks in perpetuity for the benefit of all.

26 CIRCULATION AND MIXING IN COASTAL REGIONS AND ESTUARIES

Donald W. Pritchard

Man's most intimate contact with the marine environment occurs in coastal waters and in estuaries. It is in these areas that man harvests the largest part of the living resources he takes from the sea. At present, virtually the only nonliving resources, such as minerals, oil, and gas, which man extracts from the sea and the sea bottom are taken from the coastal regions and estuaries. A large fraction of the unwanted byproducts of man's activities, that is, waste products, enter the estuaries and coastal regions either directly as discharges from industrial and municipal sewage outfalls, or indirectly via rivers into which wastes have been discharged from interior regions of the continents.

Approximately 50 million people live within the coastal belt bordering the estuaries and ocean shore lines of the United States, and the rate of growth of population and industry in this belt exceeds that of the rest of the nation. Consequently, use of estuarine and nearshore coastal waters as receivers of waste materials is increasing at a rapid rate. During the next several decades the open coastal waters, between one-quarter of a mile and twenty miles off-shore, will in particular feel the impact of this growth in waste discharges. Despite this fact, more is known about the currents in the open ocean than is known about the circulation patterns in this nearshore zone of the coastal region.

Studies conducted over the last twenty years have provided

considerable information on the general character of the circulation pattern and the mixing processes in estuaries. An increased awareness of the need for knowledge of the physical processes of movement and mixing of the waters of the open coastal zone has led to the initiation of studies which are now providing some information on the basic character of the physical processes in these waters.

Historically, the term "estuary" has been applied primarily to the lower tidal reaches of a river. A review of some of the dictionary definitions is appropriate as a starting point. *The Concise Oxford Dictionary* gives, simply: "Tidal mouth of a large river." *Webster's New 20th Century Dictionary* states: "An army of the sea; a frith or firth; a narrow passage, or the mouth of a river or lake, where the tide meets the river current." *Webster's New International Dictionary* has: "(a) A passage, as the mouth of a river or lake where the tide meets the river current; more commonly, an arm of the sea at the lower end of a river; a firth. (b) In physical geography, a drowned river mouth, caused by the sinking of land near the coast."

The French dictionary, *Larousse,* brings in a somewhat different concept, giving as a definition of an estuary (when translated into English): "A coastline bight which is covered with water only at high tide. A gulf formed by the mouth of a river." The second sentence refers to a drowned river mouth. However, the first part of this definition seems peculiar to the French. It describes, for example, the region near Mont St. Michel where a curving region of the coast is covered at high tide and bare at low tide. This area cannot be described as a coastal embayment, and there is no dilution of sea water—features that are important in defining an estuary.

From a physical standpoint, the definition of an estuary should recognize certain basic similarities in the distribution of salinity and density, as well as the circulation pattern and the mixing processes; it should also point out the importance of the boundaries that control the distribution of properties and the movement and mixing of waters.

Taking these features into account, an estuary can be defined as a semienclosed coastal body of water that has a free connection with the open sea and within which sea water is measurably diluted with fresh water derived from land drainage.

First, consider the requirement that an estuary be "a semienclosed coastal body of water." The circulation pattern in an estuary is influenced to a considerable degree by its lateral boundaries. This control of the water movements by the lateral boundaries is an important feature of an estuary and should be taken into account in the definition.

Furthermore, the definition states that the estuary is a coastal feature and hence limits to some extent the size of the bodies of water under consideration. The intent here is that the estuary be a part of the coast and not form the coast. Admittedly, the application of this restriction involves somewhat arbitrary decisions. By this part of my definition I would exclude the Baltic Sea, the adjacent Gulf of Bothnia, and the Gulf of Finland from being designated as estuaries, despite other similarities. To me, the Baltic Sea and the adjacent Gulf of Bothnia and Gulf of Finland form the coastline rather than being a feature of the coastline. The physical significance of this restriction is that the lateral boundaries of such relatively large bodies of water are less important to the kinematics and dynamics of water movement than they are in a true estuary.

The next requirement of the definition, that of "a free connection with the open sea," is included to indicate that communication between the ocean and the estuary must be adequate to transmit tidal energy and sea salts. The free connection must allow an essentially continuous exchange of water between the estuary and the ocean. Again, it must be admitted that the definition does not perfectly delimit the character of the connection between the ocean and the coastal indenture required for the body of water to be classed as an estuary. In the great majority of cases, however, there should be no problem in concluding whether the connection is, in fact, "free."

We come finally to the phrase in the definition requiring that, within the estuary, sea water be "measurably diluted with fresh water derived from land drainage." This dilution of sea water provides the density gradients that drive the characteristic estuarine circulation patterns. There are embayments in the coastline in which evaporation equals or exceeds the freshwater inflow; these water bodies are not considered to be estuaries, although much that we learn about water movement and mixing in estuaries can, with appropriate modification, be applied to these other coastal bays and lagoons.

Having now defined an estuary, we should consider some possible subclassifications based on physical characteristics. From a geomorphological standpoint, there are four primary subdivisions of estuaries: (1) drowned river valleys, (2) fjord-type estuaries, (3) bar-built estuaries, and (4) estuaries produced by tectonic processes.

Drowned river valleys are the classical estuaries of the physical geographer. Because they are most commonly found along a coastline with a relatively wide coastal plain, and are generally confined to that geological regime, I have called these waterways coastal plain estuaries. This designation has received relatively widespread use in the United States.

The Chesapeake Bay is a prime example of this type of estuary. During the last glacial period, the Susquehanna River reached the ocean about 180 kilometers seaward of the present shoreline; the York River and the other rivers now entering the Bay to the north of the York were then tributaries of the Susquehanna. The James River probably reached the sea separately. The rise in sea level by about 100 meters following the glacial period, roughly 10,000 years ago, flooded the valleys of these rivers to form the Chesapeake Bay System.

Drowned river valleys are not only typical of the eastern seaboard of the United States, but are widespread throughout the world. It should be pointed out, with respect to the coastal plain estuaries, that by the definition given here not all the length of the drowned river valley would be classified as an estuary. The phrase "within which sea water is measurably diluted by fresh water" implies not only that there must be a supply of fresh water to mix with the sea water, but conversely that the estuary proper extends up the drowned river valley only as far as there is a measurable amount of sea salts. In most coastal plain estuaries the river bottom does not rise above sea level for a considerable distance landward from the point at which the last vestiges of sea-derived salt can be measured. The "fresh" water of the river of course has some dissolved solids, and, therefore, has a salt content. Even so, the upper limit of the estuary, as defined by the most landward intrusion of sea-derived salt, can be quite sharply delineated, because the ionic ratios of the major constituents in the river water are quite different from those in sea water. For example, the ratio of chloride ion to total dissolved solids in the sea is about 1:1.8, whereas this ratio in "freshwater" rivers is more characteristically 1:10 or 1:20.

Above this upper limit of the estuary there is usually a stretch of the freshwater river that is still subject to the oscillation of the tidal currents. The duration of the flood period as compared to the ebb period will decrease until a point is reached where the downriver flow just ceases at what would be maximum flood. There then occurs a further stretch of the river that is subject to a tidal variation in water elevation, and within which there is a time variation in the downstream velocity, but without any flood flow. The tidal effect on surface elevation frequently can be traced, under certain flow conditions, to the point at which the river bed rises above sea level. The stretch of the fresh river above the upper limit of intrusion of sea-derived salt that is still subject to tidal action is called the tidal section of the river.

Fjords are coastal indentures that have been gouged out by glaciers. They are generally U-shaped in cross-section, and frequently have a shallow sill formed by terminal glacial deposits at their mouths. The basins inside the sills are often quite deep: 300 or 400 meters. Most fjords have rivers entering at the head and exhibit estuarine features in the upper layers. The sill depths in Norwegian fjords are often so shallow that the estuarine features develop from the surface to the sill depth, while the deeper basin waters remain stagnant for prolonged periods. Some fjords along the British Columbia coast have greater sill depths, and the estuarine layers do not extend down to the sill.

In this case the basin waters are subjected to a slow but steady exchange with the adjacent open sea waters.

When offshore barrier sand islands and sand spits build above sea level and extend between headlands in a chain, broken by one or more inlets, bar-built estuaries are formed. The area enclosed by the barrier beaches is generally elongated parallel to the coastline. Frequently more than one river enters into the estuary, although the total drainage area feeding a bar-built estuary is seldom large. The lower valleys of such rivers have frequently been drowned by the rising sea level, and hence the bar-built estuary might be considered as a composite system, one part being an outer embayment partially enclosed by the barrier beaches, and another part being a drowned river valley or valleys. Because the inlets connecting the bar-built estuary with the ocean are usually relatively small as compared to the dimensions of the sound within the barrier, tidal action is considerably reduced in such estuaries. These systems are usually shallow, and the wind provides the important mixing mechanism. Albemarle Sound and Pamlico Sound in North Carolina are examples of bar-built estuaries.

The fourth category, estuaries produced by tectonic processes, is a catchall classification for estuaries not clearly included in the other three divisions. Coastal indentures formed by faulting or by local subsidence, and having an excess supply of freshwater inflow, are covered by this category. San Francisco Bay is an example of this group of estuaries.

It is an interesting fact that estuaries are transient geological features, peculiar to a relatively short geological period following a rise in sea level. The coastal plain estuaries we find today along coastlines throughout the world were formed by rivers that cut valleys through the coastal plain during the last glacial period, which terminated about 10,000 to 12,000 years ago. At that time the sea level stood about 100 meters below its present level, and rivers cut valleys through not only the present coastal plain but also across what is now the continental shelf. As the great continental ice sheet retreated, the sea level rose in several steps, with periods of relatively stable sea level occurring between periods of abrupt rise. During the early periods following each abrupt rise, new areas of the continents previously covered with ice were exposed. These areas, initially lacking an adequate stabilizing cover of vegetation, were subjected to rapid erosion, providing a large mass of sediment that filled the outer reaches of the then drowned river valleys on the continental shelves.

Following the last abrupt rise in sea level, about 4,000 years ago, sediment carried into estuaries by rivers was redistributed by tidal currents and by the nontidal estuarine circulation, thus shaping each estuary into a geomorphological form approximating that which we observe today.

During any prolonged period of relatively stable sea level, the ultimate fate of estuaries is to be filled with sediment and hence disappear. Man interacts with this natural process in two ways. First, man's activities on land generally increase the rate of erosion and hence the supply of sediment to the estuary; thus man tends to contribute to an increase in the rate at which the estuary is disappearing. On the other hand, most major harbors are within estuaries, and there is an ever-increasing demand for deeper and wider navigation channels serving such harbors. In some cases the dredged spoil from the construction and maintenance of such navigation channels is deposited in adjacent shoal areas of the estuary, and hence man is merely redistributing the sediment, without really modifying the ultimate fate of the estuary, that is, the filling of the estuary with sediment. In other instances, however, dredged spoil from navigation projects in estuaries is not returned to the estuary, but is either put on adjacent low-lying lands, or is carried out of the estuary to sea for disposal. In these cases man's activities are tending to delay the ultimate fate of the estuary. In addition, dams built on the rivers that ultimately discharge into estuaries, for the purpose of creating reservoirs for water supply, flood control, and hydroelectric projects, entrap some of the sediment supply and thus act to temporarily delay the ultimate fate of the estuary.

The mixing between the fresh water flowing into the estuary from the river or rivers, and the salt water from the sea provides the density distribution which drives the characteristic estuarine patterns. The density of natural waters increases as the salt content of water increases. Typically the salinity of an estuary increases more or less regularly from the head of the estuary toward the sea, and also increases with depth. Consequently, the density of the estuarine waters increases toward the sea as well as with depth.

Consider an elongated coastal indenture connected to a sea that has relatively small tides, such that the tidal currents in the estuary are relatively small. If there were no freshwater inflow into the head of the estuary, sea water would fill the embayment to the position where the bottom rises above sea level. An inflow of fresh water, as from a river discharging into the head of the embayment, would push the sea water down the estuary toward the sea, and also, because it is less dense, the fresh water would flow over the top of the intruding layers of sea water. The intruding ocean water would take the shape of a wedge underneath the seaward-flowing fresh water. The position of the edge of the sea-water wedge, that is, the extent of intrusion of the sea water up the estuary, would depend upon the rate of flow of fresh water. The tip of the salt water wedge occurs further down the estuary as the river inflow becomes larger. As the fresh water flows over the top of the salt water wedge, waves form on the very sharp density interface between the fresher upper layers and the wedge of sea water. At a critical relative velocity between these two layers of water, these interfacial waves break. However, these waves always break upward, thus cascading salt water from the wedge into the seaward flowing fresh water. As a result of the turbulence caused by the breaking waves, and by the seaward flow of the upper layer past roughness in the side boundaries of the estuary, the salt water thrown into the upper layer by the breaking waves is mixed into this layer. Consequently the salt content of the upper seaward flowing layer increases as the water in this layer moves seaward. Since no fresh water is concurrently mixed downwards, the salinity in the underlying salt wedge remains virtually constant along its length. However, since salt water is lost from the wedge into the upper layer by the breaking of the interfacial waves, and since we observe that, for a given river flow, the position of the wedge remains fixed, there must be an inflow of salt water from the ocean into the estuary in the lower layers which constitute the salt wedge.

Estuaries that have these characteristics are called, appropriately, salt-wedge estuaries. The lower reaches of the Mississippi River is a classical example of a salt-wedge estuary. During periods of low freshwater discharge, the wedge of virtually undiluted sea water extends along the bottom of the Mississippi for over 100 miles upstream. During periods of high river flow, the wedge is limited to a short stretch in the lower reaches of the delta of the Mississippi. Sediment that is carried down the Mississippi by the river flow, and that sinks into the salt wedge, is carried back up the river by the flow in the salt wedge, to become deposited at the upstream tip of the wedge. Thus the position of the wedge determines the areas of maximum shoaling, and hence the areas requiring most frequent dredging in order to maintain a navigation channel.

When the velocities associated with the oscillatory flow of the tidal currents in an estuary become large as compared to the net nontidal motion required to transport the inflowing fresh water on through the estuary to the sea, the tidal currents dominate the mixing processes. The sharp boundary between the upper, seaward flowing layer of relatively low salinity and the underlying layers of higher salinity is weakened such that mixing takes place in both directions. That is, the fresh water is mixed downwards at the same time that the saltier water is mixed upward. Consequently the underlying wedge of virtually undiluted sea water is replaced by a lower layer in which the salinity decreases more or less regularly from the mouth of the estuary toward the head of the estuary. These estuaries are called partially mixed estuaries. There remains a net nontidal circulation pattern with the upper layers moving seaward and the lower layers moving up the estuary. The volume rates of flow in the nontidal circulation of partially mixed estuaries is often very large compared to that found in salt wedge estuaries. Thus the seaward flow of lower salinity water in the upper layers is often found to be about ten times that of the freshwater river discharge, while the flow up the estuary of higher salinity water in the lower layers would then be nine times that of the river discharge. Note that the net seaward flow through the upper portion of any cross-section in the estuary must on the average exceed the flow up the estuary through the lower portion of that cross-section by a volume rate of flow just equal to the river discharge.

Most estuaries are of the partially mixed type in which the most obvious water movements to the casual observer are the oscillatory tidal currents, with water flowing up the estuary during the flood period and down the estuary during the ebb period. A careful observation of the distribution of current velocity and direction with depth reveals that in the near surface layers ebb currents are stronger, and last longer, than is the case of the near bottom layers. Conversely, flood currents are stronger and last longer in the near bottom layers than in the layers near the surface. The difference between the transport of water seaward during ebb tide and the transport of water up the estuary during flood tide gives the net nontidal flow which, as already noted, is directed down the estuary in the upper layers and up the estuary in the lower layers. The magnitude of the velocities associated with this net nontidal flow is generally only 10 to 20 per cent of the tidal velocities, and for this reason the tidal currents represent the most obvious water movements. The net nontidal circulation is, however, of primary importance in determining the flux of salt, or of some other dissolved or suspended material. The importance of the tidal currents is that these currents provide the energy for the turbulent mixing between the salt and fresh waters. This mixing in turn provides for the distribution of density, which again in turn provides the potential energy that drives the large scale, nontidal circulation pattern.

In order to consider the various mixing processes that occur in estuaries in greater detail, consider a waste effluent introduced via an outfall into the estuary. The subsequent fate of the introduced pollutant will be influenced by the physical properties of the effluent, and the method and the depth of its introduction. If the density of the effluent stream is less than that of the receiving waters, and the stream is introduced at the surface of the estuary, vertical mixing of the waste materials with the receiving waters will be inhibited. However, if this waste stream is introduced into the estuary near the bottom, the effluent will initially rise as a buoyant plume, entraining diluting water from the environment enroute to the surface. Since the estuary is seldom deep enough so that the ascending plume reaches the density of the receiving waters at an intermediate depth, the plume will spread out on the surface still somewhat lower in density than the surrounding estuarine waters.

If the waste effluent is denser than the estuarine waters, the waste stream will tend to spread out on the bottom. Initial mechanical dilution can be enhanced in this case by the introduction of the waste stream near the surface, thus providing for a descending plume that will entrain diluting water enroute to the bottom.

The major sources of pollution to an estuary are usually introduced into the waterway in effluent streams that are less dense than the receiving waters; therefore, further discussion will be limited to this case.

As indicated previously, the most effective way to introduce a waste stream that is less dense than the receiving waters would be as a bottom discharge. The effectiveness of the dilution of the ascending plume is enhanced by discharging the waste stream through a multiport diffuser, which is designed so that the ascending plumes just overlap on reaching the surface. This method produces an elongated volume source in the surface waters, which is then further subjected to the physical processes of movement and dispersion in the estuary.

If the method of effluent introduction produces a sufficient initial mechanical dilution so as to significantly reduce the density difference between the waste stream and the estuarine waters, further dilution by turbulent mixing is enhanced.

In the surface layers the diluted effluent will be extended into an elongated horizontal plume by the prevailing tidal currents. During ebb tide the plume will extend down the estuary, and during flood tide the plume will extend up the estuary. Turbulent diffusion will act along the length of the plume to spread the waste materials and to continually reduce the contaminant concentration at greater distances from the source. Each reversal of the tidal current will result in a folding back of the spreading plume. However, because of the large-scale turbulent eddies, the plume will seldom fold exactly back on itself and will also seldom follow the same path on successive tides. A widespread contaminant field of relatively low concentration will therefore develop on which is superimposed, on each tide, a relatively narrow plume of higher concentration.

Vertical mixing distributes some of the introduced waste material, after initial dilution in the surface layers, down into the deeper layers of the estuary. Hence the waste material will be transported up the estuary in the nontidal flow of the lower layer as well as down the estuary in the surface layers.

In the region of the estuary headward from the point of introduction, the concentrations of the pollutant will always be greater in the deeper layers than in the surface layers, while seaward from the point of introduction the converse will be true. These conditions prevail regardless of whether the wastes are initially introduced into the surface layers or into the deeper layers.

The pollutant is ultimately flushed from the estuary in the seaward-directed flow of the surface layers.

Tidal oscillations past irregularities in the shoreline are an important mechanism in the longitudinal dispersion of an introduced pollutant. This is made most evident by considering a contaminated volume produced by an instantaneous release as it is carried up and down the waterway by the tidal currents. Frequently eddies associated with slight embayments or with points of land that project into the waterway will temporarily trap water containing a high concentration as the contaminated volume moves past the shore features on one or the other phase of the tide. The main bulk of the contaminant is carried on past the shore feature by the tidal current, while the material trapped by the shore feature slowly spreads out into the main stream, leading to an effective dispersal behind the bulk of the contaminated volume. When the tide reverses, the process is repeated, with a resulting dispersion on the opposite side of the contaminated volume.

Thus we see that mixing between the fresh water derived from land run-off and salt water from the ocean provides the characteristic distribution of density in the estuary that drives the estuarine circulation pattern. Tidal currents are of primary importance in providing the energy for this mixing. Our knowledge of these primary mechanisms in an estuary is sufficient to allow us to describe, with some confidence, the fate of a pollutant introduced into an estuary.

Comparable knowledge is not yet available for the open coastal waters of the continental shelf. It is important that studies in these waters, which constitute the environment most likely next to feel the adverse impact of man's activities, be augmented and intensified so that the knowledge necessary for sensible management of man's use of these waters can be provided.

27 INTERNATIONAL COOPERATION

C. E. Lucas

The sea is our major highway. It is the very active, natural boundary of all our lands, with all that that signifies, as well as a vast natural source of power. Together with the atmosphere, the sea controls our weather and influences our climate. It is a natural solution of almost all the chemical elements along with an extraordinary variety of inorganic and organic compounds. The waters of the sea and the sea floor beneath cover 70 per cent of the earth's surface, and may be as rich as or richer in minerals than the land. The sea is also the source of our valuable marine fish supplies. The sea thus certainly merits intensive research and development by all nations.

Although most scientific research on the sea is now being done on a national basis, we have become used to the idea in recent years that in some fields progress can best, and sometimes can only, be made by international collaboration. What is often regarded as a new development in collaboration, however, is the international pooling of national resources on a considerable scale, to undertake investigations that would be beyond the resources of even a large country or to make progress faster than would be possible if only a single nation were performing the research.

In December 1966, the United Nations General Assembly passed a Resolution (2172) that called upon the Secretary General, in cooperation with the United Nations Educational, Cultural and Scientific Organization (UNESCO), the Food and

365

Agriculture Organization (FAO), and the World Meteorological Organization (WMO) to survey the world's activities in marine science and technology. In the light of this survey, the Secretary General was to formulate proposals for an expanded program of international cooperation, together with a strengthening of international efforts in education and training in marine science. Through such a program, better understanding of the marine environment would lead to improved methods for exploiting the ocean resources. Since then, there have been further UN resolutions in the general context of cooperative marine research, one of which refers specifically to a proposed International Decade of Ocean Exploration as an important element in this expanded program.

One major milestone of large-scale international cooperation was the International Geophysical Year in 1957–1958, when the International Council of Scientific Unions organized a loose coordination of the scientific efforts of many nations, to study natural phenomena (largely physical) on a worldwide scale during a year of intense sunspot activity. Among the programs carried out were very extensive oceanographic investigations involving government scientists along with academic marine scientists. International collaboration in oceanographic research on an extensive scale is not new. In the field of marine studies, it is now nearly seventy years old. As long ago as 1902, a group of distinguished European marine scientists, under the sponsorship of the King of Sweden, founded the International Council for the Exploration of the Sea (ICES). The Council was formed in order to furnish the knowledge essential to a rational utilization of the seas and their resources, that is, to turn the ocean's resources "to the best advantage in the present without prejudice to the future." The record of the International Council over the years has thoroughly justified the foresight of these early marine scientists and one would not find it easy today to improve on the objectives that they set for themselves.

In addition to its more normal activities of coordinating national marine programs where they can be conducted in collaboration to the greater benefit of all, of exchanging information,

366

and of compiling data, this Council over the years has sponsored a number of specifically "combined operations." These range from the famous international hydrographic and plankton surveys of 1904–1919 to contributions to the IGY in 1957, and the Council's three successive surveys of the northeastern Atlantic "oceanic front" in 1960, involving the integrated operation of nine ships from five countries. Other examples of the Council's activities include international assessments of fish stocks in different parts of the northeast Atlantic area, and predictions of the effects of different regulatory schemes on fisheries.

Although no other international bodies have modeled themselves precisely on the International Council, its example has been followed by a number of other regional bodies, especially those concerned with fisheries regulation. Examples are the International Commission for the Northwest Atlantic Fisheries (with which the Council has close relations, although ICNAF has its own Research and Statistics Committee), and the Northeast Atlantic Fisheries Commission, which received its scientific advice by agreement specifically through the Liaison Committee of the Council. Other commissions have been initiated in the Atlantic Ocean, as well as a number of fisheries bodies in the North Pacific Ocean and elsewhere. All are concerned in one way or another with coordinating international research or administration in the fisheries field. The North Pacific Fisheries Commission has been responsible for one of the most extensive international biological surveys, involving large-scale experimental fishing and tagging of the principal species of Pacific salmon, along with surveys of the environmental conditions over which the several stocks of salmon range and find their way to and from the rivers of their origin. ICNAF also has been responsible for a number of regional fish stock assessments, and for a major environmental survey, extending from Newfoundland to Greenland and Iceland using the vessels of seven countries. But international collaboration has been by no means limited to intergovernmental arrangements of these kinds. Take, for example, the famous *Challenger* expedition of which we celebrated the centenary in 1972. The production of its many vast reports was made possible only by the collaboration of scientists from many countries. A significant fraction of the progress made in marine science has been through the collaboration between individuals and laboratories, both within and between countries.

Because of the nature of marine problems, such collaboration across national boundaries has been more common in oceanography than in any other research field. There are several nongovernmental international scientific groups within the International Council of Scientific Unions (ICSU) that are specially interested in the field of marine science, such as the International Association for the Physical Sciences of the Ocean, the International Association of Biological Oceanography and the Commission on Marine Geology. The essential support for each of these groups comes from the various national scientific academies. Arising out of the collaboration involved in the marine aspects of the International Geophysical Year is ICSU's Scientific Committee on Ocean Research (SCOR), which is the principal body for liaison and cooperation between the academic oceanographers. Perhaps SCOR's main achievement was the initiation of the International Indian Ocean Expedition, in which scientists from twenty-three countries collaborated on twenty-one research vessels belonging to thirteen countries in the first extensive investigation of the Indian Ocean. While its responsibility for the Indian Ocean Expedition was in due course handed over to the Intergovernmental Oceanographic Commission of UNESCO, SCOR continues as a very active and valuable international body.

The Intergovernmental Oceanographic Commission (IOC) is a world governmental body, which was founded in 1961 and now has over seventy members. Its principal function is to promote and coordinate the study of oceanography throughout the world. It has only just begun this task, but in addition to the International Indian Ocean Expedition, it has already coordinated the International Cooperative Investigations of the Tropical Atlantic, which surveyed the biological and physical oceanography of the equatorial waters, and the Cooperative Study of the Kuroshio region of the Pacific. Other studies in the Mediterranean and the Caribbean seas are planned. The IOC also collaborates with regional bodies such as the ICES and ICNAF and takes into account the oceanographic results of their surveys when planning further joint investigations.

The IOC has a number of other coordinating responsibilities, including the exchange of oceanographic data and information, and the promotion of mutual assistance in the research field. In its planning, the Commission has had the advice of the SCOR, thus drawing on the whole of academic oceanography, and of the Advisory Committee on Marine Resources Research (ACMRR) of the FAO for the fishery aspects of oceanography. It is noteworthy that both the SCOR and ACMRR are composed of scientists nominated in their personal capacities.

The FAO was founded after World War II, and immediately established a division to be concerned with fisheries, under the world food objective of promoting "the common welfare by furthering separate and collective action" to raise levels of nutrition of the member nations. Although the FAO has a small permanent technical staff for fisheries it is not their principal task to conduct research. They have a heavy responsibility to help the developing countries, where high-grade fish protein is urgently needed and is often available locally in ocean waters, if the means of obtaining it can be developed. The FAO fisheries staff gleans scientific and technical information from the various national and international research organizations, participates in their work at times, and assists them where possible with the application of knowledge of the sea and its resources. The small permanent staff of the FAO is truly international, and is supplemented from experienced laboratories, by secondment of temporary staff to supervise its projects in various parts of the world. The larger laboratories are thus able to help others, indirectly, and even the largest at the same time gain, not only by the world-collating activities of the FAO (statistics, bibliographies, symposia on key problems, and the like), but by the stimulus and widened experience provided by the members of their staffs on return as well.

In all these instances, the reasons for international collaboration have been compelling, as the founders of the ICES foresaw. These reasons range from the very size of the oceans (even viewed on a regional basis) and their resources, in relation to the scientific effort available, to the need for the various countries concerned to pool all data and knowledge concerning the waters and their inhabitants if the maximum understanding and utilization of the resources is to be achieved: from the necessity for standardization of methods in many investigations, to the need for binding agreements to be reached at the international level if fish stocks are to be fished with the maximum efficiency.

There are now more than thirty regional bodies in existence, some of which (such as the ICES) are as much concerned with oceanography as they are with fisheries research, together with two UN bodies and the ICSU system. It might be asked whether more organizations are needed, but there are major gaps in the present system as well as some overlapping. These gaps, together with an increasing recognition of the complexity of oceanic interrelationships, and the rapid changes in the efficiency with which fisheries have developed, have led a number of people to consider whether the present ocean research organization is adequate to world requirements.

Added to the tendency of men to overexploit any stock they fish, even while international regulations are being formulated, is the formidable development of large freezer-trawlers, factory ships and the mother ship with its fleet of smaller vessels. These enable fishing enterprises to deploy rapidly and to transfer their efforts from one stock to another as they begin to feel the effects of fishing, so that even the most developed regional organization may prove inadequate to modern requirements.

Not only do the seas (and their inhabitants) have no national boundaries, but effects in one area or region may be caused by, or associated with, processes developing far from that region (and indeed outside the oceans themselves). The fish may migrate over hundreds and even thousands of miles, spending part of their lives in one region and equally important parts in another, and be fished in both. Moreover, the world oceans and atmosphere together make a gigantic world heat engine so that atmospheric conditions must be taken into account in understanding marine processes, and ocean conditions are fully relevant to meteorological understanding.

Furthermore, the world has suddenly become conscious of the truly great potential of the oceans, ranging from marine life to minerals (to say nothing of its significance for transport, and communications).

Finally, world opinion is no longer satisfied that industrial development within the marine field shall be solely by and for the benefit of the developed countries.

More specifically, the scientific activities of the IOC have remained primarily basic in nature. Although oceanographers must be concerned with the meteorological aspects of oceanography, the World Meteorological Organization has its own concern for the ocean aspects of meteorology, as evidenced by the World Weather Watch. While all research operations are being brought into closer relationship by joint working groups of the three bodies, both the FAO and the WMO are formally distinct world organizations from the IOC itself under UNESCO, despite existing arrangements for coordinating the oceanographic aspects of their activities. It was with these (and many other) points in mind that UN Resolution 2172 was considered.

It so happened that the FAO's Advisory Committee on Marine Resources Research met shortly after this Resolution was adopted and, in response to a request for advice on its scientific aspects, in January 1967 the committee invited the SCOR to join forces in attempting to formulate the requirements from the viewpoint of the scientists concerned. As a result, these two bodies invited the Scientific Advisory Committee of the WMO to participate in their deliberations so that for the first time global research on the oceans, on their resources and on their relations with the air above them, could be considered together.

The nominees of the three organizations met in Helio Cabala near Rome in July 1967, and prepared a report entitled *International Ocean Affairs*. This report was later taken as the basis for most of the recommendations made by the UN Secretary General in his report *Marine Science and Technology: Survey*

371

and Proposals, submitted through the Economic and Social Council to the 23rd Session of the General Assembly.

Briefly, the Secretary General called on member governments, UNESCO, FAO, WMO, and various other bodies to agree "as a matter of urgency to broaden the base of the IOC, so as to enable it to formulate and coordinate" an expanded program of ocean research. Among other things, the Secretary General requested the member nations to coordinate their activities so as to provide adequate support for the proposed expanded program, in "proper interrelation" with the UN agencies in particular, but including intergovernmental regional organizations as well as nongovernmental international bodies. His report specifically maintains the value of the IOC in seeking independent expert advice in identifying the scientific content of the expanded program.

The IOC welcomed the Secretary General's proposals and arranged to study the implications of an expanded program for a broadened IOC. At the same time they requested specific proposals for its "scientific content" from the Commission's two advisory bodies and from member countries. On this occasion, the Executive Committee of the SCOR was the first among the bodies concerned to meet, and it recommended the establishment of a second Joint Working Group of scientists in their individual capacities, but individually selected for this particular purpose.

In due course the SCOR, ACMRR, and WMO nominated twenty scientists from various parts of the world who, together with *ex officio* representatives of the sponsoring bodies, met in April 1968 in Rome and on the neighboring Island of Ponza to undertake their task. I had the privilege of serving as Chairman of this group, which included leading scientists in the several scientific disciplines concerned with oceanography and I was tremendously impressed, not only by their ability, which I expected, but by the sense of proportion and humility with which they tackled this task; indeed, I have never worked with a pleasanter, abler and more collaborative group.

The group's recommendations were published within the record time of one month, under the title "Global Ocean Research." With respect to research proper, the proposals made by this group fall under the following four headings.

First, there is a series of projects in the field of air-sea interaction and problems of motion in the ocean. These projects are focused primarily on the concept of the ocean-atmosphere complex as a vast heat engine, which must be understood if we are to be able to adequately predict weather and climate over the long or short term. In order to be able to make such predictions, the scientists must have a prediction "model" on a world scale, but first we need to fill many gaps in our knowledge of ocean characteristics and movements. We need much more information than we now have of daily processes in many parts of the ocean and in the air above them, together with an improved understanding of short- and long-term variations in these processes. The scientists must then proceed step by step, first developing prediction techniques on a small scale say, for one of the major ocean basins such as the North Atlantic or Pacific oceans. A particularly interesting proposal is to investigate instances of the abnormal accumulation of heat in and above some tropical waters with all their consequences for major ocean phenomena such as the monsoons and tropical storms. Even on these more limited scales, adequate observations and data can only be obtained by considerable international effort; indeed, they are as good examples as any of the need for international cooperation in marine research. This is partly because of the scale of effort required even for prediction at the ocean basin level, but it is also because of the truly international value of the predictions that should become possible, ranging as they do from the ocean weather itself, so important to mariners, to weather and climate over the land, with all that such predictions could mean in agricultural terms, perhaps especially for the developing countries.

A second set of recommendations concerns life in the ocean. The principal objects here are, first, to improve the understanding of the complex ecosystems on which fisheries depend, and the flow of energy through them. Then we need to assess production on a global basis, both of the familiar fishery objectives of today but as well of those less familiar animals (and plants) that live at lower levels in the ecosystem and we know are far more abundant; for some at least of these will undoubtedly be the basis for the next stage of fishery development. Life in the ocean is inseparable from the physical and chemical conditions that sustain it, and detailed studies are required of the ways in which the life and death of the organisms in which we are interested depend on the ever moving and ever varying physical environment. This improved knowledge about the bases of productivity, and especially about the physical processes of nutrient enrichment and concentration in coastal waters, should also be useful in the further development of coastal aquaculture, and perhaps ultimately in mariculture itself. Here we need and must visualize international cooperation in another aspect. While some of the biological objectives demand a large-scale cooperation effort much as in physical oceanography, many others demand a much more detailed and intimate observation and experiment, both at sea and in the laboratory. If we are to be successful, a fully coordinated effort will be required. Again, new methods and new instruments are needed for many aspects of these biological investigations, which will most likely be developed in individual laboratories but if successful, will be adopted as standard on an international scale.

A third set of proposals concerns marine pollution. So much attention has been devoted recently to the various ways in which our environment is being adversely influenced by man's activities that the importance of ensuring the minimum of harm to the oceans and their inhabitants will be appreciated by all. In order to reduce the known dangers, and to anticipate others, these proposals advocate first the recording of, and then the investigation of the likely effects of, all substances being released deliberately or accidentally into the ocean. This should be followed by a worldwide system of monitoring the entry of harmful substances into the ocean; it is most important that this monitoring be coupled with an annual report on the health of the ocean. Many of the problems involve those of the motion of the ocean, and require comparable methods and efforts. Other problems, again, are much more intimate and demand intensive small-scale studies at sea and in the laboratories. No work will call for more international coordination and cooperation if we are to secure the controls necessary for conserving this two-thirds of the world's surface, its coasts and its river tributaries.

A fourth section concerns the dynamics of the ocean floor. Mineral exploitation demands prior knowledge and understanding of the structure of the earth's crust (here, the sea bed) and of the general processes that are continually modifying it, from sediments to physical movement. Whether this knowledge will reveal vast and accessible mineral resources below the deep ocean remains to be seen, but we will never know without it. If, however, we could only survey and chart in detail the geology and geophysics of the ocean shelves and slopes there is little doubt that the mineral potential there would prove attractive and that the world could be a great deal wealthier. Again, there is an important international aspect, although much of the work can and will doubtless be done on a national basis. Yet again, there are important interactions with the other sections of the program, perhaps especially relating to geological sediment, of which so much is derived from the continuous rain of dead and dying organisms.

Under these four headings we believe that we have identified a number of new and major projects which, if they could all be tackled during the next 10–20 years, would greatly advance our knowledge of our planet and inner space and equip the developed as well as the less developed nations to considerably increase their profitable use of the oceans. Moreover, we believe that such knowledge will assist the nations in reaching international agreement regarding the use of the oceans.

If some of the projects at first sight seem to be rather academic, they were selected because they concern the basic research necessary to provide the understanding required for successful exploitation. Others are more obviously directed to applied ends. Many other problems remain, of course, and another group might have emphasized them differently. In any event, other scientists will contribute further ideas as plans develop for the expanded program. Any of the projects submitted that finds approval is only at the beginning of its evolution into a specific program, which it will be the duty of the IOC to coordinate. It will be the task of further working groups of scientists, from various disciplines, organizations and countries, to plan these projects in detail. During that planning the proposals may even change considerably; possibly some will be withdrawn, either as being impracticable, or to provide resources for something we did not foresee which may be viewed as even more profitable.

In addition to the four sections concerning research projects proper, a separate chapter of the report attempts to list the facilities and resources that would be needed to implement them, and to indicate where possible the order of the requirements, from ships to training programs. The requirements are extensive, but so are the oceans, and so are the present and future uses to which we can put them. If this seems to be a formidable list, and we did not attempt to estimate the cost of these requirements, the cost would still be far less than that which is being spent on space research, and the likely benefits are much more immediate. What we had continually in mind was not only improving our understanding of the oceans, but increasing their use, as UN Resolution 2172 required. In the conviction that a world international body should be concerned only with those questions that cannot be adequately dealt with by regional or national bodies alone, we gave principal attention in our considerations to investigations that demand extensive international cooperation and/or coordination for their success. Continuation of existing marine research at various levels is essential to the success of any expanded program and many existing programs will prove to be complementary to those proposed by the group and *vice versa*.

This brings me to three questions specifically posed by the IOC, concerning the peaceful uses of the ocean, the needs of the developing countries, and the value for them of their active participation in ocean research and development. Despite the many battles that have been fought at sea, by far the greatest use of the ocean in the past has been peaceful, in fishing, in trade, in travel and communication, and in recreation. Our thinking was dominated by the view that the oceans are essentially international, and that they can only be understood, and their potential made available to all mankind, by international collaboration in research, in development, and in use. At the research level this must be by collaboration between scientists and engineers of many disciplines, and from many countries; as such the programs will be unsuccessful unless scientists and engineers find them stimulating and worthwhile and so can contribute to them whole-heartedly. Both at the level of research and development, however, collaboration and coordination are ultimately matters for government, both as representing nations and as working together in world and/or regional bodies.

The seas are the world's last great resource to be relatively unexploited, and all countries have much to gain from their exploitation, especially the less developed countries with their urgent needs for food and currency, both of which might be eased substantially by the exploitation of the riches lying off their shores. But this will be possible only if they have the necessary information, and the necessary skill to interpret it, which alone can come from possessing scientists and engineers who are able to communicate and collaborate with their fellows on equal terms. It is an essential part of the content of this or any other relevant international program for the more developed countries to help, by training and mutual assistance, in the creation of such scientific corps in those less developed countries that are interested. Those countries can gain the essential skills only by participating in the fullest way possible in projects such as are being proposed, and their participation should be enthusiastically encouraged.

These proposals of the Ponza group of scientists were in due course to be considered by the IOC itself, and indeed a specially appointed working group of the IOC did consider them, at a meeting in Paris along with the national proposals of more than thirty member countries. Their report and specific plans for an

377

expanded program were then considered by the IOC at its sixth session in September 1969. It would have been presumptuous to anticipate their recommendations and decisions, which in any event were forwarded as advice to the Secretary General of the United Nations for consideration. But one important point, if additional resources over the continental shelves are to be revealed as speedily as possible, will undoubtedly be the maintenance of the tradition of the freedom of research for all throughout the world, in accordance with the scientific custom that the results should be made available to all quickly and completely.

I have indicated the possible evolution of the present arrangements for international cooperation in marine research, taking account of the interests and requirements of the different agencies and member governments, and the necessity for working in close collaboration with not only the various national laboratories concerned, but also with the existing regional bodies in the marine field. Just how the arrangement will evolve and how it will work in practice, assuming it is adopted by governments, remains to be seen, although certain features seem obvious. First, none of the participants, member governments, regional bodies, UN agencies, and the like, lose anything of their present responsibilities. The proposals envisage that they will use the Commission as an instrument for discharging certain of these responsibilities in the field of marine science. These responsibilities, of course, vary according to the constitution of the different bodies. Governments will, and must, remain the controlling bodies, as the owners of the various national laboratories and facilities, and as members of the IOC and of each of the other UN agencies. But, under these proposals, they have better opportunities to coordinate their programs and facilities so that overlapping may be avoided and other uses may be suggested for the scientific effort made available; gaps may be assessed and priorities set for filling them; and information, data and plans can be made available for all. For fisheries research, just as an example, there should be the advantage of the resources of academic oceanography and of meteorology not only becoming more directly available, but (through a review of their ocean programs along with fisheries programs) of being coordinated so as to be of the greatest use for fisheries development.

Thus, it is not intended that the IOC should become a vast research organization, with all the bureaucracy that might be envisaged. Some increase in the IOC's resources would be needed, but a relatively small one. The IOC as such will conduct no research but would be used to permit member governments to arrange more efficient growth and deployment of the world's marine research resources, either as national units or as member governments of other, and frequently regional, bodies. Governments will, and must, remain the arbiters of what the research resources are and how they can best be applied; but the potential benefits are so large and important and the problems so great that, whether their countries are developed or developing, governments will recognize that international collaboration will be essential to solve the problems and secure the benefits of the sea for all mankind.

28 THE FUTURE

Paul M. Fye

Ten years ago I did not dream that oceanography could accomplish in so short a time what it has achieved to date. My views of the future, though optimistic at that time, now turn out to have been embarrassingly modest.

Science and technology should be thought of together when we consider the future of oceanography. In the past decade, we have barely begun the engineering necessary to harvest the riches of the sea. True, men have already descended to the deepest parts of the sea, have already traversed the Arctic Ocean under and through the polar ice, have already lived for weeks within the sea and have attempted the harvest of minerals from the ocean floor. But much remains to be done. Engineering for ocean projects is mostly in the future.

In oceanography, the decade of the sixties resulted in a transition from the observational, descriptive regime of the explorer to the more precise realm of the formal scientist, whether he be a chemist, a biologist or a physicist. Yesterday each scientific voyage resulted in the discovery of a new seamount, the identification of a new species of marine life or the tracking of a different ocean current. Today, theories are explored, fundamental questions about the oceans are asked and answers sought. Tomorrow, man will be able to devote more of his energies and talents to managing our affairs so as to use the Earth's oceans as wisely as possible.

Only recently have oceanographers been able to develop

theories about ocean circulation and then test these theories by massive experiments in the deep ocean. It is scarcely more than a decade since Professors Henry Stommel and Arnold Arons, working at Woods Hole, developed a theory of deep circulation and thus provided a basis for prediction of deep ocean currents. It is even more recent that we have had experimental confirmation of this theory by the use of newly developed seagoing techniques.

Now that we have bigger and faster research ships and improved instrumentation and data processing techniques, we find we can no longer consider the oceans as unchanging. A few years ago we were combining data taken by *Challenger* in the 1870's with that taken by *Meteor* in the 1920's or even *Atlantis* data from the 1930's and '40s with *Atlantis II* data of the '60s and '70s. A different class of questions is now being asked about changing ocean characteristics and will be studied in the future. These questions concern the dynamic fluctuations in the oceans both in time and space. Theories which satisfactorily explain and predict all of the many fluctuations already observed must still be developed. This is the type of problem which will challenge the best oceanographers of the future. Solutions to problems of this kind will be a part of our future and will surely assist in wise management of ocean resources.

Technological developments follow scientific knowledge in all aspects of our cultural developments and so it will be with ocean science and engineering. But before we examine engineering developments, let us explore some of the potentials in the various areas of marine science. In marine biology, there is a growing interest in farming the seas, particularly in the coastal regions. This new emphasis on marine aquaculture will provide an exciting impetus to many basic biological investigations. As biologists study the problems of cultivating, growing and harvesting marine products, they will necessarily become deeply involved in the fundamental aspects of genetics, pathology, nutrition, and behavior of marine organisms. There will be a parallel development of new engineering designs and techniques in the operation of aquaculture stations.

The natural quality of water to transmit sound rapidly provides the best present means for long-range communication under water. We will expand the use of this important tool (and perhaps of other new tools such as lasers) to study the distribution of living organisms in the sea. There will be increasing emphasis on the importance of knowing more about the behavior of marine animals. The peculiar behavior of swordfish in attacking research submarines lends importance to this subject at least in our laboratory in Woods Hole; both the Woods Hole *Alvin* and the Grumman *Benjamin Franklin* have experienced such attacks. We are beginning to learn about the importance of chemical substances in extremely dilute solutions which attract or distract marine animals. Research in this new area of *chemotaxis* is discovering the techniques used by salmon, alewives, and other fish to navigate back to their native streams. Already it has been demonstrated that chemicals found in oysters, even in dilutions less than one part per thousand million, will still attract predatory starfish and that the branched-chain hydrocarbons in kerosene attract lobsters, which perhaps explains why bricks soaked in kerosene have sometimes been used as bait by lobstermen.

In chemical oceanography, perhaps the single most important achievement is the development of analytical techniques of very high precision. We already have demonstrated that chemicals in solutions as dilute as one part per trillion and less are significant in the marine life cycle. Many chemical measurements of the past are being drastically revised, leading to better understanding and prediction of the distribution of organic matter in the oceans. We now urgently need an understanding of what happens in the ocean when wastes of all kinds are released into it. We will depend heavily upon the chemist in the future to show us how to avoid poisoning the sea with the waste products of our rapidly growing cities and their industries.

It is important to continue the present comprehensive programs in marine ecology but in the future these studies will be integrated into a coordinated study of the cycle of organic matter in the sea. The ultimate practical objective of these studies is a thorough understanding of the production, distribution and utilization of food from the world's oceans.

In the field of marine geology and geophysics, we have seen in the last several years how an exciting "new" idea like sea-floor spreading (which can be as much as four or five inches a year in the Mid-Atlantic Ridge area) can revitalize a field. For centuries, man had assumed that the land mass under the ocean was forever inaccessible. Modern technology has changed all that, and today marine geoscientists are opening up this new frontier with dramatic speed. The deep-drilling program of the *Glomar Challenger* is a precursor of deep-ocean exploitation.

Engineering developments in the ocean have followed hard on the heels of recent scientific discoveries. At Woods Hole, our three-man research submarine, the *Alvin*, has dived repeatedly to the fantastic depth of 6,000 feet, photographing the bottom, retrieving samples with its mechanical arm and even drilling cores from selective outcroppings. But 10 years from now we will look back upon the *Alvin's* capabilities and describe them as "primitive." We will soon develop capabilities for the wise exploitation of the large ocean areas both on the continental shelves (which will dominate our commercial interests for the rest of this century) and in the deep ocean.

For centuries, man's use of the sea has been restricted to its surface or near surface. Even oceanographers, who have had an abiding interest in the deep sea and who have long had a need for an improved capability for studying the ocean depths, have had to be satisfied with lowering instruments and sampling devices from the sea surface on long cables. This has even constricted our thinking in strange ways. We have thought about the oceans in much the same way—from the surface down rather than from the bottom up. Now that a few research submersibles, such as *Alvin*, enable us to go down into the ocean, we have begun to think of viewing the oceans from underneath and a whole new world is opening up.

Where does such thinking lead? We can easily envision work stations for free swimmers on the continental shelves at depths as great as 1,000 feet. Living quarters, laboratories, and work stations can be provided for long stays at the ambient pressure of 30 atmospheres. A pressurized elevator could carry personnel quickly to the surface, without decompression, where a stable platform, consisting of a large vertical cylinder, could have decompression chambers and other necessary life-support equipment. Workers at the bottom would be provided with improved swim-out style submersibles to extend their range beyond swimming limits.

Some researchers have speculated about free swimming, perhaps with lungs flooded and intravenous supplies of oxygen, but these seem unlikely solutions for the foreseeable future. If we wish to go into the deep ocean, it will be necessary to protect the observer from the high pressures at great depths. Even so, we can visualize a laboratory with living spaces at a depth of 20,000 feet, with elevators capable of withstanding the great pressures and of coupling with the laboratory chamber at the bottom, as well as with the support ship at the surface. In addition, workers would need work boats which could explore and work at any depth. They, in turn, would need deep underwater boathouses which would connect through a system of locks to the work station on the bottom.

A variety of other engineering skills must be developed in order to expedite the recovery of ocean mineral resources, particularly from the deep sea. At the present time, exploitation of marine mineral resources is confined mostly to the continental shelf and the most valuable products are oil and gas. Much of the shelf, however, remains unexplored and emphasis in the future must be given to its full investigation. More information will also be needed on the abundance, composition and distribution of deep-sea deposits so that their utility may be evaluated and a sensible basis established for management and jurisdictional decisions. Mapping of ocean floor contours and geological reconnaissance of the deep-sea floor will provide the basis for subsequent intensive study and prospecting by industry.

Today, the most commonplace deposits which are being used from the ocean are sand, gravel, and shells. From a tonnage standpoint, these are easily the most important mineral commodities mined in the world. Globally, offshore deposits worth about $200 million are now being mined each year; this will undoubtedly increase in the future as the efficiency of recovery techniques are improved.

Around the world, other resources are already being tapped in a small way. In Malaysia, Thailand, and Indonesia dredges are already operating in offshore tin fields. Iron ore is being mined in small amounts off Japan and some along the Newfoundland coast. Drowned river valleys off the coast of Alaska probably have substantial deposits of gold, platinum, and tin. Calcium carbonate of high purity is being mined in Bahamian waters. Diamonds have been discovered off the mouth of the Orange River in southwest Africa. Oil, gas and associated sulphur, however, are likely to remain the most profitable offshore mineral resource in the foreseeable future. In the next 10 years, the petroleum industries' investment in exploration and development of submarine oil fields may well reach $25,000 million. Even today, nearly one-fifth of the world's petroleum products are produced profitably from under offshore waters.

In the deep ocean, concentration of minerals on the seabed occurs in manganese nodules. These chemical curiosities containing manganese, nickel, cobalt, and copper were originally found during the famous *Challenger* expedition almost a century ago. From a chemical and metallurgical point of view, these nodules represent one of the most interesting of oceanic deposits. We do not understand their formation, or why they are distributed so widely on the ocean floor. No doubt in the not too distant future these nodules will be mined in commercial quantities.

Fresh water is another important resource to be derived from the sea. Twenty-nine per cent of the population of the United States resides within 50 miles of the ocean. In the year 2000 it is not unlikely that some 2,000 million of the 6,000 million world residents will live in communities which should by reason of proximity look to the oceans as a major source of their fresh water. We can anticipate continued basic research into the physical and chemical principles involved in desalination, as well as the development of more efficient engineering methods of obtaining fresh water to meet this growing demand.

A by-product of the desalination of sea water may be the greatly increased production of extractable salts contained in the sea. It has already been estimated that by the middle of this decade it may be necessary to process 35,000 million tons of sea water each year to meet our increasing water demands. The value of the minerals contained in this large quantity of water is estimated to be about $600 million. Today, the profitable recovery of salt, bromine, and magnesia from sea water is possible. It has been proposed, in addition, that sulphur, potassium chloride, uranium oxide, and silver are economically extractable from sea water, even with today's technology.

Less tangible aspects of the economic potential of the oceans— the ways in which man makes use of the ocean for improvement of his general welfare—should not be overlooked when considering the future of ocean engineering. A revolution in ocean transportation is technically feasible. Some of the problems of merchant shipping, such as the design of ships and their relationship to surface waves, are directly related to problems yet to be solved in ocean engineering. Other problems will be greatly influenced by our improved understanding, predicting or even possibly controlling some of the parameters of the oceans and the atmosphere. New methods for cargo transfer, more efficient maneuvering of large ships in confined waterways, improved charting, design of better harbors, the control of silting, the control of pollution will all be assisted by ocean engineering of the next decade. It has been estimated that such technical advances could reduce the world's ocean freight bill by several million dollars a year.

And then there is weather, both to talk about and to do something about. Improved reliability of weather forecasts will save millions of dollars each year by preventing flood damage and loss of crops. We know that much of our weather develops at sea as the hydrosphere interacts with the atmosphere and we are beginning to understand how this interaction works. A better understanding and an ability to make more accurate, long-range weather predictions depends upon an improved knowledge of major ocean currents and of their temperature and salinity variance, as well as a better understanding of the effects of wind and sun on the water. The relatively straightforward task of gathering data from so large an area is itself enormous. We have hardly begun. In fact, the total investment in the study of ocean data of this sort is so small that meteorologists and physical oceanographers generally limit their activities to a thorough study of one small plot of ocean, seeking a weather development pattern which will be superimposed on other ocean plots when the data becomes available. We must make the decision soon to invest sufficient money in ocean studies so that much better weather predictions can be made. This decision will be a rational one based on economic consideration which can no longer be ignored. For example, over a 15-year period ocean-generated storm damage has been estimated to be larger than $4,000 million. The U.S. National Academy of Science's Committee on Oceanography has suggested that oceanic research in the next 20 years could result in weather predictions which could save $2,000 million annually.

Finally, the most talked about ocean resource and, in many ways, the most critically needed, is food. Food from the sea can make an important contribution as a source of cheap, animal protein necessary to prevent malnutrition. It is estimated that more than half of the 3,000 million persons in the world today suffer from malnutrition; a major factor is a deficiency of essential amino acids which are normally supplied in an adequate diet through animal protein. Fish protein concentrate provides an inexpensive form of animal protein, which for about a penny a day per person could overcome the debilitating effects of protein deficiency. But are there enough harvestable fish in the sea to meet this need even if we know how to catch and distribute them? Today the annual world catch of edible fish is about 55 million tons. Some estimates put the annual steady-state production of the oceans at better than 200 million tons or about four times the present catch. This amount of fish could supply 40 million tons of animal protein, sufficient to supplement the diet of a population of 5,000 million persons if each received 20 grams per day. Clearly there are enough fish in the sea to assist significantly in solving the malnutrition problem. But we must first solve the many technical problems and the problems of equitable distribution which I suspect will be even more difficult to resolve.

In 1968 the United States proposed an International Decade of Ocean Exploration in the belief that scientific inquiries and engineering studies of the oceans and atmosphere could offer many real opportunities to serve the common interests of mankind and the hope that such studies could help to close the gap that exists between the rich and poor countries. The Decade is also serving to point the way to sensible and realistic approaches to international cooperative ocean studies. A description of three I.D.O.E.-sponsored investigations will illustrate the effectiveness of the concept. The first involves a study of the continental margins of the eastern Atlantic Ocean; the second, a geochemical study of the oceans; and the third, an investigation into the occurrence of chlorinated hydrocarbons and petroleum hydrocarbons in marine plants and animals.

The continental margin of the eastern Atlantic from the Cape of Good Hope to the northern tip of Norway was selected for study both because of the potential importance of the area to its many bordering nations and because of the scientific interest in comparing this little known region with the better known margins of the western Atlantic. The first phase of the investigation, currently being conducted from aboard the Woods Hole Oceanographic Institution's research vessel *Atlantis II,* involves scientists from nine countries who have made traverses totaling 45,000 kilometers, gathering geophysical data off the coast of Africa between the Cape of Good Hope and Zaire. A second phase, scheduled for 1973, will continue these investigations northward to Morocco.

The geochemical study arose from the need for much more extensive and systematic sampling of appropriate chemical properties throughout the world's oceans. The basic purpose of the program is the detailed measurement of the oceanic constituents along Arctic to Antarctic sections at all depths, to provide, for the first time, a set of physical and chemical data measured on the same water samples. These data will provide the input for quantitative studies of oceanic mixing and organic productivity, and, at the same time, serve as a base line for the levels of pollutants and of fission and waste products being added to the sea. The U.S. contribution to the program involves three long traverses from the Antarctic to the northern limits of the Atlantic, Pacific, and Indian Oceans. At each of 120 locations along these tracks water samples will be collected at intervals from the surface to the sea floor and analyzed for dissolved oxygen, nutrient compounds, alkalinity, acidity, trace metals, and rare gases. Additional programs now underway or being planned by the United Kingdom, Canada, West Germany, France, Japan, India and Italy will provide additional data.

The information obtained from these investigations will greatly improve our knowledge of the dispersal rate in the sea of the combustion products of chemical fuels, radioactive material from nuclear fission and the organic poison from pesticides. We will learn more about the rates at which these pollutants can be made harmless by dilution, by chemical degradation and by removal of the sediments. In addition, the study will contribute to work on weather prediction and climate modification, since the distribution of chemical species can provide important clues to oceanic circulation which affects the transfer of heat and moisture between the sea and atmosphere.

There is evidence that man is inadvertently changing the energy balance of the Earth by adding the combustion products of fossil fuels to the atmosphere. Solid suspensions and carbon dioxide change atmospheric transparency which changes the heat balance of the Earth. The solids scatter incoming radiation, carbon dioxide absorbs outgoing infrared radiation. At the moment, it is uncertain which effect is gaining the upper hand. If the suspensions prevail the Earth will cool off; if the carbon dioxide accumulates, it will heat up. There would also be secondary effects on cloud cover and water-vapor content of the atmosphere. The oceans are the major "sinks" or repositories for washout of solids and for solution of carbon dioxide. It is not yet known how long these heat absorbers stay in the atmosphere and this must be determined more accurately. To understand the carbon dioxide cycle, detailed knowledge of ocean chemistry and mixing will be absolutely essential.

The third Decade program relates to environmental control and the problem of control of pollution. It is becoming increasingly important to protect the environment from the damaging works of man.

Much has been written about the alarming buildup of DDT in the marine environment. Until recently ecologists had assumed that the river system is responsible for most of the DDT pollution in estuaries and offshore waters, but recent investigations in the deep ocean change this concept. We had known that this pesticide is washed from the land into the rivers, and is then transported into the estuaries and coastal waters. If this were the primary path taken by DDT as it reaches the ocean, then we could reasonably expect that concentrations of the chemical would be greatest near the mouths of rivers rather than in the open ocean. But surprisingly this is not the case. DDT is distributed widely throughout the open ocean and concentrations are often as great there as in coastal waters near rivers. This is equally true of other chlorinated hydrocarbons and of the polychlorinated biphenols (PCB's), substances presumed to be toxic and commonly used in many manufacturing processes. Presumably, then, the oceans are being substantially polluted with these compounds as they are discharged from land-based locations into the atmosphere in the form of gases and aerosols. They are then mixed with the surface waters of the oceans. This year, under I.D.O.E. sponsorship, Woods Hole scientists have begun a long-range study of this phenomenon—attempting to learn the extent of distribution of these man-made chemicals in the open ocean, how and to what degree they are concentrated in marine plants and animals and what deleterious effect these chemicals have on the organisms.

There are many other programs in the Decade which are important and which will contribute to our knowledge of our world about us. The next 10 years offer us all an opportunity to learn much more about the world in which we live.

The peaceful development of the ocean's varied resources will require great scientific effort by many nations working in harmony. All nations must recognize and abide by the common legal agreements and understanding which will enable them to develop the ocean resources to their mutual advantage. It is an exciting concept, this decade of ocean exploration. Together the nations of the world can explore the living resources of the ocean to develop, conserve and harvest great food supplies. Together they can search out the ocean floor for mineral resources. Together they can better understand fundamental ocean processes so that these can be channeled toward a better life on this planet for all mankind.

INDEX

Italicized numerals refer to illustrations.